McGraw-Hill Publications in the Zoological Sciences

E. J. Boell, CONSULTING EDITOR

METHODS AND PRINCIPLES OF SYSTEMATIC ZOOLOGY

McGRAW-HILL PUBLICATIONS IN THE ZOOLOGICAL SCIENCES

E. J. Boell, CONSULTING EDITOR

There are also the related series of McGraw-Hill Publications in the Botanical Sciences, of which Edmund W. Sinnott is Consulting Editor, and in the Agricultural Sciences, of which R. A. Brink is Consulting Editor.

METHODS AND PRINCIPLES
OF
SYSTEMATIC ZOOLOGY

ERNST MAYR

Curator of the Whitney-Rothschild Collections
The American Museum of Natural History

E. GORTON LINSLEY

Associate Professor of Entomology and Chairman
Department of Entomology and Parasitology
University of California

ROBERT L. USINGER

Associate Professor of Entomology
University of California
Alternate Member, International Commission
on Zoological Nomenclature, Paris 1948

NEW YORK   TORONTO   LONDON

McGRAW-HILL BOOK COMPANY, INC.

1953

METHODS AND PRINCIPLES OF SYSTEMATIC ZOOLOGY

II

THE MAPLE PRESS COMPANY, YORK, PA.

PREFACE

The authors have long felt the need for a treatise on the principles and methods of taxonomy. Such a work should be useful not only as an adjunct to teaching but also as a reference work for the practicing taxonomist and as a source of information to the general biologist. An analysis and full statement of the often disputed principles on which the taxonomic method is based are urgently needed. We share the view of O. W. Richards (1947) that "it is less the findings of taxonomy than its principles and methods which need to be taught" and understood. We believe that taxonomy is an important branch of biology which deals not only with the identification and classification of natural populations but with objectives that go well beyond these fundamental activities.

The teaching of taxonomic theory and method has been a seriously neglected phase of biology. Most formal courses in systematics have concentrated upon the end products of taxonomic research and have not provided the student with a means for critically evaluating these end products or for tracing the steps by which they were attained. An understanding of taxonomic theory and practice is essential not only to the beginning and the practicing taxonomist but to all those who draw upon the results of his studies. This is true to a greater or lesser extent for all biological sciences, but in particular for such fields as ecology, population genetics, comparative morphology, anthropology, comparative physiology, and applied biology. Sound taxonomy is a prerequisite to intelligent conclusions in all these fields.

At the present time there is no book available that deals comprehensively with the principles and methods of taxonomy. Available works are merely commentaries on the International Rules, or they deal with selected phases of taxonomic theory with occasional reference to taxonomic practice.

The treatment in this book of certain phases of systematic zoology has necessarily been restricted because of limitations of space. Collecting techniques, for example, are so diversely specialized in each group of animals and so completely covered in separate works that they are not discussed in detail. A full discussion of the phyla and classes of animals is considered beyond the scope of this work, although a listing is presented (Table 2).

Nomenclature, although strictly a means to an end, has occupied a disproportionate part of the time and energy of taxonomists. One reason for this is that the subject is inherently complex and that revisions of the Rules become necessary from time to time, since the practicability of the Rules, like that of any other code of law, can be tested only by application. A more fundamental reason is that a basic philosophy or theory underlies the Rules of Nomenclature. This theory has not only tended to change in the course of years (as, for instance, with respect to the significance of types), but some of it could not be fully understood until the principles of taxonomy themselves were more clearly understood (*e.g.*, treatment of infraspecific names). We feel, therefore, that a presentation of the Rules of Nomenclature would be incomplete which does not deal with the history of the field, or which omits a discussion of the basic principles. We have attempted to present both these aspects. On the other hand, it is not the purpose of this book to enter into nomenclatural controversies. Since at this writing there is no edition of the International Rules of Zoological Nomenclature which is accurate or up to date, we hope that the simplified review of the Rules in Part 3 of our book may prove to be especially useful. At the same time, the treatment is open to the criticism that it is an unofficial version of a highly technical and, at the moment, controversial subject. It has been our aim to make nomenclature comprehensible to the practicing taxonomist, leaving it to nomenclaturists to analyze the voluminous proceedings of the International Commission and to debate the various issues of the moment.

In attempting to bring together the more important elements of modern taxonomic theory and practice, we have, of necessity, selected our materials primarily from the point of view of the student of living animals and have chosen illustrative examples with preference from our own work. The problems of the paleontologist, microbiologist, and botanist have been taken into consideration as far as practicable, but the materials of these groups are often sufficiently different to require different approaches to the solution of taxonomic problems. Nevertheless, there is much common ground of theory and method shared by the workers in these diverse fields, and it is to be hoped that at some time in the not too distant future all biological taxonomy may be viewed as a single cohesive field. If this book, by focusing attention on the problems of the systematic zoologist, serves as a step in that direction, one of its goals will have been achieved. If it also assists in stimulating a more critical evaluation of taxonomic theory and methods and in a wider dissemination of knowledge concerning them, the authors will feel that their labors have been justified.

It is well-nigh impossible to acknowledge sources in a book of this kind, which has grown out of the accumulated contacts and experiences of the three authors throughout their lives. Suffice it to say that our early teachers in Germany and at the University of California and our colleagues at The American Museum of Natural History and in the Bio-systematists Discussion Group at the University of California and at Stanford University have done much to shape our thinking along the lines expressed in this book. We also acknowledge the role of several generations of students at the University of California, who have unwittingly provided opportunity to test the clarity and effectiveness of portions of the manuscript during its formative stages. Their response has been most helpful.

Formal acknowledgment of quoted material is made through literature citations. Special thanks are due to several colleagues who generously gave of their time to read portions of the manuscript. Their detailed suggestions and criticisms were carefully considered and were in most cases adopted. To these readers should go a large share of credit for accuracy of statements. On the other hand, the authors individually and collectively assume the responsibility for the errors which undoubtedly will be discovered. The following persons read the chapters indicated: R. E. Blackwelder (1 to 17); E. Dougherty (10 to 16); Alden H. Miller (1 to 9); C. F. W. Muesebeck (1 to 17); C. W. Sabrosky (1 to 17); M. A. Cazier (4, 5, 8, and 9); G. G. Simpson (7); L. M. Klauber (7); H. Levene (7), and R. F. Smith (7).

Finally, we wish to express our sincere thanks to the secretaries, who meticulously typed the various drafts of the manuscript and helped in checking the bibliography and in various other tasks connected with the preparation of this work.

Ernst Mayr

E. Gorton Linsley

Robert L. Usinger

New York, N. Y.
Berkeley, Calif.
January, 1953

CONTENTS

PART 1

TAXONOMIC CATEGORIES AND CONCEPTS

CHAPTER 1

TAXONOMY, ITS HISTORY AND FUNCTIONS

Taxonomy, or systematics, is the science of classification of organisms. The term *taxonomy* is derived from the Greek τάξις, arrangement, and νόμος, law, and was proposed by de Candolle (1813) for the theory of plant classification. *Systematics* stems from the Latinized Greek word *systema*, as applied to the systems of classification developed by the early naturalists, notably Linnaeus (*Systema naturae*, 1735). In modern usage both terms are used interchangeably in the fields of plant and animal classification.[1]

Taxonomy is built upon the basic fields of morphology, physiology, ecology, and genetics. Like other scientific disciplines it is a synthesis of many kinds of knowledge, theory, and method, applied in this case to the particular field of classification. Its potentialities and its limitations are largely those of the basic fields whose raw materials it utilizes.

The first step in the resolution of any kind of biological knowledge is the classification of phenomena in an orderly system. This means ultimately the naming, description, and classification of all plants and animals. Something of the diversity of organic nature and the magnitude of this task may be indicated by the following figures. There are now known more than one-third of a million species of plants, sixty times as many as at the time of Linnaeus (Merrill, 1943). Every year about 4,750 new species of plants are described. Including synonyms and subspecies, more than 1 million names were proposed for phanerogams and cryptogams between 1753 and 1942.

The number of known species of animals is much greater than that of plants and has been estimated at about 1 million (Table 1). Including subspecies, there are probably more than 2 million named forms of animals, and new ones are being described at the rate of about 10,000 per year. For the insects alone, Metcalf (1940) calculates that $1\frac{1}{2}$ million names are already applied. Accepting an estimate of 3 million probable insect species (Silvestri, 1929), and assuming that each species has on the average five distinct developmental or morphological phases, 15 million descriptions will eventually be required to characterize the stages of all insect species! When we superimpose the necessity for arranging 3 million species in a framework of higher categories express-

[1] For different usage see Mason (1950).

3

ing inferred natural relationships, and analyzing the population structure of the species concerned, something of the magnitude of the task facing just one group of taxonomists may be seen.

The objectives of taxonomy can only be achieved by sustained cooperative effort. Furthermore, the ability of the individual taxonomist to contribute to this effort depends on the breadth of his training as well as on his native talent. The complexities of modern systematics, its dependence on related fields, the refinement of modern techniques, and the magnitude of the literature have made it inevitable that the days of

TABLE 1. ESTIMATED NUMBER OF KNOWN SPECIES OF RECENT ANIMALS (Mayr)

Protozoa	30,000	Linguatula	70
Mesozoa	50	Chelicerata	35,000
Porifera	4,500	Crustacea	25,000
Coelenterata	9,000	Other arthropods	
Ctenophora	90	(excl. insects)	13,000
Platyhelminthes	6,000	Insecta	850,000
Acanthocephala	300	Mollusca	80,000
Rotifera	1,500	Pogonophora	1
Gastrotricha	175	Bryozoa	3,300
Kinorhyncha	100	Brachiopoda	250
Nematomorpha	100	Echinodermata	4,000
Nematoda	10,000	Phoronidea	4
Priapulida	5	Chaetognatha	30
Nemertina	750	Hemichordata	80
Entoprocta	60	Tunicata	1,600
Annelida	7,000	Fishes	20,000
Echiuroida	60	Reptiles and amphibians	6,000
Sipunculoidea	250	Birds	8,590
Tardigrada	180	Mammals	3,200
Onychophora	65	Total	1,120,310

One of the objects of this tabulation is to indicate the relative size of the various groups of animals. Even the smallest phyla have therefore been included, because they are quite important from the points of view of phylogeny and comparative anatomy. The number of species of birds is based on an accurate count. All other figures are estimates, subject to two sources of error. Only 60, 50, or 40 per cent (or even less) of the existing species have as yet been described in many animal groups. On the other hand, in the less-known groups of animals, many populations have been described as full species which appear to be merely subspecies of widespread polytypic species. The two sources of inaccuracy thus cancel each other to some extent.

the untrained taxonomist are limited. The amateur will always play a most important role in assembling much of the raw material with which the taxonomist works, but he needs a broad background and special training if he is to make direct taxonomic contributions of the quality which will be required in the future. Even the trained taxonomist can no longer cover the entire field in any major group of plants or animals.

Greater specialization has been the inevitable consequence of the tremendous growth of our knowledge of living things.

HISTORY OF SYSTEMATIC ZOOLOGY

The history of taxonomy may be divided into a number of periods. These in turn correspond loosely to the various levels of taxonomy (alpha taxonomy, beta taxonomy, gamma taxonomy, see below). Definitions of these periods facilitate the understanding of the progress that has been made in the field. The complexity of taxonomy must be kept in mind when studying its history. Progress in the taxonomy of various animal groups (and in the study of animals from different regions) has been very uneven. Taxonomy is most advanced in the most popular groups (birds, butterflies, mammals, some genera of beetles), while in others it may still be on an elementary level. It is most advanced in the North Temperate Zone and lagging behind in the tropics and other distant places. Consequently the three historical periods here outlined are not strictly consecutive but largely overlapping.

First Period—the Study of Local Faunas. The history of taxonomy is almost as old as man himself. Natives of even the most primitive tribes may be excellent naturalists, with specific names for local trees, flowers, mammals, birds, fishes, and the more conspicuous (or most edible) invertebrates. A tribe of Papuans in the mountains of New Guinea was found to have 137 specific names for 138 species of birds. Only one species was confused with another. Often the nomenclature of such tribes is clearly binominal, with a generic and a specific name (Bartlett, 1940).

Several early Greek scholars, notably Hippocrates (460–377 B.C.) and Democritus (465–370 B.C.) included animals in their studies. However, only fragments of the works of these earlier authors are in existence. Apparently it was Aristotle (384–322 B.C.) who brought together the knowledge of his time and formulated it into the beginnings of a science. Aristotle did not propose a formal classification of animals, but he provided the basis for such a classification in his statement that "animals may be characterized according to their way of living, their actions, their habits, and their bodily parts." He referred to such major groups of animals as birds, fishes, whales, and insects, distinguishing among the last both mandibulate and haustellate types and winged and wingless conditions, and utilizing certain terms for lesser groups, such as Coleoptera and Diptera, which persist today. Aside from these larger groupings, his categories, according to Nordenskiöld (1928) were but two in number, the *genos* and the *eidos*, "the latter corresponding to the individual animal form—horse, dog, lion—the former to all combinations of a higher degree." The Aristotelian philosophy—it can scarcely be called a system—sufficed for the students of animals for nearly two thousand years. It is only in the works of the immediate predecessors of Linnaeus that we find more than probing attempts at animal classification.

The botanists were far ahead of the zoologists during this period, since they were the first to break away from the Aristotelian tradition and describe and classify local plants. From Brunfels (1530) and Bauhin (1623) there has been a continuous refinement of concepts and techniques (*e.g.*, Tournefort and Plumier). The contemporary writings of zoologists

Fig. 1. Carolus Linnaeus (1707–1778) and title page from the foundation work in systematic zoology.

(*e.g.*, Gesner, Aldrovandi, and Belon) were, on the whole, still dominated by Aristotelian concepts and showed only rudiments of a consistent nomenclature and of principles of classification. Of all the earlier authors, the one who had the greatest influence on Linnaeus was John Ray (1627–1705), who recognized the difference between the genus and the species and who, through evaluation of both similarities and dissimilarities in animals, arrived at a more natural higher classification than did those who had gone before him (Raven, 1942).

The type of taxonomy that is based on the study of local faunas reached its peak in the great Swedish naturalist Linnaeus (1707–1778), whose contributions were so influential on subsequent students that, with much justification, he has been called the father of taxonomy.   In the tenth edition of his great work *Systema naturae* (1758) (Fig. 1), the binominal system of nomenclature was for the first time consistently applied to animals, and this work became the foundation of systematic zoology.   In addition to his new system of nomenclature, the work of Linnaeus was characterized by clear-cut species diagnoses and by the adoption of a hierarchy of higher categories: genus, order, class.   The methods of Linnaeus were by no means wholly original, but his eminently practical system was quickly adopted, expanded, and elaborated because of his great personal prestige and the influence of his students.   It dominated taxonomy for the next century, and most of the essentials of the Linnaean method are still components of modern taxonomy.

It is generally assumed that Linnaeus accepted the doctrine of fixity of species, *species tot sunt, quot formae ab initio creatae sunt.*   Indeed, despite certain evidence to the contrary (Ramsbottom, 1938), systematic concepts of the Linnaean period were static concepts.   Higher classification was largely mechanical and showed what we now recognize to be natural relationships only in cases where fundamental characters happened to be selected.   The thinking of this period was characterized by the concepts of classical typological taxonomy.   The species was the nondimensional species of the local naturalist.   The particular importance of this period for the history of taxonomy is that at that time biology consisted almost entirely of taxonomy, and nearly all the eminent biologists of that day were taxonomists.

Linnaeus was not only the classical representative of this first period of taxonomy, his work also heralded the coming of the second period. Although Linnaeus in his earlier writings (*e.g., Fauna suecica,* 1746) exemplified the local naturalist, he became more and more cosmopolitan in his later publications, utilizing the discoveries of naturalists in faraway countries.   Still, his philosophy remained that of the student of local faunas, except that the *Systema naturae* was the product of the joint labors of many local naturalists.

Second Period—the Acceptance of Evolution.   Evolutionary thought was already widespread in the eighteenth century (Maupertuis, Buffon, Lamarck, and many others), but it owes its firm foundation to the second period in the history of taxonomy, the period of exploration.   This movement started modestly during the previous period and reached a grand climax during the middle of the nineteenth century.   It was characterized by an intense interest in the faunas of faraway places, in magnificent world voyages and expeditions, and in the accumulation of vast numbers of specimens from all over the world, which permitted the monographic treatment of genera and families.   Charles Darwin (1809–1882) was the naturalist on one of these expeditions (Voyage of the Beagle) and worked up some of its results.   He became the world's leading specialist of the Cirripedia (barnacles) and wrote a monograph of this group that was authoritative.   It was largely on the basis of his experiences as a traveling naturalist and taxonomist that Darwin conceived the theory of evolution.   Combined with the reading of Malthus's *Essay on Population*, it also gave him an answer to the problem of the cause of evolution, the theory of natural selection.   It is more than a coincidence that another traveling field naturalist, Alfred R. Wallace (1823–1913),

FIG. 2. Charles Robert Darwin (1809–1882) and title page from the foundation work in evolutionary theory.

came simultaneously to the same conclusions.   The views of both men were jointly presented in 1858 to the Linnaean Society in one of the most dramatic episodes in the history of science.   That Darwinism was to a large extent based on taxonomic work is perhaps one of the reasons why it did not actually alter taxonomic arrangements very basically, as has been pointed out by Dobzhansky (1951).

The publication of Darwin's *On the Origin of Species* (1859) (Fig. 2) resulted in a tremendous stimulation of biological thought and work. The decades immediately following 1859 were principally taken up by the question, Is evolution a fact?   Or, stated differently, Are all the living organisms descendants of common ancestors?   The interest of this period was preeminently phylogenetic.   The chief effect of the acceptance of the theory of evolution on taxonomy has consequently been a greater preoccupation with phylogeny.

Ernst Haeckel (1866), more daring and speculative than Darwin, introduced (Fig. 3) the method of representing phylogeny by means of trees or branching diagrams (see Chap. 8). Although his formalized diagrams resemble but little those that are in use today, the method itself was useful and stimulating, and it provided the taxonomist with a graphic means for expressing supposed relationships. The search for facts to improve the designs of phylogenetic trees dominated biology during the second half of the nineteenth century and led to a boom in the fields of comparative systematics, comparative morphology, and comparative embryology. In taxonomy, in particular, it spurred the search for "missing links" and "primitive ancestors." These efforts were not wasted but led to a far-reaching understanding of the animal forms and to the establishment of a natural system that is still considered essentially valid.

This was an exciting period in the history of taxonomy. Not only were new species and genera discovered daily, but with reasonable frequency even new families or orders. The reward of such exciting discoveries attracted the keenest minds to the field of taxonomy. Alas, the wealth of nature is not inexhaustible, and the period of major new discoveries in the higher animals was over well before the end of the nineteenth century. Those who were anxious to describe new orders, families, and genera had difficulty discovering them. As an alternative choice they resorted to the splitting of the existing categories. Some splitting was justified and led to an elucidation of classification by doing away with heterogeneous, polyphyletic groups. In other cases, however, it led to a disintegration of natural categories. It appears, in retrospect, as the most retrogressive period in the history of taxonomy. Few of the splitters were good biologists, nor did they understand the proper function of the taxonomic categories. Part of the disrepute into which taxonomy fell during the latter part of the nineteenth and early twentieth century was caused by the activities of those who unnecessarily split well-known and well-founded taxonomic categories, thereby hopelessly concealing natural affinities.

Third Period—the Study of Populations. While the preceding period was dominated by the study of evolution of the higher categories, with a great interest in ancestral forms or missing links (such as *Amphioxus* or *Peripatus*), the most recent phase in the history of taxonomy is characterized by a study of the evolution *within* species. The typological concept of the species, which was already shaky in the preceding period, was abandoned and replaced by a dynamic, polytypic concept. Interest reverted to the fauna of local areas and to the study of variation within

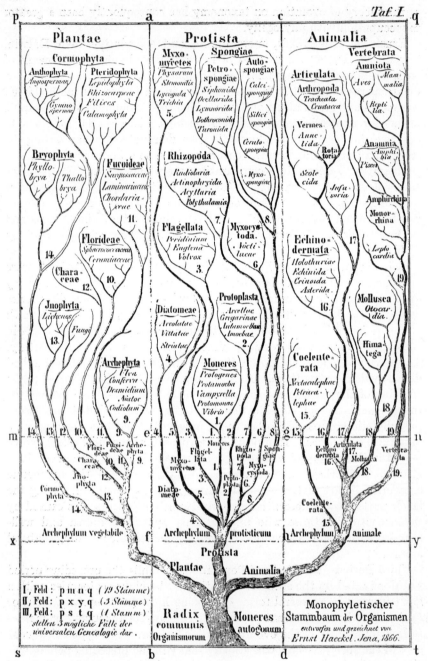

FIG. 3. The phylogeny of living things as conceived by Haeckel (1866) and expressed in a formal tree-like diagram.

populations and the slight differences between adjacent populations. The taxonomist is no longer satisfied to possess types and duplicates; he collects series and analyzes them quantitatively.   This type of study was commenced almost simultaneously by ornithologists, entomologists, and malacologists in the second half of the nineteenth century.

The detailed history of this phase of taxonomy has not yet been written, but it would be well worth the attention of historians of biology. Although the study of populations reached its dominant position in systematics only within recent generations, its roots go back to the pre-Darwinian period.   In ornithology, after the pioneer efforts of Schlegel, the systematic collecting of series was particularly in vogue among the American school, following the leadership of Baird (1854):

As the object of the [Smithsonian] Institution in making its collections is not merely to possess the different species, but also to determine their geographical distribution, it becomes important to have as full series as practicable from each locality. . . .   The number of specimens to be secured will, of course, depend upon their size, and the variety of form or condition caused by the different features of age, sex, or season.   In gathering specimens of any kind, it is important to fix with the utmost precision the localities where found.

Among the malacologists are to be mentioned particularly Kobelt (1881), Gulick (1905), the Sarasins (1899), as well as Crampton, whose biometrical studies in the local geographical variation in the genus *Partula* (1916, 1932) have become classical.

The results of this work caused the abandonment of the typological species concept.   Species were no longer considered as something fixed and uniform, but rather as polytypic, consisting of many subspecies and local populations, each differing from the others and each showing considerable variability within itself.   Two facts, in particular, were outstanding.   First, that the differences between subspecies and species were compounded of very numerous small variations; and second, that much of the local and geographical variation was closely correlated with the environment.   The working and thinking of the leading taxonomists of this period was thoroughly modern and biologically correct, except in one respect.   Most of them interpreted the close correlation between variation and the environment as indicating a direct effect of the environment.   They were Lamarckians.   In spite of this error they were essentially much closer to the truth than the early Mendelians.

It was during this period that the Mendelian rules were rediscovered (in 1900), an event which eventually led to the spectacular rise of the field of genetics.   However, the early Mendelians emphasized the role of large mutations (De Vries and Bateson) and thought that they produced new species by a single step.   They minimized the role of the environment, even as a selective agent. This attitude was in part due to the unfortunate choice of some of the most popular genetic material of that period, namely, the aberrant plant *Oenothera* (by De Vries) and the normally self-fertilizing, nearly homozygous garden plant, the common bean (by Johannsen). The early conclusions of the geneticists, which differed so drastically from those of the students of natural populations, explain the fact that the first two and one-half decades of the twentieth century were the period of the greatest cleavage between the naturalist-taxonomist and the laboratory biologist.

Further discoveries helped to resolve the conflict, and it was eventually realized that both groups were in part right, in part wrong. The geneticists began to appreciate the extreme importance of small and very small genetic changes, and the concept of mutation was extended to include these. The choice of more suitable material for genetic studies, *Drosophila* by Morgan and *Antirrhinum* by Baur, was also helpful. Fisher's (1930) demonstration that even a very small selective advantage of a new gene or gene combination would cause in due time a genetic transformation of populations was a tremendously important contribution. Perhaps the most important factor in bringing taxonomists and geneticists together was the work of three animal geneticists who had been trained as taxonomists and who studied material from natural populations, Goldschmidt, Sumner, and Dobzhansky. They introduced the population concept of the taxonomists into genetics and prepared the foundation for the establishment of the new prosperous science of population genetics, which is, so to speak, an offspring of the harmonious union of taxonomy and genetics. In turn, the genetic results, together with their mathematical interpretation by Haldane, Fisher, and Wright, forced taxonomists to give up their Lamarckian thinking and made them realize that the small variations which they had known so long were actually small mutations.

THE NEW SYSTEMATICS

The taxonomic work of the twentieth century is characterized by a continuous refinement of the methods and concepts developed in the nineteenth century. Current taxonomy is customarily referred to as the *new systematics* (Huxley, 1940), but it must not be forgotten that its roots go back to the first half of the nineteenth century, and that even the concept of geographical speciation was expressed in an almost modern form as early as 1825 by Leopold von Buch (translated, from Mayr, 1942):

The individuals of a genus spread out over the continents, move to far-distant places, form varieties (on account of differences of the localities, of the food, and the soil), which owing to their segregation [geographical isolation] cannot interbreed with other varieties and thus be returned to the original main type. Finally these varieties become constant and turn into separate species. Later they may reach again the range of other varieties which have changed in a like manner, and the two will now no longer cross and thus behave as "two very different species."

Huxley (1940) considers the new systematics as a synthesis of such modern approaches as the geographic, ecologic, cytologic, and physiologic, and of population genetics. He adds that

To hope for the new systematics is to imply no disrespect for the old. . . . Even a quarter of a century ago it was possible to think of systematics as a specialized, rather narrow branch of biology, on the whole empirical and lacking in unifying principles, indispensable as a basis for all biological workers, but without much general interest or application to other branches of their science. Today, on the other hand, systematics has become one of the focal points of biology. Here we can check our theories . . . , find material for innumerable experiments, build up new inductions: the world is our laboratory, evolution itself our guinea-pig.

To bring out more clearly the change of concepts that has occurred in the field of taxonomy, the old and the new systematics may be contrasted as follows:

The *old systematics* is characterized by the central position of a species, typologically conceived, morphologically defined, and essentially non-dimensional. Very little significance is attached to geographic variation. Many species are known from single, or at best a few, specimens; the individual is therefore the basic taxonomic unit. There is great preoccupation with technical questions of nomenclature and the identification and description of "types."

The *new systematics* may be characterized as follows: The purely morphological species definition has been replaced by a biological definition which takes ecological, geographical, genetic, and other factors into consideration. The population, represented by an adequate sample, the "series" of the museum worker, has become the basic taxonomic unit. Most taxonomic work is done with subdivisions of the species. Nomenclatural problems occupy a subordinate position in systematic work. The interests of the taxonomist are those of a biologist.

This seems like a far cry from the simple taxonomy of a Linnaeus or Fabricius, and new terms have been suggested for the new science. Although modern taxonomy may be referred to as new systematics or (so far as it applies) as experimental taxonomy, it would be misleading to use these terms in contradistinction to taxonomy. There has been such a gradual change from classical taxonomy to the new systematics, and the change has been so uneven in the various groups of animals (and in various geographical regions), that it would be misleading to refer to parts of it as taxonomy and to other parts under a different name.

We use the term *new systematics* descriptively rather than in a formal sense. There are various grades of new systematics, depending upon the degree to which a group is known. Some traces of the new systematics are found in the writings of taxonomists as far back as one hundred twenty-five years ago. No one can foresee what refinements of technique and what changes in point of view may occur in the future. What we consider as new systematics in the year 1950 may, indeed, be very old systematics fifty years hence. There is an unmistakable trend among taxonomists to approach their material more and more as biologists and less and less as museum cataloguers. The modern systematist is showing an increasing interest in the formulation of generalizations, for which the naming and describing of species is only the first step.

Many groups of animals are still so poorly known that the newer principles and techniques of taxonomy cannot be applied to any great extent. In such cases it is inevitable that the attention of the taxonomist is still almost entirely taken up with the describing of new species, the construction of keys, and similar preliminary tasks. On the other hand, the taxonomy of a few groups is far advanced. There is no group in which the new principles are being applied as extensively as to birds. Less than 200 new species have been described during the past twenty-five years; the last North American species was discovered in 1889, the last Australian, in 1911. Thus the bird taxonomist is able to concentrate his efforts primarily on intraspecific analysis, although studies of bird phylogeny lag far behind other groups.

Some nontaxonomists have formed the erroneous impression that all animal groups are rather well known taxonomically. Actually, the study of many groups of animals has hardly begun (Mayr, 1942). A striking illustration of this is presented by Remane's (1933) work on the microscopic marine fauna of the Kieler Bucht, an area previously considered to be well known. By thorough search and with the application of new methods, Remane found 300 new species in ten years, including representatives of 15 new families. Sabrosky (1950) has recently pointed out how poorly much of the North American insect fauna is known. Many so-called "common species" actually represent whole complexes of good species not previously discriminated. He writes,

A few examples will suffice for illustration. Ross (1937) in the neuropteran genus *Sialis* (alder flies) recognized a number of new species with this comment: "Critical study of the genitalia has revealed no less than ten eastern and six western species grouped under the name *infumata*." Oman (1933), who studied the important economic group of agallian leafhoppers, recognized in one part of the genus *Aceratagallia* a total of 26 species that had previously been placed under five names, besides considerable confusion among these five in their proper application. Shewell (1939) revised the dipterous genus *Camptoprosopella*, a genus of small yellowish flies commonly collected on grasses and other low vegetation, and described twelve new species, most of which had been recorded for years under the name *C. vulgaris* (Fitch), a species which, incidentally, could not even be recognized with certainty because the type is a female. The present writer (1949) found twelve new species, with characteristic terminalia in both sexes, in what had been widely determined for many years as a common Holarctic species, *Leptocera lutosa* (Fallén) (Diptera). In the abundant and persistently annoying eye gnats or *Hippelates* flies, which have been of some interest as vectors of yaws and various eye diseases, the writer has found no less than nine distinct species of three genera standing in collections under the name *Hippelates pallipes* (Loew), in this case all named species whose correct recognition requires painstaking attention to minute details.

Even less known is the taxonomy of tropical animals. Thus the major portion of the work of the taxonomist still remains to be done.

CHANGE IN TAXONOMIC CONCEPTS

Another way of bringing out the revolutionary change in the thinking of the taxonomist is to define the two concepts that are most characteristic for early and for recent taxonomy.

The Type Concept. Taxonomy in its early history was completely dominated by the type concept. The type concept goes back to Greek philosophy. The "ideas" of Plato are such "types."[1] Applied to taxonomy, the type concept postulates that all members of a taxonomic category conform to a "type." Whether a taxonomist adhered to the type concept consciously or unconsciously, it inevitably affected his methods and results. In particular, the type concept tended to exaggerate the constancy of the categories and the gaps that separate them and to minimize variability. Typologists have often either denied evolution altogether or explained its operation by macromutations. This philosophical type concept should not be confused with the type method of modern taxonomy, discussed in Chap. 12.

The Population Concept. During the past seventy-five years the population concept has gradually replaced the type concept, but by no means completely. According to this view, species are composed of variable populations, and even within the higher categories there may be considerable deviation from the "type" of the category.

[1] The early nineteenth century was the heyday of the "typologists," the adherents of the type concept. Cuvier was an outstanding representative of this school, and so were the German *Naturphilosophen* (Schelling, Oken, Carus, etc.) of that period. Students of the higher categories were particularly strong typologists, but this philosophy also affected taxonomists who worked at the species level.

The impact of this change of concept on the working methods and results of the taxonomist has been enormous. Populations are variable and, consequently, the description, measurement, and evaluation of variation has become one of the principal preoccupations of the student of lower categories. A typologist needed only one or two "typical" specimens of a species; if he had more, he disposed of them as "duplicates." The modern taxonomist attempts to collect large series at each of many localities throughout the range of a species. Subsequently he evaluates this material with the methods of population analysis and statistics. The use of statistical methods has become a standard part of the taxonomic technique in many groups and is becoming more widely used all the time. This refinement is greatly improving the quality of certain kinds of taxonomic work.

It must be recognized that with all the advances of the new systematics, the taxonomist is still forced to depend upon comparative morphology for his primary data and to fit, as well as he can, information derived from related fields into a classification scheme which is primarily morphological. The theory of evolution and the science of genetics have given meaning to his work and have provided methods for approaching the problems associated with natural populations. Finally, the new systematics has brought recognition of the true role of taxonomy and placed it at the very heart of modern biology.

THE TASKS OF THE TAXONOMIST

There is considerable uncertainty in the minds of some taxonomists, and even more in those of many nontaxonomists, as to what the real functions of the systematist are. Some laboratory men and ecologists seem to think that the taxonomist should content himself with identifying material and devising keys. Beyond that he should keep his collections in good order, describe new species, and have every specimen properly labeled. According to this view, systematics is the mere pigeonholing of specimens. No taxonomist will deny that these particular tasks are part of his job, and the worker in the less-known groups may not yet be able to go much beyond the cataloguing phase of taxonomic work. The systematist of the better-known groups, however, is not restrained by such a limitation; for him, systematics is more than an auxiliary science. He can inquire not only into the "what" but also as to the "why."

The modern taxonomist is more than the mere caretaker of a collection. In most cases he gathers his own material, carries his studies into the field, and develops thereby the technique and point of view of the ecologist. Most younger systematists have had a thorough training in various branches of biology, including genetics. This experience in both field and laboratory gives the well-trained systematist an excellent background for more fundamental studies.

The three principal tasks of the systematist are:

Identification (Analytical Stage). It is the basic task of the systematist to break up the almost unlimited and confusing diversity of individuals in nature into easily recognizable groups, to work out the significant characters of these units, and to find constant differences between similar ones. Furthermore, he must provide these units with "scientific" names which will facilitate their subsequent recognition by workers throughout the world.

Even this "lowest" task of the taxonomist is of tremendous scientific importance. The entire geological chronology hinges on the correct identification of the fossil key species. No scientific ecological survey should be carried out without the most painstaking identification of all the species of ecological significance. Even the experimental biologist has learned to appreciate the necessity for sound, solid identification. There are great numbers of genera with two, three, or more very similar species. Such species very often differ more conspicuously in their physiological traits than in their morphological characters. It has frequently happened that two workers have come to different conclusions concerning the physiological properties of a certain "species" because, in fact, one student was working with species A and the other with species B or with a mixed stock of A and B. Every biologist will recall such cases in his own field.

Classification (Synthetic Stage). The recognition and accurate description of the species is the first task of the systematist. But should he stop there, he would soon be confronted with a chaotic accumulation of species descriptions. To prevent this, the systematist must try to find an orderly arrangement of the species; he must characterize and arrange higher categories; in other words, he must devise a classification. This is the second task of the taxonomist. The devising of a classification is, to some extent, as practical a task as the identification of specimens, but it involves more speculation and theorizing. The taxonomist must decide whether two similar forms should be considered one species or two. He must also determine whether the similarities of two species are due to convergence of habitus or to close phylogenetic relationship. This leads to the question of whether or not the higher categories represent monophyletic groups.

These are some of the questions that confront the systematist who is trying to classify the bewildering multitude of organisms, and they lead inevitably to a study of the factors of evolution.

Study of Species Formation and of the Factors of Evolution. Work in this field comprises the third task of the systematist. It is here that he comes into closer contact with the other branches of biology, with genetics and cytology, with biogeography and ecology, with comparative anatomy and paleontology.   All these sciences pursue the study of evolution in their own way, with their own questions, and with their own methods.   One of the principal differences, for example, between the systematist and the geneticist is that the geneticist can test many of his conclusions by experiment, whereas the systematist can rarely do this and usually has to rely on the implications of observed data.   He can therefore say very little as to either the origin of taxonomic characters or their mode of inheritance.   On the other hand, the geneticist has difficulty in duplicating in the laboratory the conditions under which speciation proceeds in nature and can conduct experiments only at the level where some interbreeding is possible.   Many animals cannot be kept in a laboratory, and others will not reproduce in captivity.   Furthermore, the enormous time which the thorough genetic analysis of even a single species requires (it is still very far from complete in the two best-studied organisms, the fruit fly, *Drosophila melanogaster* Meigen, and the corn plant, *Zea mays* Linnaeus), makes it impossible for the geneticist to study more than a very small proportion of the known organisms.   Up to the present time only about $\frac{1}{500}$ per cent of the known species of animals have been studied with any degree of thoroughness by geneticists. It is therefore obvious that the systematist can and will have to fill many very large gaps.   But there is a more basic difference between the approach of the geneticist and the taxonomist to the problems of evolution.   The geneticist, in his analysis, seeks the "biological atoms," the genes, and other basic units.   The taxonomist, on the other hand, works with much more comprehensive entities: with the carriers of taxonomic characters, with individuals, populations, species.   There is, of course, some recent overlapping of the two fields owing to the development of population genetics, but the difference is striking enough to lead to a considerable difference in outlook and sometimes even in conclusions.

The systematist who studies the factors of evolution wants to find out how species originate, how they are related, and what this relationship means.   He studies species not only as they are, but also their origin and changes.   He tries to find his answers by observing the variability of natural populations under different external conditions and he attempts to find out which factors enhance and which retard evolutionary changes.   He is helped in this endeavor by his knowledge of the habits and the ecology of the studied species (Mayr, 1942).

LEVELS OF TAXONOMY

The three tasks of taxonomy are rarely undertaken simultaneously. Evolutionary studies cannot be pursued unless a satisfactory classification is available, and this in turn is based on the prior identification and description of species. The taxonomy of a given group, therefore, passes through several stages. These have sometimes been informally referred to as alpha, beta, and gamma taxonomy. Alpha taxonomy refers to the level at which the species are characterized and named; beta taxonomy to the arranging of these species into a natural system of lesser and higher categories; and gamma taxonomy to the analysis of intraspecific variation and to evolutionary studies (see above). Actually it is quite impossible to delimit alpha, beta, and gamma taxonomy sharply one from another, since they overlap and intergrade. However, the trend is unmistakable. It is the endeavor of the biologically minded taxonomist to pass from the alpha level through the beta level to the gamma level. Still, even in the taxonomically best known groups, there is need for more refined work on the alpha and beta levels.

THE RELATION OF TAXONOMY TO OTHER BRANCHES OF BIOLOGY

This is an age of specialization. Every aspect of life is studied by a different branch of biological science. Biochemistry and much of physiology deal with life at the molecular level, cytology with cells and their components, histology with the tissues that are formed by cells, anatomy (and parts of physiology) with organs, sociology and psychology with the behavior and the interaction of individuals, and embryology with problems of growth and development. The next higher levels of integration of life are dealt with by the science which used to be called natural history but is now referred to as taxonomy and ecology. Taxonomy deals with natural populations, subspecies, species, and higher categories. No other science takes care of this level of integration in the organic world. A study of systematics is therefore an integral part of the background of every well-trained biologist.

As long as a science is strictly descriptive, it usually has little contact with other sciences. When the descriptive stage has passed, however, and the comparative and functional stages are reached, contact and overlap with neighboring sciences is established. The two sciences with which modern taxonomy has the closest contact are population genetics and ecology. Familiarity with these two fields is an indispensable part of the training of the taxonomist.

Contributions of Systematics to Biology. Some idea of the scope and objectives of systematics may be gained from a consideration of the contributions of systematics to other branches of science and to mankind as a whole. Simpson (1945) has commented that

Taxonomy is at the same time the most elementary and most inclusive part of zoology, most elementary because animals cannot be discussed or treated in a scientific way until some taxonomy has been achieved, and most inclusive because taxonomy in its various guises and branches gathers together, utilizes, summarizes, and implements everything that is known about animals, whether morphological, physiological, psychological, or ecological.

Or, according to Pearl (1922),

It is the systematist who has furnished the bricks with which the whole structure of biological knowledge has been reared. Without his labors the fact of organic evolution could scarcely have been perceived and it is he who today really sets the basic problems for the geneticist and the student of experimental evolution.

According to Elton (1947),

The extent to which progress in ecology depends upon accurate identification, and upon the existence of a sound systematic groundwork for all groups of animals, cannot be too much impressed upon the beginner in ecology. This is the essential basis of the whole thing; without it the ecologist is helpless, and the whole of his work may be rendered useless.

Systematics has contributed to the applied sciences both directly and indirectly. This is true of medicine, public health, agriculture, conservation, management of natural resources, etc. A few examples may be mentioned from the field of applied entomology. Here insect identification has provided a filing system for economic entomologists, a convenient method for assembling the vast amount of detail accumulated over the years. It has also provided a useful tool, the natural classification, by means of which generalizations may be made as to the distribution and habits of economic insects. This is especially true of the new pests which appear from time to time and about which little or nothing was previously known. Generalizations drawn from near relatives may provide valuable clues as to probable habits, future importance, and means of control of an insect whose economic importance has just been recognized.

Systematics has proved to be the key to the solution of some of the most perplexing problems in economic entomology. For example, malaria is distributed unevenly over Europe. The supposed vector, the malaria mosquito, *Anopheles maculipennis* Meigen (1818), was reported throughout the continent, and large amounts of money were spent to control it in certain areas with no corresponding decrease in the incidence of the disease. At the same time, there was no malaria in some parts of the range of the malaria mosquito. Careful systematic studies, summarized by Hackett (1937) and Bates (1940) finally provided the key to the situation. The *maculipennis* complex was found to consist of several sibling species, distinguishable at first only in the egg stage, each with its own peculiar breeding habits, each with decided host preferences, and usually only one species actually responsible for the transmission of malaria in a given area. Armed with this information, it was possible to direct control measures to the exact spots where they would be most effective.

Applied entomological taxonomy is the basis of quarantine procedure. Here the taxonomist finds himself working under intense pressure with the fate of carload shipments of produce hanging in the balance, dependent upon his identifications. An example (Keifer, 1944) is "the identification of a single caterpillar from Orange County (California) in October, 1942, as the larva of the oriental fruit moth. [Before a second specimen was discovered] many meetings of fruit growers and entomologists [were held, and] the State Legislature appropriated over \$850,000 for various phases of investigation and control."

Accurate identification is essential in connection with the biological control of plant and animal pests. As Clausen (1942) has remarked,

A mistake in the identity of the host may result in the complete loss of years of work and the useless expenditure of large amounts of money. If, for instance, a pest is of oriental origin but is mistakenly identified as a closely related European species, the search for natural enemies in Europe, and their collection, rearing and colonization for biological control, might well prove utterly futile.

Pemberton (1941) cites an outstanding instance of the value of insect collections, assembled for taxonomic study, in the solution of a biological control problem. Some 20 years ago the fern weevil, *Syagrius fulvitarsis* Pascoe, became very destructive to Sadleria ferns in a forest reserve on the island of Hawaii, and control measures became necessary. Entomological literature failed to reveal its occurrence anywhere outside Hawaii except in greenhouses in Australia and Ireland. These records, of course, gave no clue as to the country of origin. However, while engaged on other problems in Australia in 1921, Pemberton had the opportunity of examining an old private insect collection at Sydney, and among the beetle specimens was a single *Syagrius fulvitarsis* bearing the date of collection, 1857, and the name of the locality in Australia from which it was obtained. This provided the key to the solution of the problem, for a search of the forest areas indicated on the label revealed a small population of the beetles and, better still, a braconid parasite attacking the larvae. Collections were made immediately for shipment to Hawaii, and the establishment of the parasite was quickly followed by satisfactory control of the pest. The data borne on a label attached to a single insect specimen in 1857, in Australia, thus contributed directly to the successful biological control of the pest in Hawaii 65 years later.

Systematics as a Profession. What opportunities exist for the student who contemplates a career as a professional systematist? As Ferris (1942) has put it,

How is he going to get an opportunity to work? Research of the quality that is needed now . . . cannot well be done by some hard-worked doctor, or policeman, or janitor or gardener, or even by every college professor, who in his few spare moments of relaxation after having earned his daily wage whiles away time with his collection . . . . The days when that could be done are passing. Systematic work of the kind that we need now most of all is a full-time job for a trained professional who has the technical facilities that are needed and who, through the help of assistants, is freed from the pressure of routine so that he can concentrate on his essential task.

There are not many positions of this kind in the world. Probably less than 1,000 professional taxonomists are employed in the world today. Many of these serve their governments in a capacity where their first duty is identification for economic purposes. At the state level, Illinois, California, and the Territory of Hawaii employ systematists to identify animals in connection with quarantine work and state surveys. Curators of the zoological collections of the world are full-time workers in the field of systematics, and a few of the larger universities have one or more staff members employed as taxonomists. It should be noted, however, that the above-mentioned positions do not fulfill the need expressed by Ferris. Although they fall within the definition of professional systematics, the salaries are paid for identification, curatorial, or teaching activities. Pure systematic work thus becomes a side issue, accomplished by zealous workers who are willing to burn the midnight oil.

Adding to the bulk of systematic work are a great many amateur taxonomists, a few hundred applied zoologists who maintain an interest in special groups as a hobby or who produce systematic work as a by-product of their applied studies, and several hundred students in each college generation who select and carry out a taxonomic problem in order to fulfill the requirements of a thesis for a higher degree.

It has been stated that the applied science of the future will lean even more heavily than now upon the diagnostic work of the taxonomist and the systems he devises. Taxonomy, of itself, is not spectacular and has little appeal in legislative halls or budgetary hearings. Applied science has a real and serious responsibility from the standpoint of its own selfish needs in guaranteeing that its reciprocal partner, taxonomy, has the opportunity and funds to function as it should. Officials in responsible Federal and state administrative positions must insist that funds and personnel for more comprehensive taxonomic studies be secured.

CHAPTER 2

THE SPECIES AND THE INFRASPECIFIC CATEGORIES

The following sections will be devoted to a discussion of taxonomic categories. A taxonomist cannot work with these categories unless he understands their meaning and how each category differs from the others. Some of the purely practical difficulties of assigning individual specimens to the right category will be treated in the section on taxonomic discrimination (Chap. 5).

KINDS OF TAXONOMIC CATEGORIES

The 20 or more categories that are used by the taxonomist in his classification (Chap. 3) are of unequal value and of different significance. Essentially there are three kinds of categories:

1. The species
2. Groups of populations within species (= infraspecific categories, *e.g.*, subspecies)
3. Groupings of species (collective categories = higher categories)

From evidence to be presented later it will appear that the species occupies a unique position in the taxonomic hierarchy. The discussion of taxonomic categories will begin, therefore, with the species.

As stated above, the alpha level of taxonomy is an essentially analytical stage. It consists of the distinguishing, identifying, describing, and naming of the species. At this stage no building up of a classification is undertaken, only fabrication and accumulation of the bricks of which the natural system is composed. A study of species and other lower categories is therefore essentially an analytical study. Classification, on the other hand, is synthetic, and the principles of classification will be discussed together with the higher categories in Chap. 3.

THE SPECIES

The species is the most important taxonomic category, not only for the taxonomist but also for the general biologist. An understanding of the nature of species is indispensable for taxonomic work and has to precede any attempts at giving a formal definition of the term. The word *species*, meaning originally kind, is older than the current biological concept. Even today the term is sometimes used for inanimate objects, for instance, species of minerals. The Greeks, in particular Plato and his followers, used the word *eidos* in much the same sense. The species concept of the biologist goes back to J. Ray, who in his *Historia plantarum* (1686) used the term *species* much as it was used later by Linnaeus and the nineteenth-century taxonomists. The modification of the static and morphological species concept of Ray and Linnaeus during the twentieth century will be discussed presently.

The Species in Nature. A species definition is merely the verbalization of a species concept. Species concepts are derived from a study of species in nature. A student of any local fauna finds that it is composed of well-defined "kinds" of animals and plants. Around New York City, for instance, there are about 125 "kinds" of breeding birds. These are the species. The individuals within a local population of such a species are freely interbreeding but are separated by a distinct gap from individuals of all other species.

In eastern North America there are five species of thrushes of the genus *Hylocichla:* wood thrush (*Hylocichla mustelina*), hermit thrush (*H. guttata*), olive-backed thrush (*H. ustulata*), gray-cheeked thrush (*H. minima*), and veery (*H. fuscescens*). These five kinds of thrush are quite similar to one another, and some can be told apart with certainty only by the more experienced bird student. In spite of the morphological similarity of some of these five species, each one is separated from every other one by a definite gap. No intermediate or hybrid has ever been found. They do not interbreed; they are reproductively isolated.

Taking any pair of species of a local fauna, no matter how closely related, they will be found to be separated from each other by a definite gap. It is this discontinuity between natural populations that impressed the early naturalists from Ray and Linnaeus on, and which remains the cornerstone of the species concept of the modern systematist.

Species Definitions. Taxonomists have always been faced with the problem of making their working concept of species conform to the species in nature. The pioneers were impressed by the fact that the species in nature usually differ by clear-cut characters, the "species characters." They concluded, therefore, that species should be defined on the basis of the degree of morphological difference. Morphological species definitions, however, sooner or later ran into difficulties. First of all, many kinds of individuals were found that were clearly conspecific, in spite of striking differences in structure owing to sexual dimorphism, age differences, polymorphism, and other forms of individual variation. Such forms were often described as species, but as soon as they were found to be members of a single interbreeding population, they were deprived of their species status, regardless of the degree of morphological difference. At the other extreme, sympatric (that is, occurring in the same area) natural populations have been found which are almost indistinguishable on the basis of structure, but which fail to interbreed (sibling species, see below).   These are recognized as distinct species in spite of the lack of morphological differences.   It is for these reasons that a species definition based solely on morphological criteria has proved to be unsatisfactory.   Taxonomists have therefore been obliged to seek another philosophical basis for their definition of species.   In spite of practical difficulties in its application, reproductive isolation has proved to be the soundest theoretical criterion.

Species therefore may be defined as follows: *Species are groups of actually (or potentially) interbreeding natural populations which are reproductively isolated from other such groups.*

Such a definition is called a biological species definition, because it is based on the biological criterion of reproductive isolation (Mayr, 1942). How this species definition can be applied to the specimens of the taxonomist will be discussed in Chap. 5.

Sibling Species.   Among the species is one kind which deserves to be singled out for purely practical reasons, the *sibling species* (Mayr, 1942). This name is applied to pairs or groups of very similar and closely related species.   It has been found that such groups occur commonly from protozoa to mammals.   For a more detailed discussion see Chap. 5. Sibling species are not a separate taxonomic category.   They do not differ from other species in any respect except for the minuteness of their structural differences.

The Subjective Element in Classification.   Simpson (1943, 1945), in particular, has called attention to the subjective element in much of classification, particularly in paleontology.   The student in many cases does not classify species but samples from natural populations:

From a series of concrete specimens in hand an inference is made as to the nature of a morphological group from which the sample came, and an endeavor is made to frame the morphological concept in such a way that the inferred morphological group will approximate a genetic group.   The thing that is actually classified is an inference, a purely subjective concept, which approximates a real, but unobservable, morphological unit, which in turn approximates an equally real but even less observable genetic unit.

It may seem that Simpson's views on the observability of genetic species are unduly pessimistic when applied to easily observable species like the monarch butterfly or the wood thrush.   In these cases, and they are actually very common, it appears that the classifier has much more information available than a mere inference.   In rare and localized species, like the whooping crane (*Grus americana* Linnaeus) all the living representatives of the species may be observable simultaneously.   The philosophical basis of Simpson's argument is, however, correct.

The Species without Dimension.   The original concept of a species, the species of the local naturalists Ray and Linnaeus, was a species without the dimensions of space and time.   Such a species is always separated by a complete gap from other sympatric species.   In its purest form it is clear-cut and has objective criteria, because it is defined by the gap that separates it from other sympatric species.   This local species is the yardstick by which all other situations are measured.   Lacking the dimensions of space and time, such a species is not evolving, it is static. It is for this reason that the *nondimensional species* has a great deal of objectivity and can be defined unequivocally (Mayr, 1949).

The modern concept of a species is multidimensional and often lacks the preciseness of the "ideal" nondimensional species.

Polytypic Species.   In the period of exploration which followed Linnaeus and which continues into our own day, it was found that some species are widespread and consist of many local populations.   If these local populations are sufficiently distinct from each other, they are called *subspecies* (see below for details).   Species which have no subspecies or which, to be more precise, consist of only a single subspecies are called *monotypic species*.   Species that consist of two or more subspecies are called *polytypic species*.   Recognition of the significance of polytypic species was one of the most important developments of the new systematics.   It is therefore appropriate to discuss the polytypic species in more detail.

Populations that are mutually exclusive geographically are called *allopatric*.   About one hundred years after Linnaeus it was found that certain local species that had been described from various parts of the world could be combined into groups of allopatric "species" that were obviously more closely related to one another than to any other species. Finally, when the gaps between the ranges of such species were explored, it was often found that they were occupied by intermediate populations. In other words, it was found that these allopatric species intergraded with one another.   Whenever this was the case, these allopatric "species" were united into a single polytypic species (Fig. 4).

The reclassification of all related forms originally described as monotypic species into polytypic species has led to a tremendous clarification of the system.   This reorganization of species classification is virtually completed in birds.   It is in full swing for mammals and under way for butterflies, beetles, and land mollusks but has hardly begun in most groups of animals.   Only after it has been completed will it be possible to say how many species of animals exist.   In 1870 about 11,000 and in 1910 about 19,000 species of birds were listed, but in spite of numerous subsequent discoveries, only 8,600 species of birds are now recognized (Mayr, 1946).   A similar reduction of numbers is to be expected in many

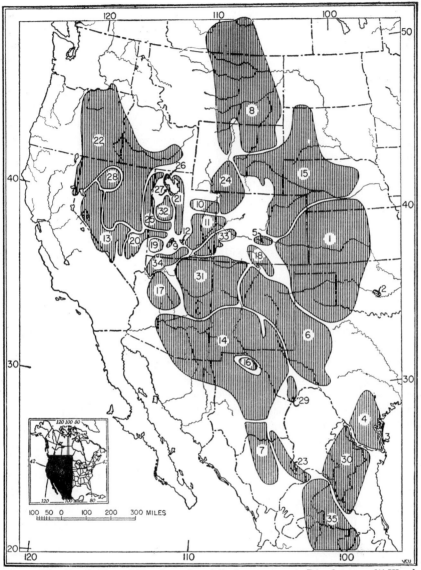

FIG. 4. The distribution of 35 subspecies of the kangaroo rat, *Dipodomys ordii* Wood-house, as an example of a range map of a polytypic species (*Setzer*, 1949).

1. *D. ordii richardsoni*	13. *D. ordii monoensis*	25. *D. ordii celeripes*
2. *D. ordii oklahomae*	14. *D. ordii ordii*	26. *D. ordii cineraceus*
3. *D. ordii compactus*	15. *D. ordii luteolus*	27. *D. ordii marshalli*
4. *D. ordii sennetti*	16. *D. ordii extractus*	28. *D. ordii inaquosus*
5. *D. ordii evexus*	17. *D. ordii chapmani*	29. *D. ordii attenuatus*
6. *D. ordii medius*	18. *D. ordii montanus*	30. *D. ordii fuscus*
7. *D. ordii obscurus*	19. *D. ordii cinderensis*	31. *D. ordii longipes*
8. *D. ordii terrosus*	20. *D. ordii fetosus*	32. *D. ordii pallidus*
9. *D. ordii panguitchensis*	21. *D. ordii utahensis*	33. *D. ordii nexilis*
10. *D. ordii uintensis*	22. *D. ordii columbianus*	34. *D. ordii cupidineus*
11. *D. ordii sanrafaeli*	23. *D. ordii idoneus*	35. *D. ordii palmeri*
12. *D. ordii fremonti*	24. *D. ordii priscus*	

groups of animals, especially terrestrial mollusks and fresh-water fish, as soon as a biologically defined polytypic species concept is applied. The consistent application of the polytypic species concept to all groups of animals is one of the chief tasks of the taxonomy of the future.

Dualistic Taxonomic Terminologies.   The deficiencies of the simple Linnaean terminology of *species* and *variety* became more and more apparent as the knowledge of species increased during the latter half of the nineteenth century and during the first two or three decades of the present one.   The polytypic species of the new systematics differs from the Linnaean species particularly by being a collective category.   It is in many instances a compound of several "species" originally proposed as monotypic.   What scientific name should one give to this new collective category, and who should be the author?   Two solutions have been proposed.

Although trinominals had been used since 1844, Kleinschmidt (1900) was the first zoologist to recognize this problem clearly (Mayr, 1942). He proposed that a new category be established between the (Linnaean) species and the genus.   He gave to it the term *Formenkreis* and proposed that the first taxonomist who gathered the various allopatric Linnaean species into this new collective category (= polytypic species of modern authors) should provide a new name for it of which he would be the responsible author (Stresemann, 1936).   Although we consider this proposal as inconvenient (and contrary to the International Rules), there is nothing wrong with Kleinschmidt's logic.   When Linnaeus named the white wagtail *Motacilla alba*, to cite one example, he had in mind the European population with the specific characters described by him. The *M. alba* of Linnaeus is what is now referred to as the nominate subspecies *M. alba alba* Linnaeus.   The collective category formed recently by uniting *M. alba* of Linnaeus with *M. lugubris* Temminck, *M. dukhunensis* Sykes, *M. baicalensis* Swinhoe, *M. leucopsis* Gould, *M. personata* Gould, *M. hodgsoni* Blyth, *M. ocularis* Swinhoe, *M. lugens* Kittlitz, and other species is a far cry from the *M. alba* of Linnaeus.[1]

Rensch (1929), dissatisfied with the term *Formenkreis*, with Kleinschmidt's evolutionary philosophy, and with his failure to distinguish between superspecies and polytypic species, coined the term *Rassenkreis* for the latter, distinguishing it sharply from the ordinary monotypic species, to which alone he restricted the term *species*.

These were the foremost attempts in zoology to solve the change in

---

[1] Several recent authors refrain from associating an author's name with the binominal of polytypic species, thereby meaning to indicate that the author of the name of the nominate subspecies is not the responsible author of the collective species to which the nominate subspecies belongs.   This practice is not sanctioned by the International Rules.

the species concept by introducing a dual system of terminology, for the Linnaean species on the one hand and the modern, polytypic species on the other. These attempts were not successful, because the vast majority of zoologists preferred a different procedure (A.O.U. Code, 1885). Instead of using two terms, one for the Linnaean species and the other for the species of the new systematics, they broadened the species concept so as to include both kinds. They no longer restricted the term *species* to the nondimensional species of the old naturalist but included also species which are variable in space and time. The qualifying adjectives, monotypic and polytypic, were proposed by Huxley to distinguish between the two kinds of species in conformance with the use of these terms for higher categories (monotypic and polytypic genera, etc.). Kleinschmidt had no followers, while Coues, Allen, Hartert, K. Jordan, and others were so energetic in the consistent application of the polytypic species concept that no lasting terminological dualism developed in zoology.

The Superspecies. Closely related allopatric forms are usually subspecies of a polytypic species. Occasionally, however, the evidence indicates that these allopatric forms have attained species rank (particularly if effectively isolated for a long time). It is frequently important in evolutionary and zoogeographical studies to single out such groups of entirely or largely allopatric species and apply to them a unit term. The term *superspecies* was proposed for these (Mayr, 1931) as a substitute for the earlier term *Artenkreis* proposed by Rensch (1929).

A superspecies is a monophyletic group of very closely related and largely or entirely allopatric species.

When the ranges of its component species are plotted on a map, the superspecies usually presents the picture of a polytypic species. However, there is evidence that the component species have attained reproductive isolation. This evidence is threefold. Either the species, although completely isolated from each other, are morphologically as different as are normally sympatric species, or they are in geographical contact without interbreeding, or there is actually a slight distributional overlap.

Superspecies are not distinguished by a special nomenclature. They are, however, listed as such in monographs and catalogues. They are chiefly important in zoogeographical and speciation studies.

The unique position of the species has been pointed out by many recent authors (Dobzhansky, 1951; Mayr, 1942; Huxley, 1942; Simpson, 1945; and others). It is the only taxonomic category which, at least in its nondimensional expression, can be objectively defined and delimited. Occupying a definite ecological niche at a given locality, it has a precise ecological meaning. The infraspecific categories are groupings of populations within species. The supraspecific categories are groupings of species into "higher" categories. The species is the "base line" in either case.

Practical difficulties in delimiting species may arise from two causes. Either they are due to insufficient information (such difficulties are discussed in Chap. 5), or they are due to the multidimensional character of species in nature. Species are evolving systems, and the paleontologist should in theory be entirely unable to delimit species vertically. This has been pointed out by several recent paleontologists (Arkell and Moy-Thomas, 1940; Burma, 1949; Dunbar, 1950; etc.). Actually, the fossil record is in most instances sufficiently incomplete to provide artificial breaks in the sequences that can be utilized by the taxonomist as species borders. Some of the unbroken vertical sequences of species recorded by paleontologists show such slight degrees of difference that they could equally well be considered as subspecies and be combined into vertical polytypic species. However, this still leaves some instances in which the paleontologist will have to break continuous sequences arbitrarily into separate species.

THE SUBSPECIES

The subspecies is the only infraspecific taxonomic category. The status of other infraspecific forms is discussed in Chap. 5, their nomenclature in Chap. 13. The subspecies may be defined as follows:

Subspecies are geographically defined aggregates of local populations which differ taxonomically from other such subdivisions of a species.

Not more than one subspecies of any one polytypic species can exist in breeding condition in any one area. Adjacent subspecies interbreed or are potentially capable of doing so if separated by extrinsic barriers.

It may be helpful to make the following comments on the above-stated specifications of subspecies:

"Differ taxonomically": The subspecies concept has an old philosophical tradition, rooted in typological philosophy. When the species concept was developed by Ray and Linnaeus, the species was first thought to be something stable and uniform, composed of individuals that conform to the type. Individuals that did not agree with the type were segregated as "varieties." Subsequently it was found that the "variety" (see below) was a composite concept, including both variant individuals and variant populations. The name *variety* for the latter category was eventually replaced by the term *subspecies*. At first only the most distinct subspecies were described, but after taxonomists in certain groups, particularly birds, had nearly completed the describing of conspicuously different species and subspecies, some authors began to name as subspecies every population they could prove distinguishable. Although such populations may be statistically different, they are not necessarily taxonomically different, for the two terms do not coincide.

This is important, because the work of the population geneticist has proved that in sexually reproducing species *no two natural populations* are genetically identical.   If large enough samples are available and a sufficiently accurate analysis is made, it can usually be proved that a statistically significant difference exists not only genetically but also in morphological characters.   Many species will have several hundred, and some widespread species many thousand, populations that differ from each other significantly (in the statistical sense).   The naming of all these slightly different populations was proposed by some authors in order to establish uniform categories that conform to the type concept as we have described it earlier.   However, this endeavor was doomed to failure from the beginning, because completely uniform population groups do not exist in sexually reproducing species.   The typological approach has led the splitter astray.

It is now realized that all taxonomic categories are somewhat heterogeneous.   Not only the species but the subspecies also is *an assemblage of populations*, except in the rare cases of exceedingly localized relict forms or insular populations.

To qualify as a subspecies, such an assemblage of populations must be *taxonomically different* from other subspecies.   What is taxonomically different can be determined only by agreement among taxonomists. The difference must be sufficiently great so that it is possible to identify the great majority of specimens without knowledge of their provenience. For that purpose, many taxonomists adhere to the *75 per cent rule* (see Chaps. 5 and 7).

Subspecies as Geographical and Ecological Races.   The word *race* is not used consistently by taxonomists.   The majority usage is that which is current among the taxonomists of mammals, birds, and insects, namely, to use the terms *subspecies* and *geographical race* synonymously and interchangeably.   Ichthyologists and anthropologists sometimes apply the word *race* to local populations within subspecies.   Other taxonomists refer to them simply as local populations.

A subspecies is *geographically localized* and consequently a *geographical race*.   However, since no two localities are exactly identical with respect to their environment, every subspecies is, at least theoretically, also an ecological race.   Warm-blooded and highly mobile animals, such as birds, are rather independent of local environmental factors, and subspecies in such groups are primarily geographical races.   Plants and many sedentary cold-blooded animals are broadly exposed to the effects of local environmental conditions, and subspecies in such groups impress the observer as ecological races.

The case of host races of parasites on plants and animals is particularly suitable to demonstrate the dual aspect of races.   Host races are

ecological races because they occur in different niches. However, they
may also be regarded as "geographical" races, because they are spatially
separated, with gene flow severely inhibited. When parasites have the
ability to get from host to host, they generally fail to produce host races.
The spatial isolation of races of parasites is thus often one between hosts
rather than a geographical one in the strict sense of the word.

It must be emphasized that there is no geographical race that is not
also an ecological race, nor an ecological race that is not also a geographical, or at least a microgeographical, race. The geographical and
the ecological aspects are two facets of the same phenomenon, the
subspecies.

Polytopic Subspecies. If subspecies of a species differ in only a single
diagnostic character, such as color, size, or growth form, it may happen
that several unrelated and widely separated populations acquire independently the same character. Dice (1941) has described this for
Peromyscus populations in the mountains of Arizona and New Mexico;
Cazier (ms.) for tiger beetles (*Cicindela*) on alkali flats; Vaurie (1949)
for East Indian drongos; and so forth.

Although such populations may be morphologically indistinguishable,
they are not necessarily more closely related to each other than to other
populations, and they are unquestionably genetically different in various
cryptic characters. However, if such populations do not differ from each
other in any taxonomic character, they must be united under a single
subspecific name (Mayr). A subspecies is a composite, heterogeneous
category, even where it consists of contiguous populations.

The criteria to be utilized in considering whether a given isolated population should be classified as a species or a subspecies will be discussed in
Chap. 5.

Intermediate Populations. Intermediate populations are usually
found in the area of contact of two well-defined subspecies *a* and *b*.
Such intermediate populations may have an extensive range, or they
may be restricted to a narrow belt. Individuals of such intermediate
populations may either be more or less uniform in character, namely,
intermediate between the topotypical populations of the two adjacent
subspecies *a* and *b*; or else this intermediate population may be composed
of a mixture of individuals, some of which resemble *a*, others *b*, while still
others are intermediate.

What should be the taxonomic treatment of the individuals of the
intermediate populations? First of all, let us state what should not be
done: They should not be described as a separate subspecies if they do
not satisfy the requirements of the 75 per cent rule (see Chap. 7).

The best solution is to find the halfway point between the "most
typical" population of subspecies *a* and that of subspecies *b*, and use

this halfway point (in phenotype, not in distance) as the dividing line between subspecies *a* and *b*; or else specimens of the intermediate populations are labeled as *X-us albus* subsp. or *X-us albus albus* $\lessgtr$ *secundus*.

If there is a definite "step" in the character change between subspecies *a* and *b*, that step should be chosen as the subspecies border, even if it is not exactly at the halfway point. If, on the other hand, there is a perfect gradation between two extremes, then the term *cline* (Huxley) may be applied to this series of populations.

Cline. Huxley (1939, 1940) has proposed the useful term *cline* for a character gradient. A series of adjacent populations in which the gradual change of a character occurs forms a cline. At right angles to the cline are the points of equal expression of the character (of equal phenotype), and therefore these lines are referred to as *isophenes*. For instance, if in the range of a species of butterfly, the percentage of white specimens varies from north to south, the corresponding isophenes may be indicated on a map (Fig. 5).

There are clines of morphological, physiological, ecological, and other characters and also of the percentage frequencies of polymorphic characters. Clines may be smooth, or they may be stepped clines with rather sudden changes of values (Huxley, 1939). Clines do not receive nomenclatural recognition. In fact, it is advisable not to obscure the presence of clines by the recognition of too many only slightly differentiated subspecies on a single cline. Clines are usually produced by selection and are therefore usually parallel to the environmental factors that are reponsible for them. Close analysis may reveal several clines within a group of populations. These may be quite independent and may run parallel to different environmental factors.

The Local Population. The subspecies is the lowest taxonomic category which it is advisable to distinguish nomenclaturally. However, the subspecies is by no means the lowest subdivision of the species. Subspecies are not homogeneous but are composed of numerous *local populations*, all of them differing slightly in gene frequencies and the mean values of various quantitative characters.

Repeated attempts have been made during the past fifty years to give nomenclatural recognition to such slight populations. Semenov-Tian-Shansky (1910) proposed the term *natio* for them. Fish taxonomists recognize *races* within subspecies, generally without naming them. This usage is not recommended as a formal terminology, since most animal taxonomists consider the terms *subspecies* and (geographical) *race* as synonymous.

Now that it is being realized that every local population is different from every other one, even if they live only a few miles apart or less, and that these populations are not sharply separated from one another (except where separated by unsuitable areas), there is no longer a valid excuse for the formal nomenclatural recognition of innumerable local subdivisions of subspecies.   It is legitimate and even desirable to describe the trends of variation within a subspecies—particularly if material from numerous localities is available—but it serves no useful purpose and

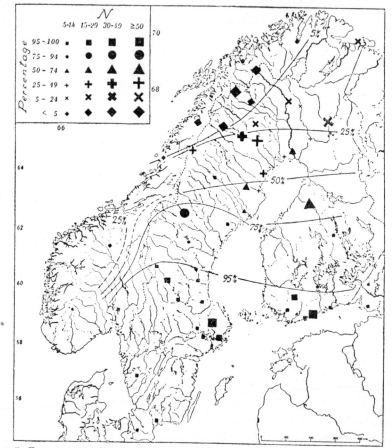

Fig. 5. Percentage at different Fennoscandian localities of white (*napi*-like) specimens of *Pieris napi* ♀, first generation (*Petersen*, 1949).

merely complicates nomenclature to give names to these localized, slightly different populations or colonies.

Variants within Populations. It is one of the most characteristic attributes of taxonomic categories that they are based on natural populations.   They may, and usually do, include many populations, but they can never include only part of a population.   Selected individuals from a population are not a population or a taxonomic category.   The males of a given species may be a different biological or genetical category from the females of that species but are not a different taxonomic category, nor are the immature forms, nor individual variants such as albinos, red-heads, or blue-eyed individuals.

This was not always so clearly recognized as it is now. In the beginnings of taxonomy no distinction was made between infraspecific variants based on populations and such variants based on individuals. Either kind was recorded under a single heading, namely, as *variety*. The variety is one of the oldest taxonomic categories. It was used by pre-Linnaean authors and also by Linnaeus. The history of the term *variety* is closely correlated with that of the type concept and of the morphological species definition. It was originally defined as an individual which somewhat differs from the type of the species but not sufficiently to require recognition as a separate species. Later analysis showed that many different phenomena were included under the heading *variety*. In addition to similar species, it included principally subspecies and individual variants of various sorts. Subspecies are a taxonomic category; individual variants are not. When the subspecies received formal recognition in the Rules as a taxonomic category, it was substituted for the "variety" of the earlier version of the Rules.

Although *not* taxonomic categories, many types of individual variants (= intrapopulation variants) have been named, especially by amateur insect collectors. No reference was made to the status of such names in the original Rules of Zoological Nomenclature. However, in order to avoid confusion, the International Commission at the Thirteenth International Zoological Congress in Paris (1948) ruled on how to deal with such names. This will be discussed in Chap. 13.

Intrapopulation variants are more important from the taxonomic point of view than from the nomenclatural one. Many of these variants are sufficiently different from each other to simulate different species. A thorough understanding of the various kinds of individual variation and of the different types that can occur within a single population is of the greatest importance in taxonomic discrimination. It will therefore be discussed in detail in Chap. 5.

NEUTRAL TERMS FOR CATEGORIES

It is very convenient in systematic work to have some terms that can be given informally to taxonomic units, particularly in incompletely analyzed cases. These are the so-called "neutral terms." The ones that are most frequently used in taxonomy are *form*, for a single unit, and *group* or *complex*, for a number of units. We often speak of a form when we do not know whether the systematic unit in question is, for example, a full species or merely a subspecies of a polytypic species, or whether it is a subspecies or an individual variant. Seasonal and polymorphic variants are often referred to as forms. The term is also used in the plural when two unequal units are combined. For example, when describing attributes common to a species and a subspecies of another species, one refers to the species and the subspecies as "these two forms."

The term *group* is most commonly applied to an assemblage of closely related species within a genus. In *Drosophila*, for example, one speaks of the *melanogaster* group, the *virilis* group, the *obscura* group, the *willistoni* group, and so forth. The usage of the term *group* for such cases is popular among taxonomists, since it eliminates the need for subgenera. Occasionally the term *group* is also applied to subspecies in species with very many subspecies. The common Palearctic jay, *Garrulus glandarius*, has a total of 41 subspecies, but they can be arranged in eight groups, the *garrulus* group, the *bispecularis* group, and others. The term *group* is also used, though more rarely, to denote a number of closely related units in the higher categories—genera, for example. The word *complex* is frequently used synonymously with the term *group*.

Terms like *section, series,* and *division* are sometimes used for groups of higher categories. Their use is, however, not standardized, and they are sometimes used above and sometimes below the family, the order, the class. They are essentially still neutral terms, corresponding to the term *group*.

Botanists use a recently coined word, the convenient *taxon* (plural, *taxa*), in place of *taxonomic category* and have recently modified their rules of nomenclature accordingly.

LOWER CATEGORIES IN PALEONTOLOGY

The categories of paleontology are those in general use elsewhere in zoology. However, the application of these categories is often different.

The samples in paleontology are often small, frequently consisting of a single specimen. When large samples are available, they are often from a single horizon or a single exposure. It is therefore often impossible to sample the represented species adequately. This uncertainty about the species leads the paleontologist to place greater reliance on the genus and to consider it "the basic unit of practical and morphological taxonomy" (Simpson, 1945).

Past paleontological practice has been to describe as a full species every sample that appeared reasonably distinct. Infraspecific categories hardly figure in the paleontological literature, except an occasional "variety," which is usually an intrapopulation variant. It is only within the last decade or so that the term *subspecies* has been used more freely in paleontology (Simpson, 1943; Newell, 1947; Sylvester-Bradley, 1951). It is applied, as in neontology, to populations (or samples of populations) that are sufficiently similar morphologically to make it probable that full reproductive isolation between them had not yet developed.

The paleontologist deals with the additional dimension of time, and his subspecies are not all synchronous. In fact, most of the paleontological subspecies are presumably ancestors and descendants. It has therefore been proposed to use two sets of terminology, one for the synchronous allopatric subspecies of the neontologist and one for allochronic subspecies. However, such a dual terminology would be impractical, for in most paleontological situations it would be impossible to determine the exact chronological relationship of allopatric populations. It is therefore most practical to follow Simpson's suggestion that the term *subspecies* be used in paleontology for any subspecific category, whether contemporary or not. However, a paleontologist must never forget that it is impossible by definition that two subspecies coexist at the same locality. If he finds two "subspecies" in one sample, he can be sure that they are either intrapopulation variants (the usual situation) or different species (see discrimination grid, Chap. 5).

THE TAXONOMIC TREATMENT OF HYBRIDS

Hybrid specimens require special nomenclatural treatment. Hybrids are often named before their hybrid nature has become apparent. Such names become invalid as soon as the hybridity of the bearer has been established.

There are three kinds of hybridism in nature:

1. Sympatric hybridization. The occasional production of hybrid individuals in the region of overlap of otherwise well-defined species is sympatric hybridization. The many hybrids in the birds of paradise and in the hummingbirds belong in this group. Such hybrids are listed as a cross of the two parental species, *Tetrao urogallus* X *Lyrurus tetrix.*

2. Allopatric hybridization. If hybridization is defined as the crossing of unlike parents, it is very difficult to make a sharp distinction between the hybridization of subspecies and of allopatric species. Until such a case is fully investigated, it is often convenient to consider as allopatric hybridization any case of interbreeding between distinct allopatric populations. No taxonomic difficulty is produced where the zone of hybridization is narrow. However, if it is wide and if a well-defined, stabilized hybrid population with intermediate characters develops, it is sometimes convenient and justified to recognize the "hybrid" population taxonomically. The fact that such complete interbreeding prevails indicates that the two parental "species" are actually conspecific. The "hybrid population" may be named as a subspecies if it satisfies the requirements of the 75 per cent rule. The taxonomic recognition of a hybrid population is not justified if it is very variable and includes a high percentage of parental types in addition to intermediates.

3. Amphiploidy. Hybridism in plants may lead to the instantaneous production of a polyploid that combines the chromosome sets of two parental species. Such a hybrid may give rise to a new population which is reproductively isolated from the parents and which may become a new species, provided that it is sufficiently fertile and able to compete with other species (including the parents).

There are a few hybrid situations which do not fit into the above scheme and for which no practicable taxonomic solution seems possible. One of these occurs when the reproductive isolation between two otherwise well-defined sympatric species breaks down locally, leading to the formation of local hybrid populations. This has happened in many species that were originally ecologically isolated, after man destroyed their habitats. The North American toads, *Bufo americanus* and *B. fowleri* (Blair, 1941), are a well-analyzed example. It is advisable in such cases to continue giving the parental populations the rank of full species and not to allow taxonomic rank to the hybrids or hybrid populations.

The second set of hybridization phenomena that causes particular taxonomic difficulties is the occurrence of "allopatric introgressive hybridization." It sometimes happens, particularly among plants, that there is a limited amount of hybridization in the zone of contact of two essentially allopatric species. The contiguous or slightly overlapping populations of the two species are more or less affected by "introgression" of genes from the other species (Anderson, 1949). Still, this introgression may not lead to a complete breakdown of the reproductive isolation between the two species. If the introgression leads to a pronounced change of the taxonomic characters of the affected populations of one of the two species, it may be justifiable to apply a subspecific name to these populations.

Parthenogenetic and Asexual Entities. The function of sexual reproduction is genetic recombination, that is, the mixing of genetic factors from two different parents. Sexual reproduction involves the fusion of the nuclei of two gametes. Deviations from this process are known as parthenogenetic and asexual reproduction. Forms of asexual reproduction include vegetative budding, as in corals and bryozoa, whereas parthenogenetic reproduction is typified by the production of offspring from unfertilized eggs. Since interbreeding is the ultimate test of conspecificity in animals, and since this criterion is only available in sexually reproducing organisms, it is evident that the species concept is difficult to apply in these cases. How should the taxonomist treat clones, pure lines, biotypes, and so-called "strains" or "stocks" of parthenogenetic or asexual organisms?

Most, if not all, forms of parthenogenetic reproduction are evidently a secondary condition. In aphids, cladocerans, rotifers, and other animals, most females are parthenogenetic during part of the year but return to sexual reproduction under certain environmental conditions. It is unjustifiable to give nomenclatural recognition as "races" or "micro-species" to such temporary clones. Such parthenogenetically repro-ducing lines will terminate sooner or later either by extinction or by returning through a sexual process to the joint gene pool of the parental sexually reproducing species.

Some exceptional cases are known in which a form that is as distinct as a good species reproduces strictly parthenogenetically, and no biparental species is known from which it might have branched off. Nomenclatural recognition is justified in such cases. Whenever several reproductively isolated chromosome types occur within such a "species," as in various crustaceans (*Artemia salina* Linnaeus) (White, 1945), it may be con-venient to distinguish them nomenclaturally. Although conventionally referred to as *races*, reproductively isolated chromosomal populations are more logically designated (*micro*)*species.*

CHAPTER 3

CLASSIFICATION AND THE HIGHER CATEGORIES

The definition, description, and naming of more than 1 million species of living animals are the analytical tasks of taxonomy, as stated in Chap. 2. The other task of taxonomy is synthetic. It consists of organizing the otherwise chaotic mass of species into a classification. Such a classification is an indispensable prerequisite to the identification, cataloguing, and arrangement in collections of these species.

Many systems of classification are possible.[1] Classifications of books in a library are often cited as an analogue to the classification of organisms. Such books may be classified according to subject matter or according to the initials of the author, or chronologically according to the date of publication or accession, or according to size, or on the basis of a combination of several of these classifying criteria. Species of animals, likewise, might be arranged according to the alphabetical sequence of the scientific names, or according to size, or to habitat, or to the climatic zone or geographical region in which they live. All these classifications have actually been proposed; they are more or less logical and sometimes useful if we are interested merely in certain practical aspects of classification. Classifications based on similar adaptations or modes of living have been particularly popular. Pliny, for instance, classified animals into those of land, water, and air. Other early authors classified bats with birds, whales with fishes, and all linear invertebrates as "worms." Many of the early classifications of the Linnaean period were also based on such adaptive features. Birds with webbed feet were classed together, and so were those with long legs. The rodents and lagomorphs were placed in a single order, owing to an adaptive similarity of the incisors; the artiodactyls and perissodactyls were classified as ungulates, owing to similarities in feeding habits, foot structure, and general body build. Actually, even some of the currently accepted categories are apparently based on convergent adaptive characters, such as the Old World warblers, babblers, shrikes, and perhaps titmice, among the birds (Mayr and Amadon, 1951).

Aristotle, almost twenty-three hundred years ago, was the first to realize that the most practical system of classification of animals is based on the degree of similarity of their morphology or anatomy. The great advantage of this system is that it is based on the sum total of many

[1] For an illuminating discussion of the principles of classification see Simpson, 1945.

40

morphological similarities or differences. Such a system is apt to indicate "natural affinities," as Linnaeus and even some pre-Linnaean authors contended, and was therefore called the *natural system*, in contradistinction to *artificial systems*, based on single characters.

Even in a strictly morphological classification, the assignment of a species to a definite category characterizes it usually as possessing a very definite combination of structures and biological attributes. So perfect indeed was the agreement of taxonomic position and structural characteristics that it became a source of considerable amazement and speculation among the naturalists in the post-Linnaean period. Although they spoke of natural systems and natural affinities, they did not understand by these terms what we do today. To explain the orderliness of the natural system, some of the natural philosophers in the first half of the nineteenth century attempted to construct systems on the basis of logical categories, similar to the periodical table of the chemical elements (Stresemann, 1950). Why these systems of horizontal and vertical columns or of concentric circles were so sterile and unsuccessful did not become apparent until it was realized what it was that made the natural system *natural*.

The theory of evolution solved this puzzle in a manner that was as simple as it was satisfactory: the organisms of a "natural" systematic category agree with one another in so many characteristics because they are descendants of one common ancestor. The natural system became a phylogenetic system. The natural system is based on similarity; the phylogenetic system on the degree of relationship. One would expect a priori that such a complete change of the philosophical basis of classification would result in a radical change of classification, but this was by no means the case (Dobzhansky, 1951). "From their classifications alone, it is practically impossible to tell whether zoologists of the middle decades of the nineteenth century were evolutionists or not" (Simpson, 1945).

The reason for the congruence is principally the fact that similarity is usually caused by relationship. The more closely two animals are related, the more morphological characters they will usually have in common. There was hardly any change even in method before and after Darwin, except that the "archetype" was replaced by the common ancestor. "The common ancestor was at first, and in most cases, just as hypothetical as the archetype, and the methods of inference were much the same for both, so that classification continued to develop with no immediate evidence of the revolution in principles" (Simpson, 1945).

PHYLOGENY AND CLASSIFICATION

One of the objects of taxonomists in the post-Darwinian period was to construct a classification of animals composed of monophyletic groups.

As we have seen, this aim had already in part been anticipated by the "natural systems" of the pre-Darwinian period. However, much of this classification was still based on conspicuous adaptive characters (*e.g.*, open incisors of rodents and lagomorphs; thickened forewings of beetles, roaches, and earwigs) rather than on true relationship. The first step, then, toward the achievement of a phylogenetic classification is an analysis of the taxonomic characters to determine which of them are derived from common ancestors (*homologies*) and which are spurious similarities (*analogies*), usually convergent adaptations correlated with similar habits.

This second task of the taxonomist is by no means completed in most groups of animals. It is farthest advanced in groups with an abundant fossil record, as mammals, reptiles, mollusks; it is most backward in essentially uniform groups, the subdivisions of which are largely based on adaptive specializations (*e.g.*, birds and many parasitic groups). The development of a sound classification which is not in conflict with phylogeny can be accomplished in these difficult cases only by utilizing every conceivable taxonomic character, not only gross morphology but also cytological characters (*e.g.*, chromosome numbers and patterns), serology, and other chemical characters, habits, ecology, and others. For a discussion of taxonomic characters, see Chap. 6.

Every one of the sources of information on phylogeny that has been used in the past has its limitations and pitfalls. This is true for genetics, physiology (including serology), embryology, and zoogeography (Simpson, 1945). It is even true for paleontology, because there are several interpretations possible for many fossil remains, particularly if they are incomplete. Still, paleontology (when fossils are available) and comparative morphology are on the whole the most productive sources of phylogenetic information.

Since it is the avowed aim of a modern classification to reflect phylogeny, one might assume that classifications could not be attempted until phylogenies are clearly and unequivocally established. This is not the case. Many of our existing classifications are actually pragmatic and based on the degree of similarity, regardless of whether they reflect blood relationship or not. Such a system may occasionally be more useful than a strictly phylogenetic system. In fact, ever since the theory of evolution was accepted, there has been a conflict among taxonomists as to whether to strive for a purely practical classification or for a classification "that expresses phylogeny." Some authors compromise; they strive for the most practical classification that is still based on monophyletic groups. But the breaking up of polyphyletic groups does not necessarily lead to a more practical system, if we do not know where the fragments belong. For instance, the large flightless birds such as ostriches, rheas, cassowaries, moas, and elephant birds were long classed in the subclass Ratites.   Eventually it became evident that these forms were unrelated, and that they have become secondarily similar only in connection with the increase in size permitted by the loss of flight. Classifying these "Ratites" in five independent orders has not simplified the classification of birds, particularly since it has not yet been established to which of the remaining orders of flying birds each of the five orders of flightless birds is most closely related.

A similar example has been related by Richards (1938):

Among the bees there is a number of cuckoo genera of which the larvae live as parasites in the nests of industrious species.   These cuckoo bees have evolved from industrious species and in favorable examples the resemblance is still so close that the ancestral genus is pretty certain.   Yet some of the genera no

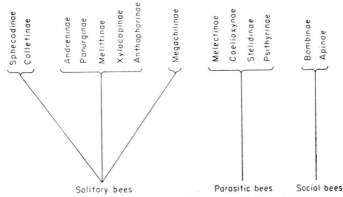

Fig. 6. A practical classification of bees (*after Friese*, 1926), in which the parasitic bees are treated as a group independent of their close relatives among the solitary and social bees.

longer closely resemble any industrious genus.   Moreover, there is a very definite "parasitic facies" dependent not only on the loss of pollen-collecting apparatus, but on the presence of bright, sometimes wasp-like colors, etc.; most parasitic bees can be recognized as such without observation of their habits.   For these reasons two different classifications have grown up.   One endeavors to place each parasitic genus next to its supposed ancestor.   This is the phylogenetic scheme and, in general, I believe the best one, but it has the disadvantage that a number of genera are hard to place.   The other scheme places all the parasitic bees together in one group which, at least in the female sex, is easily defined by the absence of pollen-collecting apparatus.   Sub-groups within this assemblage roughly correspond to the various lines of ancestry.   Although artificial this scheme has certain advantages in classifying the bees of, say, Africa which are very imperfectly known.

In order to illustrate this point, we may compare the strictly practical classification of Friese (1926) with that of Michener (1944).   Friese recognizes four polyphyletic categories of parasitic bees (Fig. 6).   Michener places a number of parasitic genera in categories with their nearest non-parasitic relatives (in the Halictinae, Anthidiini, Megachilini, Euglossini, and Bombini) but in order to do so is forced to recognize fourteen "monophyletic" categories composed wholly of parasitic bees (Fig. 7).

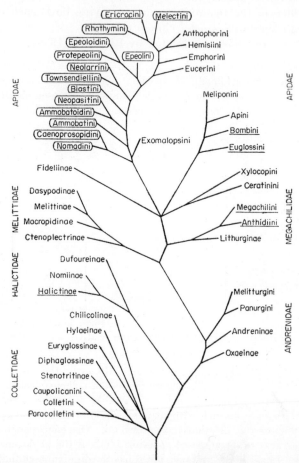

Fig. 7. A phylogenetic classification of bees (*after Michener*, 1944) in which the parasitic bees are placed according to their supposed relationships among the solitary and social bees. Wholly parasitic groups are circled, partially parasitic groups underlined.

It is obvious from these examples that a compromise must often be made between the practical aims of classification and its phylogenetic basis.

Another kind of difficulty is often encountered by the paleontologist when he finds that similar levels of morphological specialization are reached independently in unrelated or only distantly related lines. Often a real dilemma develops between the convenience of a horizontal classification and the consistency of a vertical (= phylogenetic) classification (Bather, 1927; Arkell and Moy-Thomas, 1940). For instance, in the ammonite family Cadoceratidae, four well-known genera, *Cadoceras, Quenstedtoceras, Cardioceras*, and *Amoeboceras*, follow each other in a clearly defined time sequence. Each genus is characteristic for a given geological period. However, each genus embraces many different forms which differ in some respects (but not those of the generic diagnosis) more widely from one another than from corresponding species in other genera. These forms are classed in many subgenera. "As knowledge advances, it becomes increasingly probable that each subgenus of *Cardioceras* evolved from a different subgenus of *Quenstedoceras*." There is thus often greater true affinity between subgenus *a* of Genus *A* and subgenus *a'* of genus *B* than between subgenus *a* and *b* of genus *A*. However, since the "true affinities" of many of these subgenera are obscure, and since the horizontal genera are so characteristic of well-defined geological periods, paleontologists are justifiably reluctant to replace their eminently practical horizontal classification by a more nearly "correct" phylogenetic, vertical arrangement.

Still another problem is presented by unequal rates of evolution. For instance, the class of reptiles consists of many branches, some of which branched off the main stem at an early geological date. The turtles and mammal-like reptiles are such branches. One well-defined group of reptiles (pseudosuchians, archosaurians) gave rise to the birds and the following reptilian groups: pterodactyls, saurischians, ornithischians, and crocodilians. Phylogenetically, the birds are thus more closely related to the crocodilians than the latter are to the lizards or the turtles.

It is evident from the last-mentioned difficulties that it would not always be easy to translate phylogeny into classification, even if all the facts of phylogeny were fully known. Where the phylogeny is still obscure, it would be only confusing to have anything but an openly practical classification. In spite of these practical difficulties, it should remain the ultimate aim of the taxonomist to devise a phylogenetic classification, that is, a classification in which the categories are monophyletic. Such a phylogenetic system has two advantages: (1) it is the only known system that has a sound theoretical basis (something the natural philosophers of the early nineteenth century looked for in vain); and (2) it has the practical advantage of combining forms (and there are only a few exceptions to this rule) that have the greatest number of characters in common.

The difficulties of translating phylogeny into classification are twofold. (1) There is the need for expressing different degrees of relationship through a system of categories (see below, hierarchy of categories).

(2) There is the need for presenting a multidimensional phylogenetic tree graphically and, more particularly, in a linear sequence (see Chap. 8).

SUBJECTIVITY OF HIGHER CATEGORIES

The assignment of rank to a given taxonomic group is a subjective matter. This may be demonstrated by three types of evidence.

Historical Differences. A genus, a family, or other category has a different value in different historical periods of taxonomy. While the species recognized by Linnaeus are still, in most cases, listed as species, his genera are usually completely changed. Most Linnaean genera of animals have been raised to the rank of families or even higher. Furthermore, at the end of a splitting period in some branch of taxonomy, each category has a very narrow definition. In the subsequent lumping period, the limits of these categories are again expanded.

Synchronous Differences. Even at the same period, categories are treated differently by different authors. For instance, in Parker and Haswell's textbook of zoology (1940), the insects are classified as a class of the phylum Arthropoda, and the Orthoptera as an order with four suborders. In Handlirsch's treatment of the insects in Kükenthal's *Handbuch der Zoologie* (1926–1936), the Insecta are listed as a subphylum, and the Orthoptera are arranged in two superorders and four orders.

Group Differences. The recent birds are classified in from 20 to 50 orders (by various authors). There is less difference between these orders than there is between the currently recognized orders of insects or of mollusks. Likewise the families in the order Passeres (songbirds) are much less distinct than the families in most other groups of animals. Obviously the categories *order* and *family* do not have the same meaning for an ornithologist as for most other taxonomists. Likewise, the physical anthropologists are in the habit of giving generic rank to much finer subdivisions than those so ranked by most other taxonomists.

The three types of evidence illustrate that the ranking awarded to a taxonomic group above the species is strictly subjective. However, it does not mean that in this regard any one group of taxonomists is either "right" or "wrong." Nor does it mean that the categories themselves have no objectivity (see below). It is important to keep these facts in mind.

THE TAXONOMIC HIERARCHY

The actual method of establishing a classification consists in defining groups or categories on a hierarchic scale. Each of these categories includes one or more groups from the next lower level, which is the next lower category. The result is that all the animals can be classified in a taxonomic hierarchy consisting of a series of categories of ascending rank from the species to the kingdom, each successive category embracing one or more of the next lower category. As will be presently discussed, all these categories (except the species) are both objective and subjective. They are objective because they consist of objectively definable entities; they are subjective because the categorical level, as well as the delimitation of the categories against one another, is subjective.

The function of taxonomic categories is to reduce the diversity of nature to a comprehensible system. Groups may be understood and remembered more readily than the countless units of which they are composed. Every classification involves two steps: (1) the arranging of lower units into groups and (2) the joining of these groups in an ascending hierarchy of more and more unlike groups. Both steps involve numerous practical, as well as scientific, questions.

The most essential point to be kept in mind is that primarily a classification should be practical: it should create order out of chaos. As we have already emphasized, taxonomic classification existed before the theory of evolution was accepted by biologists, and even today it may be pursued without regard to phylogeny.

Linnaeus, who founded the hierarchy of taxonomic categories, recognized within the animal kingdom only five, *classis, ordo, genus, species, varietas.* As the knowledge of animals grew (and with it their number), it became necessary to make finer divisions, of which two are now universally accepted, the family (between genus and order) and the phylum (between class and kingdom). The *varietas,* as used by Linnaeus, was an optional category under which were placed various types of variation (geographical and individual). The remaining categories form the basic taxonomic hierarchy of animals, any given species belonging thus to seven obligatory categories, as follows:

	Wolf	Honey Bee
Kingdom	Animalia	Animalia
Phylum	Chordata	Arthropoda
Class	Mammalia	Insecta
Order	Carnivora	Hymenoptera
Family	Canidae	Apidae
Genus	*Canis*	*Apis*
Species	*lupus*	*mellifera*

The respective position of two animals in the zoological system can be expressed by this hierarchy with a fair degree of accuracy. However, in most groups of animals the need has arisen for an even more precise definition of the taxonomic position of a species. This has been accomplished historically by a splitting of the original categories and by inserting additional categories between the seven basic ones. Most of these are formed by combining the original names with the prefixes *super* or *sub*. Thus there are *superorders* and *suborders, superclasses* and *sub-*

classes, etc.   Many other names have been proposed for higher categories, but none of them is in general use, except perhaps the term *tribe* between genus and family.   Some authors, as for example Simpson (1945), use a category *cohort* between order and class.   The generally accepted categories are the following:

Kingdom
  Phylum
    Subphylum
      Superclass
        Class
          Subclass
            Cohort
              Superorder
                Order
                  Suborder
                    Superfamily (*-oidea*)
                      Family (*-idae*)
                        Subfamily (*-inae*)
                          Tribe (*-ini*)
                            Genus
                              Subgenus
                              Species
                              Subspecies

In current practice the names for tribes, subfamilies, families, and superfamilies have standardized endings, which are added to the stem of the name of the type genus (Chap. 15).   No standardized endings exist for the categories above the family (Chap. 16).

THE GENUS

The genus is a collective taxonomic unit consisting of a number of similar or related species.   It is distinguished from all other higher categories by being recognized in the scientific name.   The nomenclature proposed by Linnaeus is binominal, consisting of two names, each with its own function.   The functions which Linnaeus visualized for the two components of the scientific name are diametrically opposite.   The specific trivial name signifies singularity and distinctness; the generic name calls attention to the existence of a group of similar or related species—it relieves the memory.

An objective criterion for generic rank does not exist equivalent, let us say, to reproductive isolation as a species criterion.   It is therefore impossible to give an objective definition of the genus.   A convenient definition is as follows: *A genus is a systematic category including one species or a group of species of presumably common phylogenetic origin, which is separated from other similar units by a decided gap.*   It is suggested for practical reasons that the size of the gap be in inverse ratio to the size of the unit. The latter qualification will prevent the recognition of unjustified monotypic genera.

Genera are tied down by type species, and although no one species can be "typical" of a group of species assigned to a genus, the generic type serves as a fixed point for the generic concept (Chap. 14). This situation has been likened to a flat piece of rubber nailed to a table at a single point on its surface. The rubber (generic contents) may be stretched in one direction or another by adding or subtracting species, but it always includes the nail (type species). The species which serves as the type of a genus is, in turn, tied to type specimens, so that the genus is firmly anchored. It is only the extent or limits of the genus that are arbitrary. The type system provides another aid in delimiting genera, *i.e.*, all the species in a genus must resemble the type of that genus more closely than they resemble the types of other genera.

The genus as a taxonomic category is based on the fact that species are not evenly distinct from one another but are arranged in smaller or larger groups, separated by smaller or larger gaps. Recognition of the genus is therefore based upon recognition of a natural phenomenon. How many species should be included in one genus and how a genus should be delimited from other genera are matters for the judgment of the individual systematist. Taxonomic characters that prove generic distinctness do not exist. Taxonomic literature could have been spared many unnecessary generic names if taxonomists had kept in mind Linnaeus's (1737) warning: "The characters do not make the genus, rather it is the genus that gives the characters."

Generic Characters. After a group of species has been evaluated by the taxonomist and judged to comprise a genus, it is found that such species have certain morphological characters in common. These characters are the generic characters of the taxonomist. Although they are, philosophically speaking, an a posteriori phenomenon, nevertheless they exist.

There are few practical hints that can be given as to the choice of generic characters, since as Linnaeus said, "they are given by the genus." However, a genus that has no "diagnostic character," that is, no character or combination of characters that separates it clearly from other related genera, is of doubtful validity.

The Meaning of the Genus. The genus, as seen by the evolutionist, is a group of species that has descended from a common ancestor. It is a phylogenetic unit. The characters of the genus are thus either the critical characters of the ancestral species or such characters as have been jointly acquired by all the species.

The genus, however, has a deeper significance. Upon closer examination, it is usually found that all the species of a genus occupy a more or less well-defined ecological niche.　The genus is thus a group of species adapted for a particular mode of life.　The "genus niche" is obviously broader than the "species niche," but both exist.　On this theoretical basis, it is probable that all generic characters are either adaptive or correlated with adaptive characters.　Lack (1947) has made a particularly convincing analysis of the adaptive significance of the genera of Galapagos finches.

An apparent conflict between the phylogenetic and the functional concept of the genus is that in certain groups unrelated species acquire a superficial similarity owing to parallel adaptations to similar environments.　This is particularly obvious when a loss of characters is involved and is often very confusing when reduction affects a whole series of characters which are modified concurrently (for instance, loss of wings in insects is frequently accompanied by profound changes in thoracic structure, which may involve several characters to which considerable taxonomic importance is normally attributed).

In such cases either the independent specializations (or despecializations) of such species are not recognized generically and each of the species is included with the genus from which it originated, or a separate genus is recognized for each of the aberrant species.　However, the latter alternative leads to excessive splitting and is therefore undesirable both on practical grounds and because it obscures relationships.

It is not always easy to unmask such cases of convergence.　The problems relating to the Ratites (large flightless birds) and the inquiline bees have already been discussed, and many other examples might be given. The flattened bill in insect-catching songbirds has resulted in the recognition of the presumably polyphyletic family of Old World flycatchers. The loss of eyes in cave animals has led to the recognition of unnatural categories based on the character of blindness.　Convergence of these types occurs at all levels of higher classification, and the genus is no exception.　However, a more detailed analysis usually reveals the artificiality of classifications based upon convergence.

Different Significance of Species and Genus.　The essential property of species is reproductive isolation, the essential property of genera is morphological distinctness (usually correlated with the occupation of distinctly different ecological niches).　These two properties are independent.　In one group of species there may be great multiplication of species without the acquisition of striking morphological differences, resulting in "large" genera, that is, genera with many species (as in the solitary bees).　In another group, species once formed may diverge so much from other species that they require recognition as separate genera. This leads to the recognition of many monotypic genera (as in the long-horned beetles).　In the majority of cases there will be a balance between these extremes, making possible the recognition of genera most of which are neither monotypic nor too large.

THE FAMILY

Under the International Rules the family level is the highest at which categories are tied nomenclaturally to actual genera, species, and, in turn, specimens. The type of a family is a particular genus, and this genus serves as a fixed point for the family concept.

The family concept is elusive because of varying rates of evolution and because of different levels of knowledge in the various groups of animals. Furthermore, as with other higher categories, whether or not a particular group is to be ranked at the family level is entirely subjective. In spite of these difficulties, it seems desirable to attempt a definition of the family, if for no other reason than to be consistent in treatment of the various categories. *A family may be defined as a systematic category including one genus or a group of genera of common phylogenetic origin, which is separated from other families by a decided gap.* As for the genus, it is suggested that the size of the gap be in inverse ratio to the size of the family.

Like the genus, the family is usually distinguished by certain obviously adaptive characters which fit it for a particular, though somewhat broader, niche, *e.g.*, the woodpeckers of the family Picidae, the leaf beetles of the family Chrysomelidae, etc. Unlike the genus, which is usually confined to one or several adjacent continents, the family is commonly world-wide in distribution. An entomologist who knows the 414 families of British insects can go to Africa or even Australia and recognize nearly all the same families occupying similar habitats.

Thus the family is a very useful category, the British entomologist having to learn only 414 names to place a total of 4,767 genera and 20,244 species. It is especially useful to the general zoologist, because each family usually presents a general facies which is recognizable at a glance, and all its species occupy a similar niche in their particular community, as, for instance, most of the thousands of species of Cerambycidae (long-horned beetles) in the world.

In any given locality the various families, like the various species, are generally distinct. Decided gaps between families are the rule rather than the exception, and little or no difficulty is encountered in "keying out" families in local faunal works. Unfortunately, the situation becomes much more complicated when a world-wide study is undertaken. Families are often found to break up into different distinctive groups on each continent, and types annectent with other families are sometimes found. Relict groups may exist at the family level and defy efforts to attain a clear-cut classification. Thus in many insect groups (scale insects, aphids, water striders, etc.) a choice has had to be made between enlarging the family concept beyond the limits of local convenience or recognizing exotic annectent types as separate families and using a superfamily category for the group as a whole. In entomology there appears to be a trend, not necessarily desirable, in the direction of the second of these choices. In ornithology a knowledge of the tropical relatives of the Temperate Zone forms has led to a reduction in the number of families. For instance, a study of tropical genera has induced many authors to consider the Old World flycatchers (Muscicapidae), warblers (Sylviidae), and thrushes (Turdidae) as only subfamilies.

Linnaeus did not recognize the family as a category, but it is significant that most of his genera have since been elevated to the rank of families. From this we may infer that his generic concept was not incompatible with our modern family concept, the difference between the genus and family being merely one of degree. With only 312 genera of animals in 1758, Linnaeus had no need for an intermediate category between order and genus. However, the number of newly discovered animal types increased so rapidly that the early-nineteenth-century naturalists gradually evolved and universally applied the family concept (Chap. 15).

The number of families continued to grow because of the advance in knowledge of existing animals and the discovery of new types. Thus by the end of the nineteenth century approximately 1,700 families of animals were recognized (Perrier, 1893–1932, *Traité de Zoologie*). That the trend is continuing is indicated by the fact that Brues and Melander (1932) recognized nearly 1,000 families in the insects alone.

The age of specialization has resulted in a general pushing upward of the categories, subfamilies becoming families, and families becoming superfamilies. Such a procedure is justifiable if, as indicated above, sufficiently distinctive types exist in various parts of the world. On the other hand, there is a tendency for specialists to exaggerate the importance of their groups and to split categories to an extent which is inconsistent with the practice in related groups. Dividing such groups as the Chrysomelidae or the Cerambycidae, one a group of leaf feeders and the other wood borers, destroys the biological homogeneity which is an important part of the family concept. Another family of Coleoptera, the Scarabaeidae, has been divided into 20 families, although a morphological homogeneity is broken up in the process. It is well to remember that the taxonomic hierarchy is indefinitely expandable within the limits of the family, *e.g.*, subfamily, tribe, subtribe, and even division, series, etc. The essential point, as stressed by McAtee (1926) is to preserve a sense of proportion, for in dealing with higher categories, judgment must be exercised, and conservatism should be the rule.

ORDERS, CLASSES, AND PHYLA

Taxonomic categories above the family level are not based upon type genera and species. And yet, in general, the orders, classes, and phyla have proved to be the most stable categories in our taxonomic hierarchy. It is true that a few names have been changed (these categories are not clearly subject to the International Rules of Zoological Nomenclature) and a few new phyla have been proposed within the last generation. But most of the higher categories are well known and well defined, and there is seldom any doubt as to the limits of the groups involved. As with genera and families, gaps between higher categories should be in inverse ratio to the size of the group.

The higher categories, representing the main branches of the phylogenetic tree, are characterized by a basic structural pattern which was laid down early and within which the seemingly endless adaptive modifications have taken place. In general, then, the higher categories are definable in terms of a basic structural pattern, and in most cases they are widely distributed over the earth's surface and each higher category exhibits a variety of adaptations so that each of its component families, for example, occupies a particular and usually distinctive ecological niche. Except for certain highly specialized groups such as the order Siphonaptera (fleas), the order Chiroptera (bats), etc., the higher categories are not obviously or even predominantly distinguished by adaptive characters.

As might be expected, the numbers of higher categories follow the trend noted previously for genera and families. According to recent tabulations, there are approximately 350 orders, 68 classes, and 30 phyla of recent animals (Table 2).

THE VALUE OF A CONSERVATIVE TREATMENT
OF THE HIGHER CATEGORIES

The higher categories are collective categories. Their function is not only to group together related species (genera, etc.) but also to serve as convenient labels for such groups. The terms Coleoptera and Lepidoptera must mean the same to all zoologists in order to have a maximum of usefulness. The same is true for families and even for genera.

To reach complete unanimity is quite impossible, since the limits of higher categories are subjective. However, an effort should be made to maintain some standards. Wetmore (1940) recognizes 27 orders of recent birds; Stresemann (1927–1934) places the same families in 48 orders. Rensch (1934) gives a particularly lucid discussion of such problems, supported by many instructive examples.

TABLE 2. THE PHYLA AND CLASSES OF ANIMALS
(Extinct groups are indicated by an asterisk)

Kingdom Animalia
  Subkingdom Protozoa†
    Phylum Protozoa
      Subphylum Plasmodroma (Cytomorpha)
        Class Flagellata (Mastigophora)
        Class Rhizopoda (Sarcodina)
        Class Ciliatoidea (Protociliata, Opalinidea)
        Class Sporozoa
      Subphylum Ciliophora (Cytoidea)
        Class Ciliata
        Class Suctoria
      Subphylum Amoebosporidia (Cnidosporidia, Haplosporidia)
  Subkingdom Mesozoa
  Subkingdom Parazoa
    Phylum Porifera
      Class Calcispongiae
      Class Hyalospongiae
      Class Desmospongiae
    Phylum *Pleospongida (Archaeocyatha)
  Subkingdom Metazoa
    Phylum Coelenterata (Cnidaria)
      Class Hydrozoa
      Class Scyphozoa
      Class *Stromatoporoidea
      Class Anthozoa
    Phylum Ctenophora
      Class Tentaculata
      Class Nuda
    Phylum Platyhelminthes
      Class Turbellaria
      Class Trematoda
      Class Cestoda
    Phylum Acanthocephala
    Phylum Rotifera
      Class Seisonacea
      Class Bdelloidea
      Class Monogononta
    Phylum Gastrotricha
    Phylum Kinorhyncha (Echinodera)
    Phylum Nematomorpha
      Class Gordioidea
      Class Nectonematoidea
    Phylum Nematoda
    Phylum Priapulidea

† For a different arrangement of the Protozoa, see W. Ulrich. 1950. Begriff und Einteilung der Protozoa. Moderne Biologie, pp. 241–250. See also W. Ulrich. 1951. Vorschläge zu einer Revision der Grosseinteilung des Tierreichs. *Zool. Anz.*, sup., **15**: 244–271.

Phylum Nemertina
    Class Anopla
    Class Enopla
Phylum Entoprocta
Phylum Annelida
    Class Polychaeta
    Class Oligochaeta
    Class Hirudinea
Phylum Echiuroidea
Phylum Sipunculoidea
Phylum Tardigrada
    Class Heterotardigrada
    Class Eutardigrada
Phylum Onychophora
Phylum Linguatula
Phylum Arthropoda
  Subphylum *Trilobita
    Class *Opisthoparia
    Class *Proparia
    Class *Agnostia
  Subphylum Chelicerata
    Class Merostomata
    Class Pycnogonida
    Class Eurypterida
    Class Arachnida
  Subphylum Mandibulata
    Class Crustacea
    Class Oligoentomata (Collembola)
    Class Pauropoda
    Class Symphyla
    Class Diplopoda
    Class Chilopoda
    Class Myrientomata (Protura)
    Class Insecta
Phylum Mollusca
    Class Amphineura
    Class Crepipoda
    Class Gastropoda
    Class Scaphopoda
    Class Pelecypoda
    Class Cephalopoda
Phylum Pogonophora
Phylum Bryozoa (Ectoprocta)
    Class Gymnolaemata
    Class Phylactolaemata
Phylum Brachiopoda
    Class Inarticulata
    Class Articulata
Phylum Phoronidea
Phylum Chaetognatha

Phylum Echinodermata
  Subphylum Pelmatozoa
    Class *Edrioasteroidea
    Class *Cystoidea
    Class *Blastoidea
    Class Crinoidea
  Subphylum Asterozoa
    Class Asteroidea
    Class Ophiuroidea
  Subphylum Echinozoa
    Class Echinoidea
    Class Holothurioidea
Phylum Hemichordata
    Class Pterobranchia
    Class Enteropneusta
    Class *Graptolithoidea (Graptozoa)
Phylum Chordata
  Subphylum Tunicata
    Class Ascidiacea
    Class Larvacea
    Class Thaliacea
  Subphylum Acrania
    Class Cephalochordata
  Subphylum Vertebrata
    Class Agnatha
    Class *Placodermi
    Class Chondrichthyes
    Class Osteichthyes
    Class Amphibia
    Class Reptilia
    Class Aves
    Class Mammalia

Nothing is gained by splitting well-established natural categories too fine. Arkell and Moy-Thomas (1940) cite some particularly extreme examples for fossil invertebrates:

Examples of flagrant disregard of this rule [a uniform scale of values] are Buckman's innumerable genera made by splitting up contemporary species of the single good Liassic ammonite genus *Dactylioceras*, and by Heinz's pulverization of the Cretaceous lamellibranch genus *Inoceramus*. Out of what was originally a single genus *Inoceramus* Heinz created a whole systematic hierarchy, comprising 2 families, 24 subfamilies, 63 genera, and 27 subgenera; and even so he did not take the Jurassic forms into account. [Even if this minute subdivision were taxonomically justified] it should be carried out downwards in the scale, starting with the genus *Inoceramus* and proceeding through subgenera to groups and sections. All the advantages of minute subdivisions can thus be achieved without disturbance to the whole classification of Mollusca.

Handlirsch (1929) also warned against the chaos produced by excessive splitting and cited the following examples:

In the family of the praying mantids Giglio-Tos (1927) arranges the known 1500 species in 30 subfamilies and 500 genera. There is thus an average of only 3 species per genus. Among the genera no less than 150 were made by Giglio-Tos himself; 175 are monotypic, 74 have two species. Roewer (1923) puts the 1700 species of opiliones in 500 genera, of which more than half (300) contain only 1 or 2 species. The order Strepsiptera with 150 species has been split by Pierce into 5 super-families, 20 families, subfamilies or tribes, and 45 genera or subgenera, of which 29 are monotypical.

Smith (1947) also points out how much is lost through too fine a splitting of genera.

THE MEANING OF THE HIGHER CATEGORIES

There has been much dispute as to whether the higher categories have objective reality or not. Paleontologists are almost unanimous in considering the genus a better defined, more objective category than the species. Most botanists agree with this view. Students of birds, however, and of other well-known groups of living animals insist that the species is the category that is most clearly defined in nature. Who is right?

The genus of Linnaeus was very broadly defined. As has been pointed out above, it included genera that are now considered to comprise a family or an order. With some recent authors, to mention the other extreme, the genus has become so narrow that it is monotypical in the majority of cases. Linnaeus arranged all the 554 species of birds known to him into 63 genera. Nearly all his species are still recognized as such today; most of his genera have been raised to the rank of families. Some recent ornithologists allow no less than 7,000 to 8,000 genera for the 8,600 species of birds, others about one-fifth of this number. There is thus about a 500 per cent difference between the genus of the extreme lumper and that of the extreme splitter. On the other hand, the extreme splitter recognizes less than twice as many species of birds as the extreme lumper. It is obvious from these figures that—at least as far as birds are concerned—the delimitation of species is less a matter of subjective opinion than that of genera.

To obtain a deeper understanding of the nature of the higher categories, it may be useful to consider a concrete case.

Figure 8 represents a diagrammatic family tree of the 37 living species of river ducks of the genus *Anas* (*sensu lato*). This is not a phylogenetic tree, because it is not based on any information on fossil forms which might be ancestral connections of the various branches. Such a diagrammatic illustration of degree of relationship based on degree of similarity (morphological and otherwise) may be called a *dendrogram*. There is comparatively little difference of opinion among ornithologists as to the grouping of these species. It is agreed that there are several more closely bunched clusters of species, each of which forms a natural group, such as species 32–37 (mallard group) and species 7–13 (blue-winged teal–shoveler

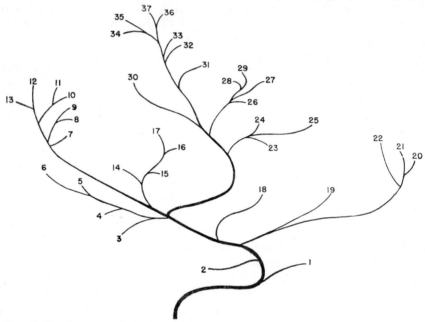

Fig. 8. Dendrogram of the genus *Anas* of the tribe Anatini (river ducks) (*after Delacour and Mayr*). 1 = *leucophrys*, 2 = *waigiuensis*, 3 = *angustirostris*, 4 = *capensis*, 5 = *punctata*, 6 = *versicolor*, 7 = *querquedula*, 8 = *cyanoptera*, 9 = *platalea*, 10 = *discors*, 11 = *rhynchotis*, 12 = *clypeata*, 13 = *smithi*, 14 = *erythrorhynchos*, 15 = *bahamensis*, 16 = *georgica*, 17 = *acuta*, 18 = *falcata*, 19 = *strepera*, 20 = *americana*, 21 = *penelope*, 22 = *sibilatrix*, 23 = *flavirostris*, 24 = *crecca*, 25 = *formosa*, 26 = *aucklandica*, 27 = *castanea*, 28 = *bernieri*, 29 = *gibberifrons*, 30 = *specularis*, 31 = *sparsa*, 32 = *undulata*, 33 = *melleri*, 34 = *fulvigula*, 35 = *platyrhyncha*, 36 = *poecilorhyncha*, 37 = *luzonica*.

group). It is also agreed that certain species, such as 1, 2, 18, 19, and 30, are rather isolated, and that some of the species and species groups are somewhat intermediate between others. Furthermore, it is agreed among ornithologists that the whole group of 37 species is fairly isolated from the other genera of the tribe Anatini.

The "splitters" interpret this evidence as indicating that this group of species should be divided into at least 12 genera, many of them monotypic. They insist that this is the only way of indicating the existence of the various groups of species.

The "lumpers," on the other hand, point out that these 37 species have numerous characters in common, and that the group as a whole is well defined and separated by a decided gap from other groups of ducks. They therefore propose to include all 37 species in a single genus. With four other genera, they make up the tribe Anatini of the subfamily Anatinae.

The important point is that both antagonists agree on the essential facts of the dendrogram. The major and minor groups of species of Fig. 8 may be objectively defined, but the higher categories based on these groupings are subjective, because it is a matter of opinion how many species groups to include in a genus. *The delimitation of the genus is subjective.* If we accept the definiteness of delimitation as a criterion, we come to the conclusion that the genus lacks the objective basis of the species, because most genera are not separated from other genera by big, clear-cut gaps. Most genera (particularly the monotypic ones) could be united with other genera, and most polytypic genera could be subdivided equally well into smaller genera. Where the limits of the genus should be drawn in any given case is left to the subjective judgment of the individual worker. The same is, of course, true for the tribe, the family, and the other higher categories.

Summarizing the essential conclusions of this discussion, one may make the following statements on the higher taxonomic categories:

The genus is a group of related species, the family a group of related genera, and the order a group of related families.[2] Each of these groups is composed of units of the next lower categorical level, which share a number of biological and structural characters that distinguish them from members of other groups. Each group either occupies a well-defined ecological niche or, particularly the family and the order, shares at least a common adaptive pattern. The exact delimitation and ranking of the groups is often subjective. Even though the higher categories, as such, are more subjective than the species category, they appear nevertheless to have a biological and structural basis with some objective criteria.

---

[2] Monotypic higher categories are recognized by the gaps which separate them, and their level is determined by evidence extrapolated from related polytypic categories.

PART 2

TAXONOMIC PROCEDURE

The selection of a suitable problem is especially important to the beginner in taxonomy. Much time and effort are wasted on groups which are too difficult or on groups which present no real problem. Some important considerations in selecting a taxonomic problem are as follows: (1) Its scope should be such as to permit completion in a reasonable period of time. (2) In little-known groups the types should be accessible. (3) The group selected should be such that the taxonomist can collect and study it in the field.

After a problem has been selected, the steps in taxonomic procedure are assembling and care of material, identification, analysis of material, preparation of descriptions, keys, bibliographies, and illustrations, synthesis of a classification, and, finally, publication. Each of these steps will be discussed in detail in the following chapters, with examples selected to illustrate pertinent points. A certain amount of imagination will be necessary in order to apply the methods illustrated to the endless variety of animal groups. Special problems demand special answers, and even routine work suffers if it becomes stereotyped. However, although originality is an asset to the scientist, new methods or novel treatment of data must be over and above the acceptable minimum requirements of standard taxonomic procedure.

In the following pages, then, are described the taxonomic practices which, through actual use, are approved by a majority of systematists. In addition to commonly used procedures, newer methods are described which, in our opinion, point the way to standard practices of the future.

The methods that are of particular importance in a given group depend on the state of taxonomic maturity of the group. In birds the methods of alpha taxonomy play a rather minor role, while in some poorly known groups of acari the methods of gamma taxonomy are inapplicable. It will be evident from the discussions in the subsequent chapters which methods are of special importance to a particular worker.

CHAPTER 4

COLLECTING AND COLLECTIONS

Students will find material of the commoner types of animals in most large museums. If they plan a monographic treatment, they may also borrow material from other institutions, which will usually send it willingly unless it is being currently studied. Such material consists of the products of expeditions and the random collections of all-round naturalists. Material of this sort has many shortcomings: the total range of a species is rarely adequately sampled, important stages in the life cycle are often missing, and there may be no data on ecological differences in the various parts of the range, to mention only a few of its many deficiencies. It is obviously quite insufficient for the kind of analysis required by systematics on the gamma level. The modern taxonomist attempts, therefore, to round out such material with his own collections. The late Admiral H. Lynes, for instance, who was especially interested in *Cisticola*, a genus of African warblers with some 40 species, made a whole series of collecting trips to nearly every corner of Africa. He combined his collecting with a detailed study of the ecology, habits, songs, and nest construction of these birds. The result is that the genus *Cisticola*, formerly the despair of the bird taxonomists, is now well understood (Lynes, 1930). Mont A. Cazier, who is now monographing the 90 North American species of the tiger beetle genus *Cicindela*, has not only devoted several seasons to collecting them but has also engaged several other collectors. His collections now total some 80,000 specimens and are being enlarged by 5,000 to 10,000 specimens annually from selected critical localities found during preliminary working out of the material.

In other cases the systematic collecting has concentrated not on certain genera but on a definite geographic region. The most ambitious single undertaking along these lines was probably the Whitney South Sea Expedition, operated under the auspices of the American Museum of Natural History in New York with the support of the Harry Payne Whitney family. This expedition visited practically every island in the South Seas, obtaining nearly complete bird collections and fair collections of other material. It operated continuously from 1921 to 1934, and its work was continued by single collectors into 1940. The student of such collections has the gratifying feeling that it is unlikely that his findings will be upset by future discoveries (Fig. 9).

WHERE AND HOW TO COLLECT

The modern taxonomist is a student of populations. He is therefore interested in adequate samples of these populations, samples that give a sufficient picture of the variability of these populations and permit, when necessary, their statistical analysis. Formerly a museum retained only a few "typical" representatives of every species and considered the rest of the material as duplicates. Nowadays a museum takes pride in

Fig. 9. Camp of a field expedition in New Guinea (*American Museum of Natural History* photo).

possessing large series of specimens of each species, originating from all parts of the range of the species. The replacement of the type concept by the population concept made such a shift of emphasis inevitable.

The choice of collecting stations should be planned carefully. Ideally the working out of the geographic variation of a species should be done in two steps: (1) All the material already available in collections should be assembled and analyzed. (2) The filling of the crucial gaps thus shown will be the goal of all subsequent collecting. Collecting stations, whenever possible, should be spaced sufficiently closely to permit an accurate mapping of the range of the species. Aberrant populations occur most frequently along the periphery of the range of a species. This area should be collected particularly thoroughly. If the species shows seasonal variation, collections should be made in various seasons.

If the species wears or bleaches, collections should be made at the time when specimens are in their best condition—in birds, for example, after they have completed their molt. In many invertebrates the season during which sexual maturity occurs is relatively short, so collecting should be done during that time. If various stages of the life cycle are of taxonomic importance, an effort must be made to have them all represented.

If a species shows noticeable geographical variation, the collections should cover the ranges of all the subspecies and should attempt to delimit the areas of intergradation. That this is not an unattainable objective has been proved by several modern collectors such as Kinsey for cynipid wasps (1936). The Whitney South Sea Expedition collected birds so systematically that up to 1950 not a single new species or subspecies had been discovered on the islands visited by that expedition.

There are almost endless techniques for collecting, different for every group of animals. These are described in standard collecting manuals, a few of the better known and most recent ones of which are listed in the bibliography of this chapter.

Labeling. A specimen that is not accurately labeled is worthless to the student of the new systematics. So important, in fact, is the label that it is sometimes stated jocularly that the label is more important than the specimen. Many kinds of information are desirable, but by far the most important single piece of information is the exact locality. In forms like certain land snails that may have racially distinct populations as little as $\frac{1}{2}$ mi. apart, the locality must be stated with great precision. If the locality is a small community, farm, hill, creek, or other geographical feature which cannot easily be found on commercial or geodetic (*e.g.*, United States topographic) maps, its position relative to a well-known place should be added on the label ("15 mi. N.W. of Ann Arbor, Mich."). The county or district should be given with all less well-known localities. If the specimen was collected in mountains, the altitude should always be given. Additional ecological information is valuable. It is essential in forms like plant-feeding insects or host-specific parasites.

Whenever possible, the label should be written in the field at the time the specimen is prepared. Any replacing of temporary labels by later permanent ones is a potential source of error. However, it cannot be avoided with insects when labels are printed for entire lots of specimens. All essential data should be recorded on the original labels. Data recorded in a field book are frequently overlooked and may be unavailable if the collection is divided. The original label should never be replaced by a museum label. A certain number of mistakes are always made in the transfer. If a museum label is desired, it should be added to the original label.

What data in addition to locality are needed depends on the given group. Most good bird collectors, for instance, record on the label not only locality, date, and collector's name but also the sex (based on autopsy), the actual size of the gonads, the degree of ossification of the skull (important for age determination), the weight (in grams), and the colors of the soft parts. The little extra time required to take these records is more than compensated for by the added value of the specimens.

THE CARE OF TAXONOMIC COLLECTIONS

The value of much taxonomic work depends on the quality of the collections on which it is based. It is therefore necessary to say a few words on the methods of curating taxonomic collections.

Preparation of the Material for Study. Bird and mammal skins are ready for study as sent in from the field by the collector. Mammal skulls have to be cleaned. Some insects should never be placed in alcohol or other liquid preservatives; others are useless when dried. Invertebrates that are preserved in alcohol or formalin are usually ready for study as preserved. Microscopic slide mounts or slides of parts of the organs may have to be prepared for the smaller forms. Instructions may be found in textbooks of microscopic technique (Guyer, 1936; Lee, 1937). Most insects are pinned (Oman and Cushman, 1946), and the wings are spread if they are taxonomically important (or beautiful), as in butterflies and moths and some grasshoppers. Species can be identified in many groups of insects only by a study of their genitalia. Microscopic slides or dry or liquid mounts of the genitalia may have to be prepared.

CATALOGUING

The methods of cataloguing depend on the group of animals. In the higher vertebrates, in which collections consist of a limited number of specimens, each specimen receives a separate number and is usually catalogued separately. The cataloguing is done geographically, that is, all the specimens collected at a given locality or district in a given period of time or by one expedition are entered in the catalogue together. This greatly facilitates the subsequent accumulation of distributional data or of faunistic analyses if the collection is subsequently broken up and the specimens entered into the collection according to their systematic relationships. The cataloguing is usually done after the specimens have been identified, at least as far as the genus. This permits a permanent reference to the contents of the collection long after it has been broken up and distributed according to the system or even to other institutions.

In groups in which the collections consist of large numbers of specimens, as, for example, in most insect collections, where additions of

100,000 specimens per year are not uncommon, it is customary to catalogue accessions by lots, each lot consisting of a set of specimens from a given locality or region. Lot numbers, in turn, may refer to collectors' diaries or to other sources of information on each collection. It is also customary to note whether a lot was received as a gift or by purchase or exchange, and the name of the collector and donor is always given.

In cataloguing, entries of vertebrates usually contain the following items:

1. Consecutive museum number
2. Original field number
3. Scientific name (or, at least, generic name)
4. Sex
5. Exact locality
6. Date
7. Collector
8. Remarks

The collections of a museum are arranged according to a system, that is, following some generally adopted classification. The sequence of orders and families is fairly standardized in many classes of animals. Unidentified material (if not to be worked out as a collection) is placed with the family or genus to which it belongs.

A properly organized and well-curated collection is a catalogue in itself, and most large museums do not maintain card files of individual specimens filed in taxonomic sequence. The maintenance of such card files, useful as they are, is too time-consuming to be practicable with the small staffs of most museums. The bird collection of the American Museum of Natural History lists on the tray labels the scientific names not only of all the available species and subspecies but also of those lacking in the collection (which is specifically stated) (Fig. 10). The names on the collection cases and trays thus constitute a check list of the known species and subspecies of birds. Such a system might be unwieldy in very incomplete collections.

The maintenance of collection catalogues and card files is a time-consuming task and should never be carried to the point where it interferes with work on the collections. A list of the accessions, however, is important, particularly since it often allows the recording of additional information on localities where the specimens were obtained, which cannot be entered in full on the labels of all the specimens.

TYPES OF MUSEUM COLLECTIONS

The modern taxonomist is expected to operate efficiently, supply precise information, and produce the very best in modern research. To do this his most important single asset is a large, well-curated, up-to-date collection. Museum collections are of various types, depending on the objectives of each museum and the purpose for which the collections are intended. For example, one museum may have all its material displayed as public exhibits, another may be connected with a university and be

Fig. 10. Method of storing study specimens of birds in open trays (collection case in American Museum of Natural History).

primarily concerned with the teaching of students, and a third museum may have as its objective the accumulation of a world-wide research collection. It is important to differentiate between these types of collections and to adhere closely to specific objectives in each case. No deviation or overlapping should be allowed without full realization of the additional demands on funds, personnel, space, and specimens already on hand.

Survey Collections. Some collections are devoted exclusively to surveying a particular geographic area, *e.g.*, the former U.S. Biological

Survey, the Illinois Natural History Survey, and the Zoological Survey of India. Such surveys may cover the entire biota, as in Illinois, where an effort is made to ascertain the total number of species occurring in the area specified. On the other hand, a survey may be designed to cover a particular group, *e.g.*, the California Insect Survey, or certain economic pests, *e.g.*, wartime airport, port, and maritime pest surveys. Survey collections may involve large numbers of specimens—often far more of a given species than is practicable in a general research collection. In an exhaustive survey a large proportion of the material may consist of immature specimens and obscure specimens of small size. This type of material is of great value for the study of variation, distribution, seasonal abundance, and density. Data should be very fully recorded and, because of the mass of material, should be kept with the specimens.

The problem of identification is the most serious obstacle in conducting a survey and the most difficult feature of survey collections. Generally a list of specialists is maintained, and material is "farmed out" to these good-natured but usually overworked individuals as long as they are willing to accept it. Since the success of any survey depends on accurate and fairly prompt identification, this is the most important part of the work.

Identification Collections. The task of identification, especially in insects, has become nearly intolerable because of congested conditions in museums, because of the tremendous number of species, and because so many of the specialists are private investigators who can work only in their spare time. As a partial answer to this, some Federal and state agencies have found it necessary to set up centers for the identification of insects more or less apart from, and simply utilizing the results of, taxonomic research. There are two primary requisites for such work: (1) an adequate library and (2) a representative reference collection. The collection must be a study collection with specimens suitable for detailed comparison. It must approach completeness in representation of the species recorded from the region covered. Long series of duplicates are neither necessary nor desirable.

Examples of identification collections are the collections of the larger quarantine stations. Although such collections inevitably fall far short of complete coverage, they are useful for the identification of the commonest species which are intercepted repeatedly. Over a period of time, collections of this type are built up out of specimens which were referred to specialists and were returned authoritatively determined. With such material at hand, an experienced quarantine inspector can identify the bulk of his routine interceptions from day to day, thus saving the time and energy of specialists.

Research Collections. Research collections aim to accumulate comprehensive material suitable for original taxonomic analysis (Fig. 10). They are the finest and highest type of scientific collection and should be prepared and preserved with great care. They may be private, in the hands of an individual; semipublic, in the laboratories of a privately endowed institution such as an academy of science or private museum; or public, in a city, state, or national museum or in public schools or universities. The methods employed in these various collections are essentially the same, differing only as the size of the collection may introduce special problems.

Sooner or later most private research collections are given or sold to the large, privately endowed or publicly supported museums. Large museums, like libraries, are the repositories of the accumulated scientific materials of our civilization. In biology they are a priceless heritage.

But far from being merely a storehouse for specimens of former years, the several great collections of the world today are actively developing, expanding centers of taxonomic research. New material is being gathered on expeditions, and specimens are being curated as rapidly as time and funds will permit. These large collections serve as the focal points for taxonomic research and publication. Volunteer workers augment the limited staffs and carry on a share of the actual research.

The inherent weakness of these research centers and, as a consequence, the inherent weakness of systematic zoology is the type of financial support of museums. Money is usually available for the accumulation of material, especially by spectacular expeditions, but additional support is rarely forthcoming to care for the material or to study it.

Few museums can afford to build up equally good collections in all branches of zoology. It is advisable, in fact, that each museum should lay special emphasis on the accumulation of as complete a collection as possible from particular areas or of certain groups that are of special interest to its curators. In view of the cordial relationships now customary among museums, such specialization will lead to greater efficiency in the working up of collections.

Type Collections. Original descriptions and all subsequent descriptions and illustrations must obviously be based on actual specimens. With advancement in technique and knowledge it almost inevitably happens that such descriptions are deficient. This may be no reflection on the original worker who failed to see in 1840, for example, that the entire classification of the Trichoptera (caddisflies) would eventually be based on the structure of the male genitalia.

The use of new characters often leads to the discovery that a so-called "species" is actually composed of several similar species. In such cases it is essential to refer to the type specimen to determine which of these species should bear the name originally given. This function of the type specimen, discussed in greater detail in Chap. 12, explains why types are nowadays considered with such respect, and why every effort should be made to ensure the safety of these irreplaceable specimens.

It has been argued that a specimen used as a basis for description or illustration becomes common property, belonging to science rather than to an individual. For this reason as well as for safety and to make them available to as large a group of zoologists as possible, types are customarily deposited in large collections of public or private institutions which have come to be recognized as standard type repositories. Although some zoologists advocate centralization of types in a single world clearing-house (to avoid the necessity of traveling thousands of miles to obscure corners of the globe to see types), and others advocate the deposition of types in collections as near as possible to the place where they were collected, the present haphazard system is likely to continue for many years. The vast majority of types today are preserved in the collections of large and presumably permanent institutions with full-time curators to care for them.

The vexing question of the lending of types is dealt with by each institution in its own way. Many institutions have entrusted types to the mails in order to lend them to competent individuals for monographic work. Although fraught with risk, such a practice has resulted in the correct placement of many species when the original types have since been destroyed.

Ideally, types should be housed in a separate collection to facilitate removal in case of emergency and to avoid the constant handling inherent in a general study collection. They should be clearly labeled with the distinctive colors described (see Chap. 12). If not previously catalogued, they should be numbered individually for convenience in referring to them in the literature and to facilitate finding the specimen in the collection. They may be arranged either systematically or chronologically as received or alphabetically according to the originally given scientific name. A card index by genera and another by species will save much time in locating the desired type.

CHAPTER 5

IDENTIFICATION AND TAXONOMIC DISCRIMINATION

After the collection and preparation of material, the next step in taxonomic procedure is identification. It is an integral part of all taxonomic work.

Identification is the utilitarian side of taxonomy. The routine task of identification is in one sense a stumbling block to progress, because it occupies much time and effort that might otherwise be devoted to monographic studies. Ironically, it is only through such monographs that routine identification is made possible. Yet, in another sense, identification is the groundwork upon which all progress in taxonomy is based. The great collections of the world are accumulations of the identifications of past generations and, as such, are the storehouses of the raw material of our science.

Identification to the species level may be a difficult task in groups with large numbers of species and scattered taxonomic literature. It is now impossible for one person to make authoritative or even reasonably satisfactory identifications in all groups of animals. Recognizing this fact, Federal and state agencies charged with the responsibility of identifying economically important animals have resorted to employing specialists, each of whom is assigned a particular group. It is the duty of these specialists to make available to others their knowledge and experience, but it is also the responsibility of the beginner, nonspecialist, quarantine inspector, or economic zoologist to show consideration to the specialist and identify his own material in so far as the available literature and collections will permit. Only in this way can the specialist render the real service for which he alone is fitted: making determinations of difficult forms, confirming identifications to be used in publications, and preparing original monographs in order to facilitate future identification.

There is no better way to learn taxonomic procedure than to try to identify material with the help of a good monograph. The student is referred to Roger Smith's (1942) *Guide to the Literature in the Zoological Sciences* or to the volumes of the *Zoological Record* for references to more recent monographs. If necessary, a specialist may be consulted to recommend a suitable publication.

Segregation of Material. Some animals are segregated roughly in the field. A careful collector of small animals, such as insects, usually keeps specimens of different species from different hosts in separate containers. But this is only a crude segregation and may not even follow taxonomic lines. After the specimens are mounted and labeled, however, they are segregated taxonomically. This process is carried as far as the knowledge of the collector permits. Beginners may have trouble placing some specimens in the correct order, whereas specialists may carry their rough segregation to the generic level or even down to species. In museums the usual practice is to segregate unstudied material according to orders and, in the case of easily recognized groups of some size, to families or even genera. This procedure varies, of course, with the animal groups involved.

One further step in segregation is very useful. Most species have a distinctive facies, and a taxonomist with a good "eye" can save a great deal of time by assembling all specimens of a given species in one place. The eye in this case may be assisted by reference to the labels bearing localities and dates of collection.

Steps in Identification. Every species name is based on a published description or figure and usually also on a type specimen. Identification, or determination, is the association of other specimens with the appropriate description or type specimen. This may prove difficult for any of several reasons: the general classification of the group may be so poor or so neglected that it is difficult to determine the genus or higher category involved; the description may be inadequate or inaccessible; the type may not be "typical" (in the zoological sense), or it may be inaccessible or lost; and finally, the specimen may represent an undescribed species.

In spite of the inherent difficulties, correct identifications are possible for a majority of specimens in most groups of animals. The steps in identification are as follows: (1) preliminary key to orders and families, (2) key to genera and species if recent monographs or faunal works are available, (3) reference to the most recent catalogues, (4) reference to current bibliographies for literature published subsequent to the most recent catalogues, (5) reference to original descriptions, (6) comparison with authentically determined specimens or with the type.

Preliminary Key to Orders and Families. This step is very necessary for the beginner and is best done with the simple keys given in general textbooks or handbooks. Even the advanced student may encounter unusual species or immature or exotic forms which cannot be placed in the proper family or order on sight. However, modern works are generally available which provide family and subfamily keys and greatly assist in this stage of identification.

Driver's (1950) *Name That Animal* is a good elementary guide to the principal groups of animals. In addition to the general keys, a bibliography to the most important works on each group of animals is given.

For example, Brues and Melander (1932) is cited among the general works on insects, and this, in turn, gives keys to the orders, families, and sub-families and cites the more important monographs under each group.

There are many works on the animals of specific regions (*e.g.*, Park, Allee, and Shelford, 1939, for the Chicago region). There is an excellent survey to taxonomic works dealing with the British Isles (Smart, 1942). Other regional works are *Die Tierwelt Deutschlands* (Dahl, 1925 *et seq.*), *Faune de France* (1921–1950 and continuing), and *Die Tierwelt der Nord-und Ostsee* (Grimpe and Wagler, 1925 *et seq.*). There is, unfortunately, no comprehensive bibliography of regional taxonomic treatises available for the United States.

Key to Genera and Species. Identification is relatively easy if a thorough monograph of recent date is available. In this case, the specimen is run through the keys; the description of the appropriate species is checked, character by character; the specimen is compared with any illustrations that may be given; and the recorded geographical distribution is checked. If all these points agree, the identification is considered as tentatively made, subject to comparison with authentic specimens, and provided that no additional species have subsequently been described.

Reference to Recent Catalogues. In the absence of a monograph or revision, or for the period since such a monograph was published, the most recent catalogue of the group should be consulted. The catalogue will give literature citations to the descriptions of all species known up to the time of completion of the catalogue. Some catalogues give more than this, *e.g.*, complete bibliographies under each genus and species, lists of synonyms, and geographical distribution. Identification is greatly facilitated by a good catalogue, because it brings together the most significant published references in the group and guides the taxonomist to the species most likely to occur in the territory in which his specimens were collected.

Reference to Current Bibliographies. Catalogues are inevitably out of date soon after they are published. This difficulty may be partially compensated for by the issuance of supplements. Nevertheless it is not at all unusual to find the most recent catalogue dated twenty years pre-viously. In some of the major insect orders there is no general catalogue since 1900, and some groups have never been catalogued from a world standpoint.

Fortunately, there exists an annual bibliography of the literature in systematic zoology. This great reference work is called the *Zoological Record*. It is the most indispensable reference publication for taxonomic work. Starting in 1864, the *Zoological Record* has appeared each year up to the present time. Each new scientific name is given, together with a reference to the place of publication and the type locality. The names are arranged alphabetically under families, but a systematic arrangement is followed for families and higher groups. Current numbers are available separately by purchase or subscription. In the United States it can be ordered through the Society of Systematic Zoology.

The usual method of using the *Zoological Record* is to start with the most recent volume and work back to the date of completion of the most recent catalogue or revision. The particular genus or other group in question may be located in the table of contents of the section devoted to the particular class of animals involved. New names, synonymy, distribution, and in some instances, even biological references are given. If the citation is not clear because of its abbreviated form, or if the exact title of the publication is important, reference may be made to the bibliography of papers arranged according to authors at the beginning of the section. For special needs there is an elaborate subject index covering various phases of morphology, physiology, ecology, and biology.

The *Zoological Record* is published by the Zoological Society of London in cooperation with the British Museum (Natural History) and the Commonwealth Institute of Entomology. The following 19 sections of the *Zoological Record* are published separately and may be obtained singly or as an entire volume each year: (1) Comprehensive Zoology, (2) Protozoa, (3) Porifera, (4) Coelenterata, (5) Echinoderma, (6) Vermes, (7) Brachiopoda, (8) Bryozoa, (9) Mollusca, (10) Crustacea, (11) Trilobita, (12) Arachnida, (13) Insecta, (14) Protochordata, (15) Pisces, (16) Amphibia and Reptilia, (17) Aves, (18) Mammalia, and (19) List of New Generic and Subgeneric Names.

Some groups of animals have never been catalogued or monographed. This is especially true of insects. In such cases it is necessary to work back through the entire *Zoological Record* (Vol. 1, 1864).

Prior to 1864 the best annual review of the taxonomic literature is found in the *Berichte über die wissenschaftlichen Leistungen* in different branches of zoology, including entomology and helminthology, published in Wiegmann's *Archiv für Naturgeschichte* (Berlin, 1835 *et seq.*). Additional important bibliographical helps covering this early period of zoology are Engelmann (1846), Agassiz and Strickland (1848), and the Catalogue of scientific papers published by the Royal Society (1800–1863). Sherborn's *Index Animalium* (1758–1800, 1801–1850) gives a complete list of generic and trivial names proposed up to 1850.

The *Zoological Record* is always one or two years behind, so other bibliographies must be consulted for the most recent literature. *Biological Abstracts* (1926 to date) is an important source of recent literature. Its section, Systematic Zoology, contains abstracts of taxonomic papers and hence is a valuable source of information for papers which are not immediately available elsewhere. However, *Biological Abstracts* covers the taxonomic field very incompletely, so it is no substitute for the *Zoological Record*.

There are numerous zoological bibliographies dealing with zoology as a whole, or with vertebrate zoology (Wood, 1931), or with special groups, such as birds, fishes, or other taxonomic subdivisions. The student of taxonomy is advised to familiarize himself with the bibliographical aids that are available in his special field.

Reference to Original Descriptions. Although keys are the greatest aid to identification, reference should always be made to original or more recent authoritative descriptions. Unless this is done, there is a possibility that the specimen in question represents a species not included in the key. Original descriptions are located by means of catalogues, monographs, the *Zoological Record*, or other bibliographical sources as described above.

Copies of original descriptions may be difficult to find. Even the largest libraries are not complete, and the average university library will be found wanting from 5 to 25 per cent of the time. This is not so much a reflection on the caliber of libraries as it is evidence of the extent and diversity of scientific publications throughout the world. Although largely confined to a half-dozen languages, taxonomic papers are published in practically every country in the world. This poses a very real problem for libraries with limited budgets. The situation is further complicated because the law of priority places a premium on the earlier works. No taxonomic work since 1758 becomes "out of date" if it contains new names, and as a result of limited editions, losses through the years, and other factors, there are not enough copies available to supply all biological libraries.

The search for original descriptions in connection with identification involves full use and familiarity with all available scientific libraries, reference to the *Union List of Serials* to locate publications in other libraries for interlibrary loan, extensive use of microfilm services, and accumulation of reprints by purchase or by exchange with other workers.

Descriptions are the foundation of taxonomy, since only the printed word is indestructible. Types may be lost, and the original author is available to pass on "his" species for only a brief span of years.

Descriptions should be read several times, first to obtain a general impression or mental picture of the actual specimen which the original author had before him. Then particular characters which the original or subsequent authors considered important should be extracted and checked against the specimens in question. Finally, any comparative notes given by the original author should be checked. In many cases such comparative characters are the most useful clues to identification.

Original descriptions are, normally, the court of last appeal for purposes of general identification. However, many original descriptions are totally inadequate. This is particularly true of the descriptions published prior to 1800. The value of a description is in direct proportion to the judgment of the author and his ability to select significant characters and describe them in words, and the extent and nature of the material available to him at the time of description. For this reason descriptions given in a thorough and authoritative monograph of recent date are usually much more usable than original descriptions.

Illustrations are often equally as valuable as, or more valuable than, original descriptions. In popular groups, such as birds or butterflies, there are many works with colored plates. Such works are often a great help in the rapid identification of specimens. It is, however, advisable to check such tentative identifications by comparison with previously identified material or to take other precautions. Colored plates are not always well reproduced, and there are many opportunities for error if too much dependence is placed on them.

If the original description is accompanied by an illustration, the difficulty occasionally arises that characters of illustration and description are in conflict. It can sometimes be proved in such cases that the artist did not have access to the type specimen and utilized another specimen that was believed to agree with the type. Such discrepancies occur not infrequently in the work of early authors.

Comparison with Types and Other Authentically Determined Specimens. It is sometimes impossible to make a satisfactory determination from the literature alone. Such a situation exists if the group has been neglected, if the keys are inadequate, or if the descriptions are poor. Even under ideal conditions, identification is greatly facilitated if types or other authentic material are available for comparison.

Comparison of specimens is a highly technical job and requires a considerable background of knowledge and preparation in the particular group in question. For this reason preliminary identifications made by direct comparison with authentic collections, without first studying the literature and the significant characters in the group, are often valueless.

Reference collections are often accumulated for the express purpose of facilitating identification. In such cases comparison is made with whatever series of specimens is available, and it is necessary to judge whether the specimen in hand falls within the possible range of variation of a given species.

Care should be taken not to rely exclusively on comparison with supposedly authentic specimens. Even "authoritative" collections may contain wrong identifications or may be incomplete. In such cases hasty comparison without the other steps in identification may lead to erroneous conclusions.

Type specimens are the most authentic of all but should not be used for routine identifications. Ideally, in the course of a monographic study of a group, all type specimens should be reexamined. At this time the significant characters are usually known and can be checked, using the same technique and the same interpretation of the characters as are applied to the rest of the material.

In work with subspecies it is not always necessary to have type specimens for comparison (if there is no question as to the identity of the species). On the other hand, a series of specimens from the type locality ("topo-typical specimens") is desirable to provide information on the characters and variability of the subspecies.

Determination Labels. Each specimen or each series should be labeled at the time an identification is made. The determination label should give the scientific (generic and specific trivial) name and author and in addition should give the name of the determiner and the year in which the identification was made. With this information on every specimen, the authenticity of the determination is established, and its dependability may be readily evaluated at any subsequent date on the basis of progress which may have been made in the study of the group during the intervening years. In bird and mammal collections these names are usually written in pencil so that they can be changed easily if there is a change of nomenclature.

It sometimes happens that existing knowledge and available material are not sufficient to place a specimen positively. In such cases the specimen should be set aside to await further material or evidence. Tentative or doubtful identifications should always be clearly indicated as such by means of a question mark. Unfortunately, most large collections contain numerous examples of doubtful or hasty determinations. In such cases the original specimen in a series may be quite authentic, but specimens may have been added subsequently with little or no regard for the critical characters of the particular species and without individual determination labels. The result may prove to be a hodgepodge including several species or subspecies. Obviously, this procedure is not only confusing but delays and complicates the task of identification.

TAXONOMIC DISCRIMINATION

When identifying material, particularly in less-known groups or from less-known regions, the taxonomist frequently comes across specimens that defy classification. They do not key out properly, or they do not agree with the specimens of the species with which they key out (or a close analysis reveals that specimens identified as a single species appear to belong to two or three distinct species). The question inevitably arises, Do these specimens belong to an undescribed species? In the past, this question has often been too hastily answered in the affirmative, with the result that we now have thousands of synonyms in zoological nomenclature. A great many of these might have been avoided if the describer had observed a few elementary precautions. A worker may greatly minimize the possibility of error if he (1) asks himself the basic questions of the taxonomist and (2) studies the discrimination grid (Table 3). This procedure is equally useful when applied to the classifi-

TABLE 3. DISCRIMINATION GRID

	Not reproductively isolated	Reproductively isolated
Morphologically identical:		
Sympatric.............	(1) Same population	(5) Sibling species
Allopatric.............	(2) Same subspecies	(6) Sibling species
Morphologically different:		
Sympatric.............	(3) Individual variants of the same population	(7) Different species
Allopatric.............	(4) Different subspecies	(8) Different species

cation of previously described but still dubious entities. In the preparation of any taxonomic revision the student is apt to come across cases in which he has to disagree with previous treatments.

The Basic Questions of the Taxonomist. If a taxonomist has before him two samples of specimens which may or may not belong to the same taxonomic category, he should ask himself the following three fundamental questions:

1. Is it likely that the two compared samples (when they are sympatric) were drawn from the same population or not?

If it is not likely, he should ask,

2. Do the two populations (from which the samples were collected) belong to the same species or not?

If the two populations appear to be conspecific, he should ask,

3. Is the difference between the two populations sufficient to merit subspecific separation or not?

Well-defined species are usually characterized by (1) morphological and physiological differences, (2) reproductive isolation, and (3) ecological differences. If a taxonomist has accurate information on these three points, he is rarely in doubt whether or not to classify a population as a species. For subspecies the additional information of geographical relationship is highly important, subspecies being allopatric.

The Discrimination Grid. In order to determine whether two given samples are intrapopulation variants, subspecies, or species, the working taxonomist relies chiefly on three sets of data: *reproductive isolation,* *presence or absence of morphological differences,* and *geographical relationship.* On the basis of this information a table with eight squares can be constructed which we shall call the *discrimination grid* (Table 3).

All three sets of information are not usually available to the taxonomist. The determination of the presence or absence of morphological differences is no major problem to the experienced taxonomist (except in the case of sibling species). Geographical relationship can nearly always be determined in properly labeled material. It is the lack of information on reproductive isolation which causes most of the difficulties. If we look at the discrimination grid, we see at once that without information on reproductive isolation we may have difficulty in choosing between the following alternatives: 1 or 5, 2 or 6, 3 or 7, 4 or 8. A high percentage of taxonomic errors is due to the wrong choice in one of these four alternatives. What can we do—in the absence of direct information on reproductive isolation—to avoid error? Fortunately, there is a great deal of indirect information available which may help us to reach the right decision.

Sibling Species (Alternative 1 versus 5, Alternative 2 versus 6). It is one of the most interesting findings of painstaking modern taxonomic work—often coupled with ecological analysis, chromosome determinations, and breeding tests—that in many taxonomic groups, exceedingly similar populations may coexist side by side without interbreeding. They satisfy every species criterion except that of morphological distinctness. Mayr (1942) has coined the term *sibling species* for such pairs or groups of morphologically nearly or completely identical species, translating into English the previously existing terms *Geschwister-Arten* (Ramme, 1930) and *espèces jumelles* (Cuénot, 1936). They have also been referred to as biological or physiological species (or races), cryptic species, and phenons.

Mayr (1948), in a recent survey, has shown how widespread and relatively common sibling species are in the animal kingdom. The discovery of sibling species is possible only in groups which are either very well known taxonomically or to which particularly refined methods of analysis have been applied. Such methods attempt to prove reproductive isolation, either directly or by establishing discontinuities between these nearly identical populations. Suitable methods are either biometrical (applied particularly in fish taxonomy), cytogenetic (*e.g.,* in *Sciara* and *Drosophila*), or combined taxonomic-ecological (*e.g.,* in *Anopheles*). Differences in parasite faunas may also provide clues on sibling species. Experimental evidence, useful as it is, is not necessarily conclusive, since the degree of reproductive isolation between two species may be different in the laboratory from what it is in nature, owing to changed ecological conditions. The absence of morphological differences is a negative character which alone is nondefinitive. Distributional data are not decisive, since sibling species may be sympatric or allopatric. For this reason elaborate studies of sibling species have thus far been carried out only in groups that are medically (*e.g.*, *Anopheles*), genetically (*e.g.*, *Drosophila, Paramecium*), or otherwise of special significance. It is therefore impossible to give the approximate percentage of sibling species in various orders. However, they appear to be particularly common among Diptera (*Drosophila, Anopheles*), Hymenoptera (ants), Lepidoptera (especially moths), and Protozoa (*Paramecium*).

Sibling species are not a different type of species; they are merely those species that are near the invisible end of the spectrum of morphological species differences. They grade imperceptibly into species that are morphologically more and more distinct from one another. Morphological differences are often eventually found after a particularly painstaking scouting of previously unstudied structures.

Sibling species are obviously inconvenient to the museum taxonomist. Often specimens of sibling species cannot be recognized in preserved material. However, since species are not a creation of the museum taxonomist but phenomena of nature, it is impossible to ignore the existence of sibling species. The museum worker will be unable in many cases to do better than to label museum specimens from a group of sibling species by the group name, *e.g.*, *Anopheles maculipennis* group.

Individual Variants or Different Species (Alternative 3 versus 7)? Different individuals that belong to the same interbreeding population may be very different. This intrapopulation variation, also termed *individual variation*, has been the source of much confusion to taxonomists. It is estimated that more than half of all synonyms owe their origin to an underestimation of individual variation. A careful study of the phenomena of individual variation in general, and specifically in the group with which the taxonomist is concerned, is an indispensable prerequisite of all sound taxonomic work.

A thorough knowledge of all the possible forms of individual variation is necessary whenever the taxonomist is forced to make a decision as to whether certain specimens represent a different species or individual variants. The tabulation and discussion of the major types of variation within a single population, as shown on page 82, may be helpful.

1. Extrinsic (Noninherited) Variation. Whether a certain variant within a population has a genetic basis or is merely a noninherited modification is difficult to determine, especially in museum specimens. Nevertheless, it is important for the taxonomist to know that various types of variation exist, and in better known groups, field observations and experimental evidence are often sufficient to decide the precise status of a given variant.

A. Progressive Individual Variation. 1. AGE VARIATION. Few species of animals are born in such an advanced condition that they resemble the adults of the species. Animals, whether they are born more or less developed or whether they hatch from an egg, in general go through a series of juvenile or larval stages in which they may be quite different from adults. The catalogues of any group of animals list numerous synonyms that are due to the failure of taxonomists to recognize the relationship between various age classes of the same species.

MAJOR TYPES OF VARIATION WITHIN A SINGLE POPULATION

I. Extrinsic (noninherited) variation
    A. Progressive individual variation
        1. Age variation
        2. Seasonal variation
    B. Social variation (social polymorphism)
    C. Ecological variation
        1. Habitat variation (ecophenotypic)
        2. Host-determined variation
        3. Density-dependent variation
        4. Climatically induced variation
        5. Heterogonic variation
        6. Neurogenic color variation
    D. Traumatic variation
        1. Parasite-induced variation
        2. Accidental and teratological variation
II. Intrinsic (inherited) variation
    A. Sex-associated variation
        1. Primary sex differences
        2. Secondary sex differences
        3. Alternating generations
        4. Gynandromorphs
        5. Intersexes
    B. Non-sex-associated variation
        1. Continuous variation
        2. Discontinuous variation (genetic polymorphism)
        3. Sex-limited polymorphism

In reptiles, birds, and mammals there are no larval stages, but immature individuals may be rather different from the adults, particularly in birds. For example, Linnaeus described the striped immature goshawk (*Accipiter gentilis* Linnaeus) as a different species (*gentilis*) from the adult (*palumbarius*) with its crossbarred underparts. Several hundred bird synonyms are based on juvenal plumages. By finding specimens that molt from the immature into the adult plumage, it is usually easy to clear up this difficulty.

In many fishes the immature forms are so different that they have been described in different genera or even families. The immature stages of the eel (*Anguilla*) were originally described as *Leptocephalus brevirostris*

Kaup. The unmasking may be difficult in neotenic animals, that is, animals that may become sexually mature in a larval stage.

The difficulties for the taxonomist are even greater in groups with larval stages which are so different that they have not even the faintest resemblance to the adult (*e.g.*, caterpillar and butterfly). The floating or free-swimming larvae of sessile coelenterates, of echinoderms, mollusks, and crustaceans are often extremely different from the adults. The taxonomic status of such larval stages can be settled either by establishing the chain of intermediate stages or by rearing them.

The taxonomic identification of larval stages of parasites of which the different stages occur on different hosts is particularly difficult. It is customary in helminthology to assign formal taxonomic names to the larval (cercaria) stage of flukes (trematodes), in order to facilitate their ready identification. Such dual nomenclature is, of course, dropped as soon as it becomes known to what trematode species a given cercaria belongs. This can be established only through rearing.

Age variation is not restricted to differences between larval stages and adults but occurs also among adults. In various species of deer (*Cervus*, etc.), for example, it is known that older stags have antlers with more points than younger ones. The shape of the antlers may also change. This age variation must be considered when the antlers of different species are compared. There is probably no more addition of points (or only an irregular one) after a certain age has been reached. It would therefore be as risky to try to determine the exact age of a stag by the number of points of its antlers as to try to determine the age of a rattlesnake (*Crotalus*) by the number of rings in the rattle, or the age of a hornbill (*Aceros plicatus* Forster) by the number of folds in the casque on the bill.

It is the aim of the taxonomist to work with samples that are as homogeneous as possible. It is much easier to achieve this in animals that have a definite adult stage (after the larval one) than in those that show continuous growth, such as snakes or fishes, which may reach maturity after having attained only half or less of their potential size. In such forms as the latter it is better to work with ratios of absolute measurements (proportions) than with the measurements themselves. Many meristic characters (*e.g.*, number of scales or fin rays) are not increased after they are formed, in spite of the enormous subsequent growth. Hence the importance of these characters in herpetology and ichthyology.

In birds it is generally assumed that final size is reached with the first completely adult plumage. There is some evidence that this is not always so. In the hornbill, *Aceros plicatus*, from the Papuan region, it is well established that "adults" with only two or three folds on the bill are younger than those with five or more folds. Birds in adult plumage with five to eight folds have a bill length of 198 to 227 mm. (average, 212.3 mm.), while birds in equally adult plumage with two or three folds have a bill length of 185 to 199 mm. In some passerine birds it has been possible through banding to show that the average size of known adult individuals increases slightly over the years (Lang, 1946).

2. SEASONAL VARIATION OF THE SAME INDIVIDUAL. In animals that live as adults through several breeding seasons, it happens not infrequently that the same individual has a very different appearance in different parts of the year. Many birds have a bright nuptial dress, which they exchange for a dull plumage at the end of the breeding season. Among North American birds this is true, for example, for many ducks, shore birds, warblers, tanagers, and others. In many cases such a change of plumage is restricted to the males.

In arctic and subarctic birds and mammals, such as ptarmigans (*Lagopus*) and weasels (*Mustela*), there may be a change from a cryptic white winter dress to a "normally" colored summer dress. In other birds the colors of the soft parts change with the seasons. In the common egret (*Egretta alba* Linnaeus) and in the European starling (*Sturnus vulgaris* Linnaeus), the bill may change from yellow to black; in the black-crowned night heron (*Nycticorax nycticorax* Linnaeus), the legs may change from salmon-colored to olive, etc. The plumage changes in birds are usually effected by molt, but wear alone may produce striking changes. In the European starling (*Sturnus vulgaris*), for example, the freshly molted bird of October is covered with white spots, and all the feathers show whitish or buffy margins. During the winter the edges of the feathers wear off, and in the spring, at the beginning of the breeding season, the whole bird is a beautiful glossy black without the molt of a single feather. A similar process of wear brings out the full colors of the nuptial plumage in the males of the linnet (*Acanthis cannabina* Linnaeus), the snow bunting (*Plectrophenax nivalis* Linnaeus), the house sparrow (*Passer domesticus* Linnaeus), and many other birds. In arid regions, particularly in real deserts, the sun bleaches the pigments. A bird before the molt will look much paler than one in freshly molted plumage.

In all these cases it is the same individual which in different parts of the year looks very different. Such seasonal variation is particularly common among vertebrates, with their elaborate endocrine systems. Many such seasonal variants were described as distinct species before their true nature was realized.

B. *Social Variation (Social Polymorphism)*. In the social insects, such as some bees and wasps, but particularly among ants and termites, "castes" have developed. These are definite groups of individuals within a colony, such as females (queens), workers (sometimes of different types), and soldiers (also sometimes of different types). In the Hymenoptera, these are most commonly modified females and genetically identical (except for the workers in some social bees; Kerr, 1950), but in the Isoptera (termites) both sexes may be involved. The structural types observed may result from different larval food or may be due to hormonal or other controls. Obviously taxonomic names should not be applied to these intracolonial variants; but invalid species have sometimes been described because it was not realized that there were different types of soldiers or workers in the same colony.

C. Ecological Variation. 1. HABITAT VARIATION (ECOPHENOTYPIC). Populations of a single species that occur in different habitats in the same region are often visibly different. The taxonomic treatment of such local variants has fluctuated between two extremes: some authors have described them as different species; others consider them all as nongenetic variants. Actually they may be (*a*) microsubspecies (or ecological races) or (*b*) nongenetic ecophenotypes. The latter are particularly common in plastic species, such as some mollusks.

Dall (1898) gave a very instructive account of all the variations he observed in a study of the oyster (*Ostrea virginica* Gmelin):

> The characteristics due to situs may be partially summarized: When a specimen grows in still water, it tends to assume a more rounded or broader form, like a solitary tree compared with its relatives in a crowded grove. When it grows in a tideway or strong current the valves become narrow and elongated, usually also quite straight. Specimens which have been removed from one situs to another will immediately alter their mode of growth, so that these facts may be taken as established. When specimens are crowded together on a reef, the elongated form is necessitated by the struggle for existence, but, instead of the shells being straight they will be irregular, and more or less compressed laterally. When the reef is dry at low stages of the tide, the lower shell tends to become deeper, probably from the need of retaining more water during the dry period. . . . When an oyster grows in clean water on a pebble or shell, which raises it slightly above the bottom level, the lower valve is usually deep and more or less sharply radially ribbed, acquiring thus a strength which is not needed when the attachment is to a perfectly flat surface which acts as a shield on that side of the shell. Perhaps for the same reason oysters which lie on a muddy bottom with only part of the valves above the surface of the ooze are less commonly ribbed. When the oyster grows to a twig, vertical mangrove root, or stem of a gorgonian, it manifests a tendency to spread laterally near the hinge, to turn in such a way as to bring the distal margin of the valves uppermost, and the attached valve is usually rather deep, the cavity often extending under and beyond the hinge margin; while the same species on a flattish surface will spread out in oval form with little depth and no cavity under the hinge.

In fresh-water snails and mussels such habitat forms are particularly common. The upper parts of rivers, with cooler temperatures and a more rapid flow of water, have different forms from the lower reaches, with warmer and more stagnant waters. In limestone districts the shells are heavy and of a different shape from those which grow in waters poor in lime. This dependence of certain taxonomic characters on environmental factors was, curiously enough, entirely overlooked by some earlier workers, a fact which resulted in completely absurd systematics. Schnitter (1922), who largely cleared up the situation, described these absurdities as follows:

> The last step in the splitting of the fresh-water mussels of Europe was done by the malacozoologists Bourguignat and Locard. According to the shape and the outline of the shell, they split up the few well-known species into countless new ones. Locard lists from France alone no less than 251 species of *Anodonta*.

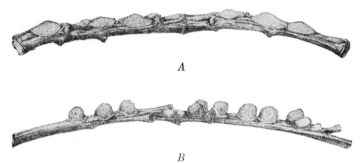

A

B

Fig. 11. Difference in structure of the scales *Lecanium corni* Bouché on different host species: *A*, on apricot (*Prunus*); *B*, on alder (*Alnus*) (× 2). (*Ebeling*, 1938.)

On the other hand, two mussels were given the same name, if they had the same outline of the shell, even though one may have come from Spain and the other from Brittany. It seems incredible to us that it never occurred to these authors to collect a large series at one locality, to examine the specimens, to compare all the individuals and to record the intermediates between all these forms. It is equally incomprehensible that these people did not see the correlation between environment and shape of shell, even though they spent their entire lives in collecting mussels.

All these "species" of *Anodonta* are now considered to be habitat forms of two species, and the other names have been sunk into the synonymy of the two valid species.

Whether a given habitat form is an ecophenotype or a microgeographic race is not always evident. It is sometimes necessary to transplant it or to raise it in the laboratory in order to solve this question. Much work of this sort still remains to be done.

2. HOST-DETERMINED VARIATION. Host-determined variations in parasites of plants and animals provide a source of taxonomic error and permit confusion with microgeographical races or with sympatric species. This

phenomenon is most commonly expressed in size differences but may involve other morphological or physiological characters.

Ebeling (1938) studied variation in the scale insect *Lecanium corni* Bouché, grown on different hosts (Fig. 11). Those from *Prunus* had large

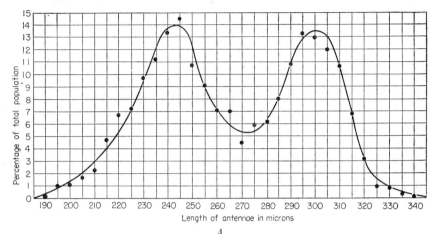

A

Fig. 12*A*. Bimodal curve resulting when individuals of *Lecanium corni* from two host species, apricot (*Prunus*) and Christmasberry (*Photinia*), are combined into one frequency distribution for antennal length (*Ebeling*, 1938).

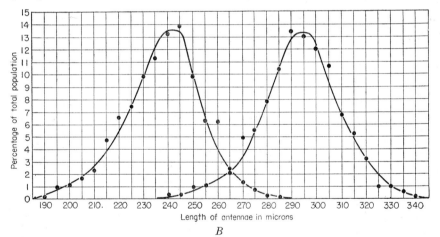

B

Fig. 12*B*. Slightly overlapping "normal curves" resulting when individuals of *Lecanium corni* from apricot (left) and Christmasberry (right) are placed in their respective frequency distributions for antennal length (*Ebeling*, 1938).

bodies and short appendages; those from *Photinia*, small bodies and long appendages. When individuals from the two hosts were combined in one frequency distribution for antennal length, a bimodal curve resulted; when plotted separately, two "normal curves" were produced (Fig. 12). Transfer of adults from *Prunus* to *Photinia* provided offspring of the *Photinia* type.   A third type on *Alnus* when transferred to *Prunus* gave progeny of the *Prunus* type.

Gerould (1921) has reported that the braconid wasp, *Apanteles flaviconchae* Riley, spins white cocoons when reared from blue-green caterpillars of *Colias philodice* Godart, golden cocoons when reared from yellow-green caterpillars from the same species.   With regard to another parasitoid, Salt (1941) found that males of the parasitic wasps, *Trichogramma semblidis* Aurivillius, tend to be wingless and otherwise modified when they develop in the eggs of the alderfly, *Sialis lutaria* (Fabricius) (Megaloptera), but not when reared from lepidopterous hosts.

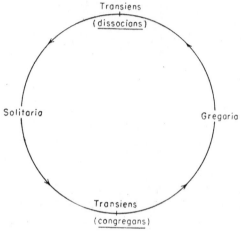

Fig. 13. Diagram illustrating the phases of locusts from solitary through transition to the gregarious phase (*Imms*, 1937).

Another kind of case is cited by H. S. Smith (1942).   He states that the encyrtid wasp, *Habrolepis rouxi* Compere, readily parasitizes red scale on citrus but is unable to do so when the red scale is reared on *Cycas*. This apparent immunization by the plant host might well confuse interpretations which utilize parasites as a taxonomic index.

3. DENSITY-DEPENDENT VARIATION.   The effects of crowding are sometimes reflected in morphological variation.   This is not uncommon where crowding produces a shortage of food materials.   However, density-dependent variation need not be related to food supply.   Uvarov (1921 *et seq.*) has shown that gregarious species of locusts exist in three unstable biological phases, solitary, gregarious, and transitional (Fig. 13).   These phases differ in anatomy (Fig. 14), color, and behavior characteristics and have often been described as distinct species.   When newly hatched nymphs are reared under crowded conditions, they mostly develop into the gregarious phase; under less crowded conditions, into the transitional

phase; and when isolated and reared separately, into the solitary phase. Similar phases have been reported by Faure (1943*a*, 1943*b*) in two species of armyworms (Lepidoptera), *Laphygma exigua* (Hübner) and *L. exempta* (Walker).

4. CLIMATICALLY INDUCED (SEASONAL) GENERATIONS. Many species of short-lived invertebrates, particularly insects, produce several generations in the course of the seasons of a single year. In such species it is not uncommon that the individuals which hatch in the cool spring are quite different from those produced in the summer, or that the dry-season individuals are different (*e.g.*, paler) from the wet-season population.

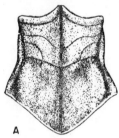 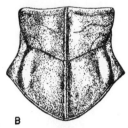

A   B

FIG. 14. *Locusta migratoria* Linnaeus. Pronotum of ♀ in dorsal view of *A*, phase *danica* (solitary), and *B*, phase *migratoria* (gregarious) (*Uvarov*, 1921).

Such seasonal forms can usually be recognized not only by the occurrence of intermediates in the intervening season, but also through identity of wing venation, genitalia, etc.

Cyclomorphosis. A special kind of seasonal variation is found in certain fresh-water organisms, particularly rotifers and cladocerans. The populations of a species undergo quite regular morphological changes through the seasons, in connection with changes in the temperature, turbulence, and other properties of the water (Coker, 1939). Many "species," particularly in the genus *Daphnia*, have been named that are nothing but seasonal variants. A study of the causes of cyclomorphosis has been begun (Brooks, 1946).

5. HETEROGONIC VARIATION. Heterogony (allometry) may result in the disproportionate size development of some structure in relation to the rest of the body. If individuals of a population show allometric growth, animals of different size will show heterogonic variability. This is particularly well marked among insects. It involves such features as the heads of ants (Fig. 15), the mandibles of stag beetles (Lucanidae), the frontal horns and thoraces in scarabs, antennal segments of thrips, etc. Failure to recognize the nature of such variations has resulted in much synonymy.

The exact causes of much of this variation are unknown. In species with continuous growth it is actually a form of age variation (see A1 above).   Some of it has a genetic basis and is properly classified under intrinsic variation (see IIB below).   In holometabolic insects, however, where this phenomenon is particularly common, it is closely correlated with size, and this in turn is thought to be the result of variation in food supply which causes the larva or nymph to metamorphose at different growth stages.

6. NEUROGENIC OR NEUROHUMORAL VARIATION.   Neurogenic or neuro-humoral variation is color change in individual animals in response to the environment.   Such changes are accomplished through the concentration or dispersal of color-bearing bodies known as *chromatophores*.   This type

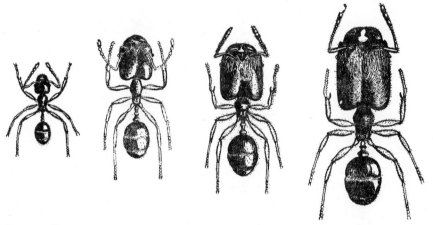

FIG. 15. Heterogony as a cause of variability.   Neuters of *Pheidole instabilis*, showing increase in the relative size of the head with absolute size of the body (*after Wheeler*, 1910).

of variation was first thoroughly studied in the chameleon (Brücke, 1852). It occurs sporadically in the lower animals but is best developed among the cephalopods, crustaceans, and cold-blooded vertebrates (cyclostomes, elasmobranchs, teleost fishes, amphibians, reptiles).   Space will not per-mit a discussion of this specialized type of variation.   For details the reader is referred to the recent review and bibliography by Parker (1948).

D. Traumatic Variation.   Traumatic variation occurs with varying frequency in different groups of animals.   The abnormal nature of this type of variation is usually obvious, but in some cases it is subtle and may be misleading.

1. PARASITE-INDUCED VARIATION.   Aside from such familiar effects of parasitism as swelling, distortion, and mechanical injury, parasites may produce conspicuous structural modifications.   In the bee genus *Andrena*, for instance, parasitism by *Stylops* frequently results in reduction in the size of the head, enlargement of the abdomen, and changes in punctura-

tion, pubescence, and wing venation. It commonly results also in inter-sexes. Since *Andrena* is markedly sexually dimorphic, these intersexes have been a source of taxonomic confusion and synonymy. However, in one case (Linsley, 1937), a stylopized intersex proved of value in associat-ing the sexes of a bee which had been described as two different species.

Salt (1927) has made the most comprehensive study of the morpho-logical effects of stylopization in *Andrena*. In females he found reduc-tion of the pollen-collecting organs, loss of anal fimbriae, changes in relative length of antennal segments, reduction of facial foveae, reduction of the sting and accessory organs, paling of ventral abdominal pubescence, acquisition of angular cheeks, and yellow on the normally dark clypeus. In males he reports the development of long hairs resembling the female flocculi, broadening of the posterior basitarsus, changes in proportions of antennal segments, loss of cheek angles and some yellow from the clypeus, indications of facial foveae, and reduction in size of genitalia.

Holmgren (1913) described some strikingly different termite soldiers from the Orient and assigned them to a new genus and species, *Gnatho-termes aurivillii* Holmgren. Kemner (1925) showed that these modified soldiers were nothing but parasitized individuals from colonies of *Macro-termes malaccensis* (Haviland).

2. ACCIDENTAL AND TERATOLOGICAL VARIATION. Accidental variation is usually externally induced, although it may work internally through some developmental or hormonal system. The external stimuli may be mechanical, physical, or chemical. Such variation is extremely diverse and in most animals may be readily identified, because the individuals involved either deviate so markedly from type as to be recognized as freaks, or because the injuries or abnormalities involved are asymmetrical. However, in those forms which undergo metamorphosis, injuries to an earlier stage may produce later abnormalities which are not so easily recognized as such. This is especially true when the anomalies involve characters which are normally of taxonomic value in the group concerned. For instance, certain types of pupal injury in beetles may produce sym-metrical abnormalities in punctation, surface sculpturing, or segmenta-tion of appendages; in butterflies, symmetrical modification of wing patterns. In most cases, however, even with such subtle differences, the abnormal nature of the variation may be detected by the specialist with-out much difficulty.

Teratological variation has been elaborately studied and classified by Cappe de Baillon (1927) and Balazuc (1948). The student interested in pursuing this subject further is referred to these works for details and for further references.

II. Intrinsic (Inherited) Individual Variation. In all the cases of variation mentioned in the preceding section, the same individual is actually or potentially subject to a change in appearance. In addition to this noninherited variation, there is much intrapopulation variation that is due primarily to differences in genetic constitution. This genetically based individual variation can—somewhat arbitrarily—be divided into two classes.

A. Sex-associated Variation. Among genetically determined variations within a population, there are many which are sex-associated in that they may be sex-limited (express themselves in one sex only) or otherwise associated with one or the other sex, or which involve sex characters or modes of reproduction. Some of these are as follows:

1. PRIMARY SEX DIFFERENCES. These are differences involving the primary sex organs utilized in reproduction (gonads, genitalia, etc.). Where the two sexes are otherwise quite similar, primary sex differences will rarely provide a basis for taxonomic confusion.

2. SECONDARY SEX DIFFERENCES. There is more or less pronounced sexual dimorphism in most groups of animals. The differences between male and female are often very striking, as for instance, in the birds of paradise, hummingbirds, and ducks. In many cases the different sexes were originally described as different species and retained this status until painstaking work by naturalists established their true relationship. A celebrated case is that of the king parrot [*Larius (Eclectus) roratus* Müller] of the Papuan region, in which the male is green with an orange bill, the female red and blue with a black bill. The two sexes were considered different species for nearly one hundred years (1776–1873) until naturalists proved conclusively that they belonged together.

Striking sexual dimorphism is particularly frequent in the Hymenoptera. The males of the African ant *Dorylus* are so unlike other ants that they were not recognized as such and were for a long time considered to belong to a different family. In the tiphiid wasps (Tiphiidae), the small wingless female and the large winged male are so different that some taxonomists use a different nomenclature for the two sexes. Whole "genera" consist entirely of males, others of females. The best way of determining with which female of "genus" *B* a given male in "genus" *A* belongs is to find a pair *in copula* or to watch a female in the field and catch the males as they are attracted to her. Once it has been established that *B* is the female of *A*, it is usually possible to associate many "species pairs" in the same genus by utilizing additional information on distribution, frequency, color characters, etc.

3. ALTERNATING GENERATIONS. In many insects there is an alternation of generations that is very confusing to the taxonomist. In the genus *Cynips* (gall wasps), the agamic generation is so different from the bisexual one that it is quite customary to apply different scientific names

to the two (Kinsey, 1930).   In the aphids (plant lice) the parthenogenetic wingless females are usually different from the winged females of the sexual generations (Fig. 16).

4. GYNANDROMORPHS. Gynandromorphs are individuals that show male characters in one part of the body and female characters in another part.   Thus the two halves of the body may be of opposite sexes, or the division may be transverse, or the sex characters may be scattered in a mosaic.   In the latter case symmetrical variants may be produced. Usually gynandromorphs may be recognized as such, and therefore they rarely provide a source of taxonomic confusion.   Gynandromorphism is produced by an unequal distribution of chromosomes, particularly the sex chromosomes.

5. INTERSEXES.   Unlike gynandromorphs, intersexes are likely to exhibit a blending of male and female characters.   They are generally thought to result from an upset in the balance between male-tendency and female-tendency genes.   This upset may result from irregularities in fertilization or mitosis or from physiological disturbances associated with parasitism (see 1 under ID).   Intersexes are particularly apt to appear in populations of interspecific or intersubspecific hybrids.   Intersexes have been studied in greatest detail in *Lymantria* (Goldschmidt, 1933) but are well known in many other animals.

B. Non-sex-associated Individual Variation.   This term is simply one of convenience applied to intrapopulation variation which is not sex-limited or does not primarily involve sex characters.

1. CONTINUOUS VARIATION.   The most common type of individual variation is that which is due to the slight genetic differences which exist between individuals.   No two individuals (except monozygotic twins) are exactly alike, genetically or morphologically, in a population of sexually reproducing animals.   One of the outstanding contributions of population genetics has been the establishment of this fact.   The differences are in general slight and are often not appreciable unless special techniques are employed.

The study of this variation is one of the foremost tasks of the taxonomist.   It is now evident that no one individual is "typical" of the characters of a population.   Only the statistics of the whole population can give a true picture of the population.   This explains why it is necessary to procure adequate samples of each population.   The collection and evaluation of the statistics of populations will be discussed in more detail in Chap. 7.

The variability of different characters of the same population is often very different.   Likewise there are different degrees of variability among related species.   Just why one species should be variable and another

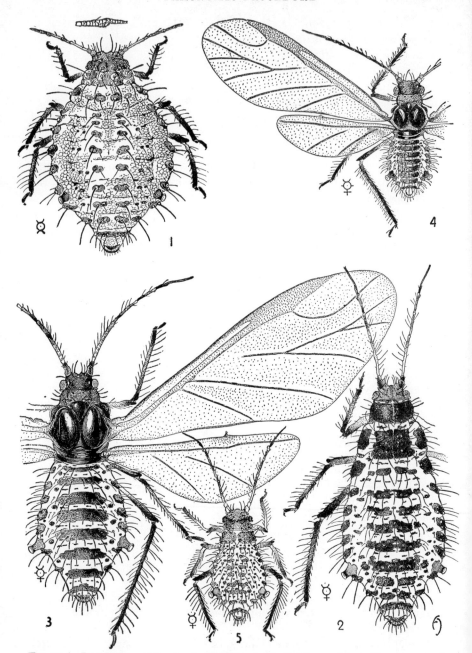

FIG. 16A. *Periphyllus californiensis* (Shinji). 1, Fundatrix or stemmother; 2, normal apterous parthenogenetic viviparous female; 3, alate of same; 4, smallest spring alate viviparous female; and 5, smallest spring apterous female (see data on facing page).

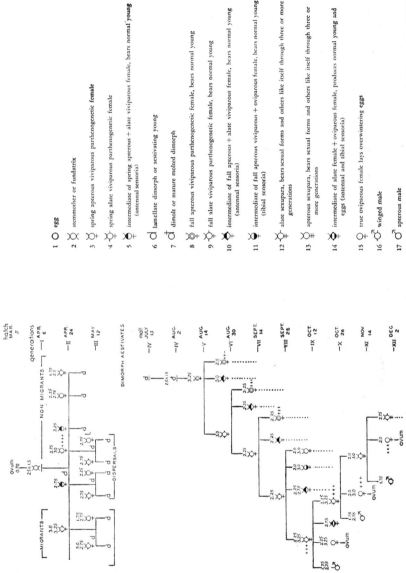

1 ○ egg

2 stemmother or fundatrix

3 spring apterous viviparous parthenogenetic female

4 spring alate viviparous parthenogenetic female

5 intermediate of spring apterous + alate viviparous female, bears normal young (antennal sensoria)

6 lamellate dimorph or aestivating young

7 dimolt or mature molted dimorph

8 fall apterous viviparous parthenogenetic female, bears normal young

9 fall alate viviparous parthenogenetic female, bears normal young

10 intermediate of fall apterous + alate viviparous female, bears normal young (antennal sensoria)

11 intermediate of fall apterous viviparous + oviparous female, bears normal young (tibial sensoria)

12 alate sexupara, bears sexual forms and others like itself through three or more generations

13 apterous sexupara, bears sexual forms and others like itself through three or more generations

14 intermediate of alate female + oviparous female, produces normal young and eggs (antennal and tibial sensoria)

15 true oviparous female lays overwintering eggs

16 winged male

17 apterous male

Fig. 16B. Sequence of forms of *Periphyllus californiensis* (Shinji) throughout a season (*Essig and Abernathy*, 1952).

one not is not always clear. A taxonomist who has adequate material of one species should not hastily decide that this will permit him to be certain of the variability of related species.

Early taxonomists vastly underrated individual variation in many genera of animals. The species of the snail genus *Melania* (fresh and brackish water) have been described largely on the basis of shell characters, such as the presence or absence of spikes and of diagonal and spiral ribs. However, spined and spineless specimens occur in the species *M. scabra*, *M. rudis*, and *M. costaba*, sculptured and smooth specimens in *M. granifera*, and so forth. In a revision of this genus no less than 114 "species" were found to be nothing but individual variants and had to be added to the synonymy of other species (Riech, 1937).

2. DISCONTINUOUS VARIATION (GENETIC POLYMORPHISM). The differences between individuals of a population are, in general, slight and intergrading. In certain species, however, the members of a population can be grouped into very definite classes, determined by the presence of certain conspicuous characters. Such discontinuous individual variation is called *polymorphism*. Frequently such polymorphism is controlled by a single gene transmitted by simple Mendelian inheritance.

Polymorphism is more pronounced in some groups of animals than in others. The spotting in lady beetles (Coccinellidae) is a well-known example of genetic polymorphism, as is industrial melanism in moths. Polymorphism has great biological importance, since it proves selective differences between apparently neutral characters. For a more detailed discussion of polymorphism, see Ford (1940, 1945), Mayr (1942), and Mayr and Stresemann (1950). The practical importance of polymorphism to the taxonomist is that it has led to the description of many so-called "species" that are nothing but polymorphic variants. In ornithology alone about 100 species names were given to polymorphs. The establishment of their true nature has led to a considerable simplification of taxonomy.

Genetically different seasonal forms. In exceptional cases of rapidly reproducing forms it happens that selection is so strong that the summer generation is genetically different from the spring and fall generations. This has been shown for *Drosophila* (Dobzhansky, 1951) and for several polymorphic species (*Adalia bipunctata* Linnaeus, and the hamster, *Cricetus cricetus* Linnaeus). These changes can only be demonstrated by special techniques and are not likely to confuse the taxonomist.

3. SEX-LIMITED POLYMORPHISM. Perhaps the most spectacular cases of polymorphism are to be seen in the Lepidoptera and more particularly in certain species of butterflies. The common alfalfa butterfly, *Colias eurytheme* (Boisduval), for example, has two strikingly different female forms, one resembling the male in ground color and the other, var. *alba*

Strecker, being largely white. The most complicated cases of sex-limited polymorphism which have been studied genetically are the examples of mimetic polymorphism in African swallowtail butterflies of the genus *Papilio*. Quite apart from the fact that allopatric populations throughout Africa show distinct subspecific differences which are correlated with differences in the species of butterflies which they mimic, we find that several distinct female forms exist within a single population. Thus in West Africa one finds, in the same population of *Papilio dardanus*

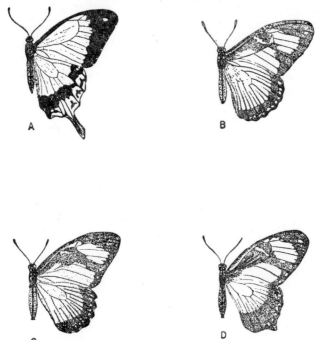

FIG. 17. Mimetic polymorphism in the *Papilio dardanus* complex. *A*, male of *cenea*— also basic type of nonmimetic female, ground color yellow; *B*, *dionysus*, nonmimetic female, ground color of forewings white, hind wings yellowish; *C*, *trophonissa*, mimetic female, ground color of forewings white, hind wings brownish; *D*, *hipocoon*, mimetic female, ground color white (*redrawn from Eltringham, 1910, by Goldschmidt, 1945*).

Brown, one male form and five female forms, three of the latter mimicking different models which belong to the families Danaidae and Nymphalidae (Table 4 and Fig. 17). The most remarkable feature of this polymorphism is that, although the various forms are so distinct as to resemble representatives of three different families of Lepidoptera, breeding experiments have shown (Goldschmidt, 1945)

. . . that this type of heredity is nothing but ordinary Mendelian heredity under the control of the respective sex and its specific physiology of development. . . .

[In a related case, *Papilio polytes* Linnaeus,] one type of female (*cyrus* Fabricius) resembles the male, another, *polytes*, mimics *P. aristolochiae* Fabricius, and a third, *romulus* Cramer, mimics *P. hector* Linnaeus. The breeding results were explained satisfactorily by a dominant factor A which converts *cyrus* into *polytes*, and one B, which only in the presence of A converts *polytes* into *romulus*" [Table 5].

Another celebrated case is that of *Pseudacraea eurytus* Linnaeus (Carpenter, 1949).

TABLE 4. MIMETIC POLYMORPHISM IN WEST AFRICAN *Papilio dardanus* BROWN
(From Goldschmidt, 1945)

Male	Nonmimetic females	Mimetic females	Models
Typical *dardanus*	Basic type ♀ similar to ♂ *dionysus* Doubleday and Hewitson	*hippocoon* Fabricius *trophonissa* Aurivillius *niobe* Aurivillius	*Amauris niavius* Linnaeus *Danaus chrysippus* Linnaeus *Bematistes tellus* Aurivillius

TABLE 5. GENOTYPES OF FORMS OF *Papilio polytes* LINNAEUS
(From Goldschmidt, 1945)

Males All Alike	Male-like Female	Mimetic Female	Mimetic Female
	cyrus	*polytes*	*romulus*
aaBB	*aaBB*		
aaBb	*aaBb*		
aabb	*aabb*		
AaBB			*AaBB*
AaBb			*AaBb*
Aabb		*Aabb*	
AABB			*AABB*
AABb			*AABb*
AAbb		*AAbb*	

The Recognition of Individual Variants. How can individual variants be recognized? There is no simple answer to this question. If a large sample of a population is available, intermediate forms between the various more extreme variants are usually found. Also, there are certain characters in every group that are less subject to individual variation than others. The genitalic armature in insects, the palpus in spiders, the radula in snails, the structure of the hinge in bivalves are such characters. If several sympatric forms agree in their genitalic armatures (or one of the other mentioned characters) it is very probable that they are conspecific.

However, even here one has to apply a balanced judgment. Although in most genera of Lepidoptera there are characteristic differences between the genitalia of related species, there are cases known in which forms have identical genitalia, even though they are different species by every other criterion.

The establishment of correlations is often very helpful. If two forms which differ in character *a* can be shown to differ also in the less conspicuous characters *b*, *c*, and *d*, it becomes very probable that they are different species. Some years ago Mayr (1940) found that among birds identified as the southeast Asiatic minivet (*Pericrocotus brevirostris* Vigors), some had the innermost secondaries all black; others had a narrow red margin on these feathers. A detailed study revealed that those birds with red on the innermost secondaries had seven additional characters: a more yellowish red of the underparts, a different distribution of black and red on the second innermost tail feather, a narrow whitish margin along the outer web of the first primary, and four other minor characters. Slight though they were, these characters were well correlated with each other and with geographical and vertical distribution. The conclusion that two full species were involved has since been confirmed by several authors.

Post-mortem Changes. The taxonomist must guard against one further type of individual variation. In many groups of animals it is impossible to prevent post-mortem changes of preserved specimens. Some extreme cases are known in birds. The deep orange-yellow plumes of the twelve-wire birds of paradise (*Seleucides ignotus* Forster) fade in collections to white. Skins of the Chinese jay (*Kitta chinensis* Boddaert), whose plumage is green in life, turn blue in collections, owing to the loss of the volatile yellow component in the pigment. Many birds that are clear gray or olive-gray when freshly collected become more and more rufous through oxidation of the black pigment ("foxing"). Many synonyms have been created in ornithology owing to the comparison of freshly collected material with old museum specimens.

Other post-mortem changes result from chemical reaction of preservatives or from killing agents. A common color change of this nature takes place when certain yellow insects, especially wasps, are overexposed to cyanide. The specimens turn bright red, and thus far no method has been found for reversing this reaction without injury to the specimens.

When preserving specimens with evanescent colors (corals, marine slugs, etc.) it is essential to take full notes and preferably color photographs or water-color sketches. This will make possible an accurate description of the living animal.

Different Subspecies or Not (Alternative 2 versus 4)? The discrimination grid indicates that two allopatric conspecific populations are to be

considered as belonging to different subspecies if they are morphologically different and as belonging to the same subspecies if they are morphologically identical. If there is a clear-cut difference between populations or none at all, there is no difficulty in making this decision. But there are many borderline cases. The term *identical* is not meant to be taken too literally. No two natural populations are ever exactly identical, at least in sexually reproducing species. The proper question then is, How different does a population have to be, in comparison with another one, in order to qualify as a subspecies?

Complete unanimity on this point has not yet been reached by taxonomists. There are two schools, the lumpers and the splitters. The extreme splitter recognizes as a subspecies every population which can be shown by statistical tests to be different. The extreme lumper recognizes as subspecies only populations of which every specimen can be identified. Very few taxonomists hold with either extreme. The two most common standards are that either more than 50 per cent of the specimens of the examined population must be identifiable with certainty, or more than 75 per cent. These are sometimes referred to as the *50 per cent rule* and the *75 per cent rule*. For practical reasons we prefer the 75 per cent standard, and it will be the basis of the subsequent discussion.

The expression *75 per cent nonoverlap*, or *75 per cent of the specimens must be identifiable* means that *75 per cent of the individuals have to be different from all other individuals of other subspecies (of the species)*. On the other hand, if 75 per cent of the individuals of population *A* are different from only 75 per cent of the individuals of population *B*, then it is possible for only 5.05 per cent of the individuals of *A* to be different from 99.865 per cent of the individuals of *B*. This means that only about 5 per cent of the individuals can be identified with certainty. Clearly this is not sufficient. A fuller discussion will be given in Chap. 7.

Two further points must be mentioned here, although they also are fully discussed in Chap. 7. One is that the overlap rule applies to populations, while the taxonomist, of course, studies only samples that are drawn from these populations. Obviously, the larger the sample, the greater the chance for overlap. The second point is that the range of variation of a sample or of a population is not linear but two-dimensional. If the wing length of a subspecies of birds varies from 70 to 80 mm. on the basis of an adequate sample, we can predict that about two-thirds of the specimens have a wing length of 73 to 77 mm. The values near the mean are much more frequent than those near the extremes.

If the *coefficient of difference* (see Chap. 7) is greater than 1.5, two different subspecies are usually involved. If the coefficient is less than 1, it is not advisable to separate the two forms.

If the coefficient of difference is between 1 and 1.5, it is necessary not only to use more refined methods of calculation, but also to take into consideration additional evidence. If the population in question has some distinctive biological characteristics, or numerous lesser characters in addition to the clearly diagnostic main character, it may be named even if the coefficient of difference is somewhat lower than average. Such biological characteristics occur when the population in question has a well-defined, isolated range, or when it is situated on the periphery of the species range. In contradistinction, the coefficient of difference has to be well above average if the population in question is intermediate between two other subspecies, or if it is situated in the middle of a cline.

Subspecies or Allopatric Species? (Alternative 4 versus 8). The word *allopatric* is essentially an antonym of *sympatric* and means therefore geographical distribution without geographical overlap. There are five kinds of allopatry that may be encountered by the taxonomist:

1. Allopatric populations *A* and *B* are in contact and intergrade in the (usually fairly wide) zone of contact.

2. Allopatric populations *A* and *B* are in contact and interbreed completely in the (usually fairly narrow) zone of contact.

3. Allopatric populations *A* and *B* are in contact but do not interbreed freely in zone of contact. Occasional hybrids occur.

4. Allopatric populations *A* and *B* do not interbreed at all, even though meeting in a zone of contact.

5. Allopatric populations *A* and *B* are separated by a distributional gap which prevents contact.

Populations that qualify under (1) and (2) are nearly always to be considered subspecies; under (3) and (4), species; and under (5), species or subspecies. The following comments, numbered to correspond to the list above, may be helpful:

(1) Allopatric populations that intergrade with each other belong to the same species. It depends on the degree of difference whether or not they are to be considered subspecifically different.

(2) There is no clear-cut distinction between intergradation and allopatric hybridization. In general, we speak of *intergradation* when a series of intermediate populations is intercalated between two subspecies, each with approximately the same amount of variability as any population of either subspecies. We speak of *allopatric hybridization* when the two subspecies meet in a well-defined zone and form there a hybrid population with greatly increased variability, often containing the entire spectrum of character combinations from subspecies *a* to subspecies *b*. There must be evidence for random interbreeding in this zone. Allopatric hybridization is sometimes also referred to as secondary intergradation, because it is a secondary event, following a breakdown of a previous extrinsic isolation of the population. Among North

American birds the flickers (*Colaptes*), juncos (*Junco*), and Canada jays (*Perisoreus*) furnish good examples of hybridization between widely divergent subspecies. For further details and additional examples see Mayr, 1942, pp. 263–270.

(3) Allopatric forms that hybridize only occasionally in the zone of contact are full species. There are a few cases where it is difficult to decide whether the hybridization is occasional or complete. Much recent evidence indicates that hybridization has to be fairly complete in order to restore secondary intergradation.

Two North American warblers, the blue-winged warbler (*Vermivora pinus* Linnaeus) and the golden-winged warbler (*V. chrysoptera* Linnaeus), meet along a front extending from the New York region to the Middle West. They regularly form a few hybrids in the zone of contact (or narrow overlap), which have been named Brewster's and Lawrence's warblers (based on different combinations of the parental character). However, the frequency of the hybrids seems not to have increased over the years, nor has the gap between the species been narrowed.

More difficult to evaluate are cases where two species remain as distinct species over most of their range but form complete hybrid populations in a few areas. This happens particularly in regions in which the natural ecological balance has been badly disturbed in recent years by human interference. It is recommended that such forms be treated as full species in spite of the occasional free hybridization under the stated conditions.

(4) Allopatric populations that are in contact but fail to interbreed are full species. The failure of interbreeding indicates reproductive isolation and attainment of species rank. The failure of overlapping may be due to either one of two opposite reasons. The zone of contact may connect two very different ecological areas (*e.g.*, savanna and forest). If one of the two neighboring species is specialized for one of these habitats and the other species for the other, the two species cannot invade each other's ranges because their ecological requirements are too different.

The other possible reason for nonoverlap of full species is that their ecological requirements are so similar in every respect that they compete with each other. On one side of the zone of contact one species is slightly superior, on the other side the other.

A full understanding of this situation is very important, because allopatry has often been taken as an automatic criterion of conspecificity. Mayr (1951) lists numerous cases of birds which have been restored from subspecies to species rank after the nature of their allopatry had been more closely investigated.

(5) Allopatric populations that are separated by a distributional gap may be either species or subspecies. The most important of the species

criteria, the presence or absence of reproductive isolation, cannot be used (except experimentally, and even then with reservations) to determine the status of geographically isolated populations. This is the reason why the classification of allopatric populations is so often subject to a considerable amount of disagreement among taxonomists. Many solutions for this dilemma have been proposed, but all of them are beset with difficulties.

Some taxonomists insist that all morphologically distinct, isolated populations be treated as full species "until it is proven that they are subspecies." This solution is, of course, impractical, because it is impossible in most of these cases ever to obtain clear-cut proof, one way or the other. Furthermore, this solution overlooks the fact that it is just as serious an error to call a population a species if it is really only a subspecies as to call it a subspecies if it is a species.

The second solution is to treat as full species all populations that are not connected by intergradation. This procedure is founded on the correct observation that populations which are connected by intergradation are conspecific, and it jumps from this observation to the reverse conclusion that populations which are not connected by intergradation are not conspecific. This conclusion is correct only so far as sympatric or contiguous populations are concerned, because with them the lack of intergradation proves the absence of interbreeding and thus constitutes *de facto* proof of specific distinctness. It does not necessarily apply to isolated, allopatric populations. Geographical isolation is not an intrinsic isolating mechanism, and there is no guarantee that the morphological hiatus caused by the temporary stop in the gene flow is proof of the evolution of isolating mechanisms. Others have proposed the opposite extreme, namely, to consider all related allopatric forms as conspecific.

A complete experimental analysis, including studies on mating preference and a cytological examination of hybrids, is usually impossible and may not be conclusive when it is possible. Ecological preferences are part of the isolating mechanisms between species, and these cannot be properly evaluated in the laboratory. For example, the sympatric sibling species *Drosophila pseudoobscura* Frolova and *D. persimilis* Dobzhansky and Epling always hybridize in laboratory populations, but no hybrid has ever been found in nature.

Since direct proof is unavailable, it becomes necessary to decide the status of isolated populations by inference. Several kinds of evidence are available. All these are based on the observation that reproductive isolation is correlated with a certain amount of morphological difference, which is fairly constant within a given taxonomic group. The taxonomist can use this evidence to work out a yardstick which can be applied to

isolated populations.   There are three sets of morphological differences
that can be utilized to calibrate such a scale.

1. Degree of difference between sympatric species.   Within a given
genus or within a group of closely related genera, there is usually a fairly
well defined amount of morphological difference between valid sympatric
species.   This difference may be great, as in the case of birds of paradise,
or it may be very slight, as in the case of sibling species.   This amount of
difference between good species can be used to determine the status of
isolated populations in these same genera.

2. Degree of difference between intergrading subspecies within widespread species.   The amount of morphological difference between the
most divergent subspecies in species of the same genus indicates how
much morphological difference may evolve without acquisition of reproductive isolation.

3. Degree of difference between hybridizing populations.   Subspecies
or groups of subspecies within a species sometimes become temporarily
separated from one another through the development of a geographical
barrier but merge again after the breakdown of the barrier.   Free interbreeding, which often occurs even after morphological difference of considerable magnitude has developed, proves conspecificity.   Good examples of such free interbreeding of morphologically strongly differentiated
populations are to be found in North American birds among some of the
juncos (*Junco*) and flickers (*Colaptes*).

Even after all these criteria have been applied, some doubtful cases
remain.   *It is preferable for various reasons to treat doubtful allopatric
populations as subspecies.*

The fact that a population has been unable to invade the range of its
nearest relative implies that it has been unable so far to develop isolating
mechanisms that would permit coexistence.   There is no zoogeographical
barrier more formidable for a subspecies than the range of another subspecies (Mayr).   Furthermore, the use of trinominals conveys two important pieces of information: (1) closest relationship and (2) allopatry.
Such information is very valuable, particularly in large genera.   To treat
such allopatric forms as separate species has few practical advantages.

CHAPTER 6

TAXONOMIC CHARACTERS

The essence of original taxonomic research is the analysis of material and the synthesis of the results into a classification. Although in practice these steps are often combined, they are really two separate operations. The first consists of finding and evaluating differences, the second of discovering points of resemblance. In both cases we are dealing with certain attributes of organisms which are known as *taxonomic characters*. The present discussion of the various kinds of taxonomic characters is given as a prelude to the discussions on analysis and synthesis of material.

Organisms differ from one another in many ways. Differences may be insignificant, as in identical twins, clones, and parthenogenetic offspring, but more often they are extensive and numerous. Individuals of the human species differ in innumerable points, some well marked and easily described, such as size and hair color, and some elusive and difficult to describe. Even greater is the number of differences between individuals representing two different species. Such individuals differ in an infinite number of characters and yet may retain certain features in common.

A taxonomic character may be defined as *any attribute of an organism or of a group of organisms by which it differs from an organism belonging to a different taxonomic category or resembles an organism belonging to the same category* (Mayr). Taxonomic characters are thus attributes which permit placement of an organism in the formal classification.

Taxonomic characters thus have a double function: (1) they have a diagnostic aspect as indicators of difference (emphasis on differentiating properties is particularly strong in the lower taxonomic categories); and (2) they function as indicators of relationship (this property makes them especially useful in the study of the higher categories).

Differences between organisms belonging to the same taxonomic category (male vs. female, immature vs. adult form, etc.) are not taxonomic characters. Most of the differences between individual variants classified in Chap. 5 are of this sort.

THE DIAGNOSTIC VALUE OF TAXONOMIC CHARACTERS

Diagnostic Characters. If we accept a recent estimate, we might assume that a higher animal may have in the neighborhood of 10,000 genes, while the number of characters is limited only by the patience of the investigator.   Even two related species of the same genus may differ in from 400 to 600 characters.   Zarapkin (1934) in a study of two races of the beetle, *Carabus cancellatus* Illiger, studied 166 characters, but these were only features relating to the sculpture and the proportions of the sclerotized exoskeleton.   In addition to such morphological characters, there exist all sorts of physiological differences, particularly those involving thresholds and rates of growth and development, inherited ecological adaptations, and psychological reaction norms, such as differences in instinctive behavior.

It would require more than a lifetime to prepare an exhaustive species description with references to all these characters.   Furthermore, the results would be so voluminous that no one would be willing to publish them.   However, not only is such a complete species description impractical, it is also unnecessary, since even a small fraction of the morphological differences is sufficient, in most cases, to ensure a correct diagnosis. In fact, the inclusion of physiological differences in a formal diagnosis is actually undesirable, since most identifications have to be made from dead specimens.

The most practical diagnostic characters are those that relate to some easily visible structure with but slight variability.   Such characters may be of no particular importance to the species, but they serve as markers for the taxonomist. To illustrate this point we might make the following comparison: If we want to direct a person to one of two houses on a street, we need not go into a detailed description of all of its features; we merely say: It is the white, not the red one! Color is a superficial attribute of a house.   Actually the white house may be built of wood, the red one of stone or brick; the white one may have six rooms, the red one ten rooms and so forth.   Even if the red house is painted white, it will remain basically different from the other white house.   The relationship of the diagnostic characters of an animal to its other species characters is frequently of an equally superficial nature.   It is necessary to emphasize the biological insignificance of many of the key characters or diagnostic characters, because this is frequently insufficiently realized by both taxonomists and non-taxonomists. For instance, if one of two related genera of insects is diagnosed as having two extra bristles on the thorax, this by no means implies that this is the basic difference between these genera.   Actually it may be the least important difference, but it may also be the one which can be recognized most quickly by the taxonomist (Mayr, 1942).

It has often been stated that taxonomy is an art rather than a science, and there is a half-truth in this statement.   It is as true as saying that a doctor who is a good diagnostician makes his diagnosis by intuition. Actually the good doctor and the good taxonomist make their diagnoses by a skillful evaluation of symptoms in the one case and of taxonomic characters in the other.

To be truly diagnostic, a taxonomic character must be constant for all members of a given category and for no others. In the case of variable characters it must be constant for a stated percentage of the population of a given category; hence the importance of the study of variability of characters. Consequently the use of taxonomic characters involves a study of their reliability. The same character does not always indicate the same amount of taxonomic difference. For instance, depending on the group of birds involved, the presence of a crest may be a generic, specific, subspecific, age, or sex character. An intimate knowledge of the group is necessary in order to evaluate properly a particular taxonomic character. By way of further example, a prominent, much-enlarged canine tooth is an important character for distinguishing species and genera in some families of mammals and quite unimportant in others. Likewise the number of premolars, whether two or three, is important in the primates, distinguishing the catarhines and platyrhines, but in other groups of mammals the mean number may vary among individuals of the same species. Furthermore, the value of a taxonomic character may change within a single phyletic series. For instance, in one section of a genus a character may be constant and useful in separating species. Elsewhere it may break down and be subject to individual variation. This fact, however, by no means invalidates the use of the character in that section of the genus where it *is* constant.

KINDS OF TAXONOMIC CHARACTERS

Early taxonomists used morphological characters almost exclusively to distinguish taxonomic categories and as a basis for classifications. Although morphological characters are still more useful than others, they are being supplemented to an ever increasing extent by other kinds of characters, as listed and discussed below. This is not only necessary to permit the application of the biological species concept, but the great broadening of the use of new kinds of taxonomic characters has increased the reliability of classifications. A single character is not as reliable as a character complex. However, we must never lose sight of the fact that characters are of unequal importance. It is here that the art of the taxonomist comes in, for he has to decide what weight must be given to each character.

The bases on which classifications are built may be greatly increased by using all stages in the life cycle of a species. In addition to the taxonomic characters presented by adult males, the taxonomist should also use those of adult females, of the various immature or larval stages, and of the eggs.

Frequently characters of immature stages are more helpful than those of the mature animal. Thus the various entities of the *Anopheles maculipennis* complex may be more readily distinguished by characters of the egg than by those of the adults, and the classification of the Aleyrodidae (whiteflies) is based primarily on the pupa, which is the stage most commonly used for purposes of identification. Furthermore, phylogenetic classifications may frequently be developed more readily from larval characters than from adults in many groups of arthropods in which the adults are degenerate or subject to convergence. In groups with complete metamorphosis, evolution often proceeds independently in larvae and adults, and conclusions drawn from characters of one stage form a very useful check on conclusions drawn from those of another.

The taxonomist in his practical work selects from the hundreds of taxonomic characters those that are most significant as being diagnostic or as indicating relationship. The ability to select these significant characters distinguishes the superior taxonomist.

The kinds of available taxonomic characters may be somewhat arbitrarily classified under five headings: (1) morphological, (2) physiological, (3) ecological, (4) ethological, (5) geographical. Within these five classes we can distinguish additional subdivisions.

KINDS OF TAXONOMIC CHARACTERS

1. Morphological characters
   a. General external morphology
   b. Special structures (*e.g.*, genitalia)
   c. Internal morphology (= anatomy)
   d. Embryology
   e. Karyology (and other cytological differences)
2. Physiological characters
   a. Metabolic factors
   b. Serological, protein, and other biochemical differences
   c. Body secretions
   d. Genic sterility factors
3. Ecological characters
   a. Habitats and hosts
   b. Food
   c. Seasonal variations
   d. Parasites
   e. Host reactions
4. Ethological characters
   a. Courtship and other ethological isolating mechanisms
   b. Other behavior patterns
5. Geographical characters
   a. General biogeographical distribution patterns
   b. Sympatric-allopatric relationship of populations

Morphological Characters. *General External Morphology.* Since external morphology has traditionally provided a primary and evident source of taxonomic characters, such characters need little discussion here. They range from such superficial features as plumage and pelage characters of birds and mammals, through linear scale counts of fish and reptiles, to the highly conservative and phylogenetically significant sutures and sclerites of the arthropod body. Animals with an external skeleton (arthropods, mollusks, etc.) present in general the greatest array and most useful range of external structural characters.

Genitalic Structures. Because of the fact that reproductive isolation is a *sine qua non* at the species level, *differences in genitalia* have been employed in many groups as the last court of appeal in delimiting species. It has even been suggested by Dufour and others that a lock-and-key relationship exists as regards the copulatory structures of the males and females of those species with sclerotized genitalia. Such appears to be the case in certain groups of insects, *e.g.*, the Fulgoridae. On the other hand, genitalic characters have been found to vary in the same manner as other characters (Jordan, 1905). In general, it may be said that genitalic differences must be evaluated just like other characters. In groups where their significance has been proved they are usually very useful, because genitalic structures appear to be among the first to change in the course of speciation.

Internal Morphology. Anatomy provides an abundant source of taxonomic characters in practically all groups of higher animals. However, the extent to which such characters have been used varies greatly from group to group, generally in inverse ratio to the abundance and usefulness of the external morphological characters. In many groups of vertebrates selected portions of the internal skeleton (*e.g.*, the skull) are routinely preserved and used in identification, but in general both the hard and soft parts of the internal anatomy of most animal groups are used primarily as a source of characters for the elucidation of higher categories. Paleontologists, of course, must deal almost exclusively with hard parts, and as a result they have focused attention on many useful skeletal characters in groups of animals with an internal skeleton.

Embryology. Comparative embryology offers taxonomic characters of great phylogenetic significance. Thus cleavage patterns, gastrulation, and other embryological phenomena may be characteristic for whole phyla or for series of phyla and thus assist greatly in the understanding of our highest categories. On the other hand, in such groups as insects, the total (holoblastic) cleavage of the Collembola (springtails) emphasizes the wide gap which separates this group from the other Apterygota (primitively wingless insects) and the Pterygota, in spite of the secondary reappearance of this cleavage type in a few highly specialized parasitic Hymenoptera near the top of the insect series (see also de Beer, 1940, 1951).

Karyology.   Karyological and other cytological characters may be useful to the taxonomist, though the degree of differentiation and limits of variation in chromosomal structure must be tested in each group before the significance of such characters can be determined.   The simplest cytological character is chromosome number.   This is determined by a relatively simple technic involving the crushing or smearing of the testes on a slide.   Chromosome numbers have been recorded for thousands of animals, and the results of such studies have been used as evidence of phylogenetic relationship by White (1945, 1949), and others.

Chromosome morphology is being used by the plant taxonomist to an ever increasing extent.   Karyology seems to be equally promising in many genera and families of animals.   Dobzhansky, Patterson, and Sturtevant, as well as several other authors, have made substantial contributions in recent years to our knowledge of chromosomal variation in *Drosophila.*   Such closely related species as *Drosophila pseudoobscura* and *D. persimilis* are diagnosed more easily by their chromosome configuration than by any other feature.   In the genus *Sciara* also the chromosomes have excellent diagnostic value.   In a study of the Finnish bugs of the family Lygaeidae, all the genera and nearly all the 56 cytologically investigated species could be identified by their chromosomes alone.   An exhaustive summary of the field is given by White (1945).   Some of these cytological differences interfere with chromosome pairing and thus serve as isolating mechanisms.   Gene arrangements on chromosomes have been used to analyze populations of *Drosophila, Anopheles,* and *Tendipes* (= *Chironomus*), and the presence of supernumerary chromosomes to study populations of grasshoppers (*Trimerotropis*).

Such studies are useful only if the student has a thorough knowledge of cytology.   The number of chromosomes may be different in close relatives (owing to the joining of two chromosomes after the loss of a kinetochore); genetically inert chromosome sections also are easily lost. Two species with superficially identical chromosomes may be much more different genetically than others with various gross chromosomal differences.   The chromosomal polymorphism in species of *Drosophila, Trimerotropis,* and others supplies excellent evidence for this.   There is a very useful recent summary of our knowledge of the chromosomes of vertebrates (Matthey, 1949).

Physiological Characters.   Physiological characters have been very unevenly exploited for taxonomic purposes.   Yet in constancy, diversity, and significance they probably far exceed morphological characters. They have, however, the disadvantage that in most cases their study requires living organisms.   Thus the most suitable subjects for this approach have been forms with a short life cycle, small body size, or other features which make for ease of laboratory experimentation or observation. However, the array of physiological characters in general increases with the complexity of the organism. We can never hope for a complete comparative physiology for taxonomic purposes (any more than we can hope for a complete comparative morphology). Nevertheless, physiological characters are coming into greater use, not only as a supplement to morphological characters, but as a means for checking conclusions based on other kinds of data and as an aid in the development of sound classifications.

Few detailed comparisons of the physiological constants of closely related species have so far been undertaken. Growth rates and egg-hatching periods in mosquitoes and growth rates and temperature reactions in various species of frogs of the genus *Rana* differ significantly.

A combination of two or three hemolysis constants is absolutely diagnostic for each examined species of the mouse genus *Peromyscus*. The amount of difference between the studied species *leucopus, gossypinus, truei,* and *eremicus* corresponds approximately with the degree of morphological distinctness. The various species of *Daphnia* differ in the spectroscopy of their hemoglobins. All this work confirms the view that many, if not most, proteins are species-specific. For a summary of this field, see Landsteiner (1945).

Metabolic Factors. Up to the present time, the microbiologists, especially the bacteriologists, who have had little morphology to rely on, have made the greatest use of physiological characters both in the development of a classification and for purposes of identification. Thus enzymatic activity is an important taxonomic character, and both anabolic and catabolic reactions are used. Cell chemistry is important in the differential ability of certain bacteria to react to certain stains (as Gram-positive or Gram-negative). Metabolic requirements are of great importance, as, for instance, whether the bacteria are aerobic or anaerobic, and how cultural growth patterns and coloration develop on standardized media. Although students of higher plants and animals have rarely used characters such as these for purposes of identification, nevertheless many broader physiological processes, especially differential growth rates and other developmental phenomena, have proved very helpful in the separation of closely related species.

Serological, Protein, and Other Biochemical Differences. These have been receiving increasing attention as taxonomic tools. Serology is concerned with the nature and interactions of antigens and antibodies. Antigens are substances capable of inducing the formation of antibodies when introduced into the blood stream of other animals. Antibodies obtained from the blood sera of immunized animals are serum globulins which are produced in response to the introduction of a foreign antigen. These are the principal substances concerned in serological reactions.

Underlying these reactions is the principle of quantitative specificity, *i.e.*, a given kind of antibody will react more strongly, under comparable conditions, with the particular kind of antigen used in its formation than with any other substance.

TABLE 6.   A COMPARISON OF THE SEROLOGICAL REACTIONS OF THE SERA OF COMMON CRUSTACEA*

Anti-serum	Homologous antigen		*Homarus americanus*	*Homarus vulgaris*	*Callinectes sapidus*	*Carcinus maenas*	*Cancer borealis*	*Cancer irroratus*	*Cancer pagurus*	*Menippe mercenaria*	*Geryon quinquedens*	*Ocypode albicans*	*Maia squinado*
142(1 + 2)	*Homarus americanus*	L3	100	54									
140(1 + 0)	*Callinectes sapidus*	L4	...	..	100	26	16						
147(1 + 0)	*Callinectes sapidus*	371A	...	..	100	44	14						
154(1 + 1)	*Callinectes sapidus*	HC38–1	...	..	100	17	17	..	...	7	3	..	1
152(1 + 0)	*Carcinus maenas*	3	...	..	34	100	22	..	...	8	...	..	1
148(1 + 1)	*Cancer borealis*	3b	...	..	...	...	100	58					
151(1 + 1)	*Cancer borealis*	HC1	...	..	...	...	100	59	41				
160(1 + 1)	*Cancer borealis*	3d	...	..	...	...	100	29	19				
161(1 + 1)	*Cancer pagurus*	39–1	...	..	...	...	41	33	100				
162(1 + 0)	*Cancer pagurus*	39–2	...	..	...	...	55	51	100				
149(1 + 0)	*Menippe mercenaria*	36–A	...	..	6	...	12	..	...	100	10		
163(1 + 2)	*Menippe mercenaria*	36–A	...	..	28	...	16	..	...	100	25	6	5
150(1 + 1)	*Geryon quinquedens*	36–1	...	..	...	...	...	19	...	24	100		
164(1 + 1)	*Geryon quinquedens*	39–2	...	..	3	...	...	...	...	6	100		

* The homologous area represents 100 per cent, and the heterologous per cent values indicate the ratio of heterologous area to the homologous area.

The precipitin reaction was discovered by Kraus in 1897 and has been widely used in the taxonomy of microorganisms. It consists in the formation of a visible precipitate at the interface when one brings together an antigen and the corresponding antiserum. The precipitin test was first applied to broad taxonomic problems by Nuttall (1901), who showed that the relative intensities of precipitin reactions paralleled the systematic positions of the species whose antigens were tested.

Boyden (1943 *et seq.*) has done much to elaborate the concepts and refine the techniques of systematic serology. He lists the basic premises of systematic serology as follows:

1. The antigenic composition of animals is an important part of their essential natures and must be considered in any sound natural system of classification.

2. Protein antigens are conservative hereditary traits.

3. Good precipitin techniques are well adapted to reveal the relative degrees of biochemical similarity of protein antigens.

Numerous examples of the application of serologic methods to taxonomy are now available, one of the most thorough of recent date being Boyden (1943) on Crustacea. Boyden summarizes the data from all his crustacean comparisons in Tables 6 and 7.

TABLE 7. THE RELATIONSHIP OF THE SERA OF DIFFERENT SPECIES, GENERA, AND FAMILIES OF BRACHYURA
(Summarized from Table 6)

I. The relationships of the sera of species of the same genus
    A. Cancer
        1. *Cancer borealis* vs. *C. pagurus*   41, 41, 19, 55, av. 39
        2. *Cancer borealis* vs. *C. irroratus*   58, 59, 29, av. 49
        3. *C. pagurus* vs. *C. irroratus*   33, 51, av. 42
    B. Homarus
        1. *H. americanus* vs. *H. vulgaris* 54   54
                 Grand average............ 46

II. The relationship of the sera of genera of the same family
    A. *Callinectes* vs. *Carcinus*   26, 44, 17, 34, av. 30

III. The relationship of the sera of different families of Brachyura
    A. Portunidae vs. Cancridae   16, 14, 22, 13, 17, av. 16
    B. Portunidae vs. Xanthidae   4, 6, 8, 7, 6 (28), average of 5 values   6
    C. Portunidae vs. Goneplacidae   3, 3, av. 3
    D. Portunidae vs. Maiidae   1, 1, av. 1
    E. Cancridae vs. Xanthidae   12, 16, av. 14
    F. Cancridae vs. Goneplacidae   24, 4, av. 14
    G. Xanthidae vs. Goneplacidae   10, 25, 24, 6, av. 16
    H. Xanthidae vs. Ocypodidae   6
    I. Xanthidae vs. Maiidae   5

The data in Tables [6] and [7] give a quantitative approximation to the serological relationship of the species tested and they appear generally to agree with their systematic positions. The data may be presented phylogenetically as in the case of *Geryon*, representing the family Goneplacidae, in relation to the families Xanthidae, Cancridae and Portunidae. According to Rathbun . . . the family Goneplacidae is most closely allied to the family Xanthidae and our data confirm this conclusion but show in addition that the Goneplacidae are almost as close to the Cancridae as to the Xanthidae. . . . The position of *Geryon* and the Goneplacidae in relation to the other families as indicated by the present data is shown in Fig. [18]. Actually three dimensions would be needed to express this relationship properly, but it can be done on a plane surface as shown here.

Still another use of serological tests is for identification.   Brooke and Proske (1946) used the precipitin test for determining insect predators of immature mosquitoes.   They tested the stomach contents of *Belostoma, Ranatra fusca* Palisot-Beauvois, a hydrophilid larva, a damselfly nymph and a dytiscid larva and concluded that "it is possible to demonstrate, by precipitin tests, the presence of mosquito larvae and pupae in the digestive tracts of aquatic insect predators."

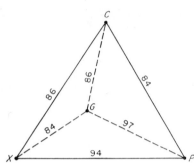

FIG. 18. A diagram to show the relative distances of four families of Crustacea from one another as indicated by serological tests.   The data are tentative, inasmuch as the families have not yet had really adequate testing.   The smaller the figure, the closer the assumed relationship.   The families concerned are Cancridae (*C*), Portunidae (*P*), Xanthidae (*X*), and Goneplacidae (*G*).   The latter family, represented by *Geryon*, is apparently closest to Xanthidae, represented by *Menippe;* a little less close to the Cancridae; and considerably more distant from the Portunidae.   Three dimensions would be required to express these relationships properly, and the plane figure is really a projection of such three-dimensional distance onto a plane surface (*Boyden*, 1943).

Body Secretions.   Another kind of physiological character which has proved useful in taxonomy involves body secretions which form consistent patterns.   The waxy secretions of scale insects and mealybugs fall in this category.   The wax patterns produced reflect, of course, the underlying morphology, especially the number, size, and arrangement of the wax glands, and therefore tend to be about as constant as the morphology of these structures.

Genic Sterility Factors.   Even the earliest taxonomists knew that there is much sterility between members of different species.   In fact, sterility has often been cited as *the* species criterion.   It is now known that sterility is only one of the many existing isolating mechanisms, and that it is gradually built up.   In some cases distinct species may be completely interfertile (as for instance *Anas platyrhynchos* Linnaeus and *A. acuta* Linnaeus among birds), while in other cases there may be a considerable amount of sterility even between subspecies of a single species (as, for instance, between the subspecies of *Drosophila pallidipennis* Dobzhansky and Pavan).   Sterility is thus a taxonomic character that must be used with discrimination.   (For a treatment of the genetic basis of sterility see Dobzhansky, 1951.)

Ecological Characters.   Through the work of field naturalists and experimental ecologists during recent decades, it has been well established that each species of animal has its own range of tolerance of habitat, food, breeding season, and other ecological factors. No two species with identical ecological requirements can coexist in the same place (Gause's rule) (Lack, 1949). Likewise it has been shown for genera and the still higher categories that each occupies a separate adaptive plateau (Sewall Wright, see Dobzhansky, 1951) or adaptive zone (Simpson, 1944). In view of these properties of the taxonomic categories, it should be possible to define them ecologically and to diagnose them with the help of ecological characters. This is, indeed, the case.

Lack (1947) showed, for instance, that each genus of Galapagos finches occupies a separate ecological zone. *Geospiza* is a ground finch (chief food, seeds); *Camarhynchus*, a tree finch (chief food, insects); and *Certhidea*, a warbler finch (chief food, small insects). Although at the present time most genera and other higher categories are defined on purely morphological grounds, it is probable that more naturally defined genera, families, etc., will result from augmenting the definition of these categories with ecological characters.

Ecological characters are of even greater practical importance in the diagnosis and separation of sibling species. The three closely related crickets of the *Nemobius fasciatus* group can be identified principally by their habitats and songs. In southern Michigan *N. fasciatus* (DeGeer) lives in dry grasslands, *N. socius* Scudder in marshes, and *N. tinnulus* Fulton in sunny oak-hickory forests (Cantrall, 1943). The various species of cave swiftlets (*Collocalia*) apparently can be better identified by the composition of their nests than by morphological characters of the birds.

The six European species of the *Anopheles maculipennis* group differ more in ecological than in morphological characters (Table 8).

TABLE 8. ECOLOGICAL CHARACTERS IN THE *Anopheles maculipennis* COMPLEX
(After Hackett and Missiroli, 1935, and Bates, 1940)

Species	Habitat	Water type	Hibernation	Malaria carrier
melanoon.......	Rice fields	Fresh water	No	No
messeae.........	Cool standing water	Fresh water	Yes	Almost never
maculipennis...	Cool running water	Fresh water	Yes	No
atroparvus......	Cool waters	Brackish	No	Slightly
labranchiae.....	Mostly warm waters	Brackish	No	Very dangerous
sacharovi.......	Shallow standing water	Often brackish	No	Very dangerous

Nearly every issue of the ecological journals describes cases of pronounced ecological differences between closely related and morphologically very similar species. As a matter of fact, a species description which does not give some account of the ecology, where such data are available, should be considered incomplete.

Specific food preferences are important taxonomic characters in monophagous or parasitic organisms. Numerous new species of insects have been discovered when those that appeared to live on the "wrong" food plant were more closely studied. At one time such bark beetle genera as *Dendroctonus*, *Ips*, and *Phloeosinus* were thought to contain but a few species, each highly variable in structure, host, and boring pattern. When these were segregated according to host plants, it was discovered that many species were involved, each with relatively constant characters of structure, host preference, and boring pattern.

The host-parasite relationship can be worked both ways by the taxonomist. A knowledge of the parasites can be used to determine differences within the host group (host discrimination), and a knowledge of the hosts can be used to discover differences in the parasites (parasite discrimination).

Host Discrimination. The method of using differences in parasites or commensals to distinguish between exceedingly similar sibling species is very useful. This method has been used advantageously by botanists. For example, *Pinus jeffreyi* Murray is now recognized as distinct from *P. ponderosa* Lawson; but entomologists were never in doubt about this, because each species of pine is attacked by a different bark beetle, *Dendroctonus jeffreyi* Hopkins on Jeffrey pine and *D. brevicomis* LeConte on Ponderosa pine. Emerson (1935) found morphological differences between two highly similar species of termites only after he had received a clue as to their distinctness by differences in the termitophile beetles found in their respective nests. Very similar species of fresh-water turbellarians may differ in the ciliates that live on their surface.

Parasites may also be used in the classification of the higher categories. The use of host-parasite relations for the elucidation of taxonomic problems has been described in detail by Metcalf (1929). Kellogg (1896, 1913) utilized this method extensively in his study of the Mallophaga. For more recent discussions of this subject see Clay (1949) and Hopkins (1949).

The flamingos (Phoenicopteri), a rather isolated group of birds, show anatomical similarities to both the storks and the geese. The bird lice (Mallophaga) of the flamingos are clearly related to those of the geese, thus (with the proper safeguards) indicating closer relationship to the geese than to the storks.

Parasite Discrimination. We have already mentioned the case of bark beetle genera, the species of which were not properly discriminated until sorted out according to host. The tapeworms *Hymenolepis nana* in man and *H. fraterna* in rodents do not differ significantly in morphology, nor do *Ascaris* of man and of pigs, although host specificity indicates the existence of differences in both cases. Many cases of this kind are recorded in the parasitological literature. On the other hand, occurrence of a parasite on a different host does not prove specific distinctness.

Ecological characters are also useful at the infraspecific level. Nearly every geographical, and often microgeographical, race differs in its ecological requirements from other races. In botany such local ecological races have been called ecotypes (Turesson, 1922) and have been studied particularly by Clausen, Keck, and Hiesey (1948). These ecotypes are discussed in Chap. 2.

In birds much geographical variation in ecological requirements has been described (Mayr, 1951). It affects particularly vertical distribution, habitat preference, food preference, and nest-site preference. The continental race of the European cormorant (*Phalacrocorax cormoranus sinensis* Shaw) nests on trees, the North Atlantic race (*P. cormoranus cormoranus* Linnaeus) nests on rocks. Instances of such geographical variation of ecological characters have also been described for other groups of animals, although the tendency is for the ecology of a species to remain fairly constant within its entire geographical range. It is this property which usually permits the diagnosis of species on the basis of ecological characters.

A special case of infraspecific variation of ecological characters is given by the host races of insects, often formerly referred to as "biological races" (Thorpe, 1930, 1940). The term *biological race* is not descriptive and has been applied to many different phenomena, particularly to sibling species. The term *host race* is more precise.

Host races are common in insects and have attained various levels of distinctness. Thus the codling moth, *Carpocapsa pomonella* (Linnaeus), has developed a distinct walnut-preferring race. This is inferred in the absence of morphological differences from the fact that "walnuts, pome fruits, and the codling moth have existed together in California since 1873, and although the moth has been a severe pest on pome fruits for many decades, only since 1918 has it become a major pest of walnuts" (Smith, 1941).

Many other host races without distinctive morphological characters have been recorded. Perhaps the best known examples in forest entomology are the races of *Dendroctonus monticolae* Hopkins and other wood-boring beetles upon which Hopkins based his "host-selection principle" (Craighead, 1921). Another case concerns the small ermine moths, *Hyponomeuta padella* Linnaeus, which, when transferred from apple to hawthorn or vice versa, develop a significant preference for the plant on which they were reared as caterpillars and proceed to oviposit on the plant of their choice as adults (Thorpe, 1930).

These examples from the field of economic entomology illustrate the importance of the ecologic approach in taxonomic research. The taxonomist of the present and future is working in a highly specialized and interrelated world. New methods must be adopted to meet changing conditions. The greatest pressure will come from applied fields such as plant quarantine, biological control, and insect vectors of plant and animal diseases, and it is here that the ecologic approach may be expected to yield the best results.

Another type of ecological character, especially useful at higher levels of classification, is the presence and kind of intracellular symbionts. According to Steinhaus (1949), Buchner (1940) describes the situation in the Homoptera as follows:

All the aleyrodids, for instance, have the same type of symbiosis and the same manner of symbiote transmission, in which a number of intact mycetocytes are carried over in the ovum. A similar uniformity exists in the psyllids. In the superfamily Aphidoidea, on the other hand, similarity of type is limited to families. Thus Aphidae and Eriosomatidae (= Pemphigidae) have rounded symbiotes, Adelgidae (= Chermesidae) have rod-shaped symbiotes, and Phylloxeridae are apparently free of intracellular micro-organisms. In the coccids there is no uniformity of type except in subfamilies. All the Lecaniinae have similar yeast-like symbiotes in the hemolymph and in the fat cells; the ortheziids contain bacteria in the fat bodies; the diaspids harbor degenerate rounded bacteroids. The mode of generation-to-generation transmission in these cases is also specific for the subfamily. Among the monophlebines all the genera have paired, elongate mycetomes, although *Marchalina* appears to be an exception. In this genus the symbiotes are carried in greatly enlarged cells in the gut epithelium. This discrepancy is clarified if one accepts the rearrangement presented by Morrison in 1928, which removes *Marchalina* from the monophlebines and places it as a tribe in the new subfamily Coelostomidiinae. One wonders if many similar changes would not be made if the taxonomist had the advantage of knowing the symbiotic arrangement of the insects with which he worked.

Finally, as a further example of ecological characters, we may mention host reactions. Where host reactions are specific and conspicuous, they have frequently been used for taxonomic purposes. Symptoms, although largely being replaced by other characters in microorganisms, still are important in the classification of plant viruses. Some of the most useful plant reactions, however, are the galls produced in response to attack by various gall wasps (Cynipidae) and gall flies (Cecidomyiidae or Itonididae). Some of these are more readily distinguished than the adult insects, and in some cases new species have been described from the gall alone. Although this practice is to be frowned on, nevertheless it is indicative of the importance that various workers have attached to such characters.

Ethological Characters. Just as morphological characteristics change from species to species and from genus to genus, thus supplying material for a taxonomic analysis, so behavior patterns change from group to group. It may be too early to speak of a science of comparative ethology, but beginnings have been made in the analysis of the unit elements of which behavior patterns of some animal groups are composed and the comparison of their evolutionary modification from species to species. This was done by Lorenz (1941) for most species of river ducks (Anatini), by Spieth (1947) for the species of the *Drosophila willistoni* group, and by Jacobs (1950) for grasshoppers. It has been found that the behavior pattern is on the whole composed of homologous elements within a given taxonomic group, but that there is great variety in the manifestations of these elements, and that many of the modifications are species-specific.

Courtship and Other Isolating Mechanisms. Differences in mating habits are especially important behavior characters, since they are more likely to result in reproductive isolation and consequent speciation. For example (Mayr, 1942),

The slugs are a group of animals which, although morphologically very similar, tend to have color phases and varieties, most of which had originally been described as good species. No two taxonomists could agree as to which of these forms were good species and which were not. In a study of the pairing behavior of these slugs, Gerhardt . . . showed that the displays that led up to copulation are exceedingly complicated and consequently highly specific. In the genus *Limax* six definite pairing types could be determined, which apparently correspond to six good species. Many of the other described 'species' of this genus are probably nothing but color varieties.

Other Behavior Patterns. In addition to behavior patterns which serve as isolating mechanisms, an infinite variety of behavior characters is available to the taxonomist. For example, the nature of the webbing constructed by various spiders, mites, and caterpillars may be used at various levels in the classification. The two bee genera *Anthidium* and *Dianthidium* were slow to be recognized on morphological grounds, yet all known species of the former construct their nests of cottony plant fibers, those of the latter from resinous plant exudations and sand or small pebbles.

The use of extraneous materials in the construction of nests or larval or pupal cases provides characters at various levels in the classification of caddisworms and bagworms, and the manner in which such materials are attached to the shell is a useful taxonomic character for distinguishing species of the molluscan genus *Xenophora*.

Finally, certain behavior patterns are more conservative than structural characters. Examples of such are the drinking habits of pigeons and sandgrouse (Pterocletidae); dust bathing of **Ploceidae** and *Passer* (but not of finches); use of mud in nest building of barn swallows (*Hirundo*) and crag martins [formerly erroneously associated with bank swallows (*Riparia*)].

Geographical Characters.   Geographical characters are among the most useful of tools for clarifying confused taxonomic pictures and for testing taxonomic hypotheses.   Most sound classifications show some correlation with geographic or associated ecologic features.   Essentially the taxonomist is interested in two kinds of geographical characters, (1) general biogeographic patterns, which are especially useful in the arrangement and interpretation of higher categories, and (2) the allopatric-sympatric relationship, which is most helpful in determining whether or not two populations are conspecific.

General Biogeographic Patterns.   The broad geographic patterns with which we are concerned have been determined by the study of distributional patterns of large numbers of groups of plants and animals.   Biogeographers have divided the world into various realms, regions, provinces, subprovinces, etc., based upon generalized comparisons of faunas and floras.   These are not rigidly defined, but in general they represent distributional centers which exist today or have existed in the past. Depending on the group, they may be expanding or retreating, and we thus find it more useful to refer to them as faunas or floras or biotas rather than zones or areas.   A taxonomist should have an understanding of the geological history of the regions in which such biotas center, as well as a knowledge of the past relationships of the faunas and floras concerned. Armed with this information, the interpretation of various higher categories can be made on a much sounder basis.

For instance, the mammals of South America are either not related to those of Africa or, if of common ancestry, have presumably reached South America by way of North America.   The hystricomorph rodents, seemingly close to the African porcupines, appeared to be an exception, the history of which was inexplicable in view of the absence of such forms in the early Tertiary period of North America.   A reexamination of these porcupines and their relatives, prompted by this zoogeographical puzzle, revealed, indeed, that the porcupines of South America and of Africa are of independent origin (Wood, 1950).   Distributional difficulties have shed light on taxonomic relationships in many other instances.   They suggest, for instance, that the New Zealand "thrushes" (*Turnagra*) are not thrushes but Pachycephalinae, and the New Zealand "tits" not Paridae but Malurinae, both reassignments leading to a considerable zoogeographical simplification.   Distribution is, thus, an important tool in taxonomic analysis.

Sympatric-Allopatric Relationship of Populations.   This is one of the most useful methods of approaching the question of whether or not two populations represent distinct species (see Chap. 5). If a series of forms shows geographic replacement, *e.g.*, a chain or ring of forms, each of which differs from its neighbors, the forms are said to be *allopatric*. Such a distributional pattern in closely related forms is now generally considered to be indicative of a polytypic species consisting of several subspecies. On the other hand, if the ranges of two or more forms partly or entirely overlap and these forms do not intergrade, they are said to be *sympatric*. Such a distributional pattern is considered to indicate that the forms involved are full species, since sympatric coexistence without interbreeding is one of the basic tenets of the species concept.

THE EVALUATION OF TAXONOMIC CHARACTERS

The determination of the characters that distinguish closely related categories or are shared by taxonomic groups (higher categories) is only one step in taxonomic research. The evaluation and analysis of these characters must go further. For instance, it must be determined how constant a given character is. Most taxonomic characters are variable, and a study of this variability is part of the taxonomic procedure. It is obvious that taxonomic characters should not be drawn from single representatives of populations, but rather from adequate samples, as described in Chap. 7.

The relation between taxonomic characters and taxonomic categories is not always clearly understood. Even though a species has specific characters and a genus generic characters, these characters have no absolute values. The taxonomic categories are not a consequence of the characters, but rather the opposite—the taxonomic characters are a consequence of the categories (Chap. 3). As stated above, the value of a given character may change from category to category. The experiences of the taxonomist in this respect may be summarized in a few simple rules.

1. The degree of difference between characters is often an indication of the degree of relationship, at least within a given taxonomic group. However, the degree of morphological difference may indicate different categorical rank in different groups. In the genus *Drosophila*, for instance, many good species (sibling species) are hardly different morphologically, while the species of birds of paradise are always strikingly different, and even subspecies may differ conspicuously. The rates of phyletic evolution of the phenotype and of speciation are only very loosely correlated.

2. A character may be of great taxonomic significance in one case and of none in another. For instance, the number of tail feathers in birds, whether eight, ten, or twelve, is sometimes a generic character, sometimes a subspecific character, and sometimes varies individually within a single population.

3. Reduced or degenerating characters are particularly unreliable. Such characters are, for instance, the presence or absence of a fourth toe in certain genera of birds, the number of teeth in certain genera of mammals (as, for instance, *Talpa*), the presence or absence of tarsal spurs or wing veins in certain insects or of wings in pterygotan groups, etc. Classifications should not be based on characters that are in the process of being lost within a taxonomic category.

4. So-called "primitive" characters are often an indication of the absence of specializations. Pseudoprimitiveness may be acquired secondarily in phyletic lines by a loss of specializations. Contrary to a widely held opinion, specializations may indeed be lost in the course of evolution, resulting in the return to what appears to be a more primitive condition.

THE BIOLOGICAL MEANING OF TAXONOMIC CHARACTERS

Up to this point we have discussed taxonomic characters primarily from the practical point of view as indicators of taxonomic difference or of relationship. Such a concentration on the practical aspect of taxonomic characters is one-sided and has been responsible for many taxonomic difficulties.

It will help our understanding of taxonomic characters to point out their biological significance. It was formerly held by many biologists that the majority of taxonomic characters were without biological significance. The modern trend is to assume that no character can become established in a population unless it has superior selective qualities. The adaptive significance of many taxonomic characters is obvious, such as those that have to do with food getting or protection against enemies and the adversities of climate. In the case of other characters, some of the morphological expressions of the phenotype may not be directly adaptive but only the by-products of the physiological actions of a superior gene complex. The analysis of the biological significance of taxonomic characters is one of the functions of the taxonomist.

Some of the species characters relate to the general adaptation of species; others have the more specific function of promoting geographical coexistence of closely related species, either by reducing competition or by functioning as reproductive isolating mechanisms. A survey of these taxonomic characters has been given elsewhere (Mayr, 1948).

TAXONOMIC CHARACTERS AND CLASSIFICATION

A satisfactory system or classification must be based on properly evaluated taxonomic characters. The more characters two animals have in common, the closer we generally group them in the system. The higher systematic categories are formed by uniting lower categories that share certain characters. We have discussed the philosophical basis of the principles of classification in Chap. 3, and we shall deal here only with some of the practical difficulties with which we are confronted in the evaluation of taxonomic characters (see also Rensch, 1934).

Linnaeus and most of his followers for nearly a century classified birds by purely adaptational characters. Birds with webbed feet were put into one category; birds with a hooked bill were considered another group; etc. Eventually it was realized that characters that are adaptations to a specific mode of living are not only subject to rapid changes by selective forces, but may also be acquired in different unrelated lines. Such characters have only limited value in establishing taxonomic categories. They are most useful in separating species and genera. When dealing with the classification of higher categories we must search for characters that tend to remain stable, characters that are phylogenetically conservative. Without entering into the controversy on homology, it should be pointed out that classifications are based on homologous characters.

TAXONOMIC CHARACTERS AND EVOLUTION

The use of taxonomic characters in classification is based on the simple fact that some characters change very rapidly in evolution, while others only change slowly. The rapidly changing characters are used to distinguish subspecies and species; the slowly changing ones are used to characterize the higher categories. If we look at a group of fossil animals, we find that they usually start with primitive forms and eventually die out with extremely specialized forms. Dollo's rule of irreversible evolution was established on this observation. As Simpson and others have pointed out, evolutionary lines do not move undeviatingly toward specialization. In fact, a character can be lost again in a phyletic line, and a similar or equivalent character can be reacquired. Specialization and despecialization often alternate in evolution. Also, each taxonomic character may evolve to a large extent independently of other characters. For this reason it is often misleading to consider the mere number of differences between two categories as indicating degree of difference. Too often several characters are partially or completely correlated. For instance, the arboreal mode of living in a group of mammals will inevitably lead to changes in the locomotor apparatus that may affect nearly every bone and muscle in the whole body. A change of feeding habits in birds may result eventually in structural modifications of the bill, the tongue, the palate, the jaw muscles, the stomach, and perhaps other features. All these characters are a single adaptive complex and should not be treated and considered as a series of independent characters. A shift into a new adaptive zone may lead to a comparatively rapid structural reorganization in order to acquire the needed specializations. Such specializations should not be overrated when making classifications.

In conclusion, a taxonomic character is any attribute by which an organism or group of organisms resembles, or differs from, another; this attribute may involve any comparative feature of the dead or living organism. Taxonomic characters which are conservative (*i.e.*, which evolve slowly) are most useful in the recognition of higher categories, those which change most rapidly, of the lower categories; taxonomic characters are subject to parallelism, especially those involving loss or reduction, and such characters should be avoided or used only with the greatest of care; character complexes which vary as a unit should be treated as a unit and weighted as though they were a single character; the same characters vary in value and constancy from group to group and even within a single phyletic series, but this fact does not invalidate their use in those parts of the series where they are constant; taxonomic characters provide our most useful tool for the recognition of taxonomic categories and thus ultimately for the interpretation of the course of evolution; the proper evaluation of taxonomic characters is thus one of the most important, as well as one of the most difficult, tasks of the taxonomist.

CHAPTER 7

QUANTITATIVE METHODS OF ANALYSIS

THE IMPORTANCE OF QUANTITATIVE METHODS IN TAXONOMY

The use of quantitative data in taxonomy is important for several reasons. First of all, they add to the preciseness of a description. The actual measurements of a series of specimens are infinitely more useful than the meaningless statement, "of medium size." "Sex comb with seven teeth" is more precise than merely "sex comb present." Such precision is important, since related species and subspecies often differ not by the presence or absence of a structure, but rather by its size, or proportions, or number. Such relative differences can be stated precisely by the use of quantitative data (figures). This has been recognized by taxonomists from the earliest times. Even in the days of Linnaeus it was the custom of many authors to record the total length of the type and similar quantitative data.

The second reason for the importance of quantitative data is that species and the other taxonomic categories are not fixed "types" but consist of variable populations. Such variability cannot be described adequately except in quantitative terms. This is particularly true when the characters of two variable species or subspecies overlap.

A third and essential reason for using quantitative data is the possibility of deriving from them (with the help of statistics) estimates of the characteristics of the natural populations from which the samples were drawn.

Descriptive methods have now become standardized (see Chap. 9) to such an extent that any description is incomplete which does not include at least a minimum of quantitative data.

The systematic presentation of quantitative data and their evaluation is the function of statistics. A detailed presentation of the principles of statistics and of the application of the various statistical methods is beyond the scope of this manual of taxonomy. Fortunately, there are a number of good texts available, among which we recommend especially Simpson and Roe (1939), *Quantitative Zoology*. A short survey of those statistical methods that are particularly useful to the taxonomist is given by Cazier and Bacon (1949). The textbooks of Snedecor (1946) and Mather (1947) present more detailed treatments, with emphasis on the analysis of variance.

Of particular interest to all taxonomists is the series of papers by Klauber on the application of statistics to the taxonomy of reptiles (*e.g.*, Klauber, 1936–1940, 1941, 1943*a*, 1943*b*, 1945), as well as Burma's (1948, 1949) discussion of the application of statistical methods in invertebrate paleontology.

Our discussion will concentrate on some of the principles of elementary statistics and their application to taxonomy.

Some taxonomists have expressed their reluctance "to become involved in statistics." Actually, they are using statistics not only when giving means and size ranges, but also when expressing the results of comparing entities. When we state that species *minuta* differs from species *grandis* in its smaller size, we are, in effect, stating that the mean length of *minuta* is less than that of *grandis*, and that the range of variation in an adequate sample of the population of species *minuta* does not overlap the range of variation in an adequate sample of species *grandis*. If we say "averages smaller," we imply that there is a difference between the means but an overlap of the population ranges.

The statistics recommended in modern taxonomic research are merely an extension of the simple statistics employed unconsciously by every taxonomist. More elaborate methods are not only made possible by the great increase in the size of the available collections (samples) but have become actually necessary in order to settle many problems of taxonomic research at the infraspecific level.

Statistics are employed most frequently in the taxonomy of contemporary species with respect to two kinds of problems:

1. The study of the consistency of expression of a taxonomic character within a population (variability). In these problems one attempts to answer the question, How constant or variable is a given character? The answer to this question is found by calculating standard deviation and coefficient of variability (see below). Knowledge of the variability of a character is indispensable to the solution of the second type of problem.

2. The study of the degree of difference between two populations in regard to one or many characters. The methods of analysis of differences between populations are described in the second half of this chapter.

Some additional problems may occur in paleontology (Simpson, 1941; Burma, 1948). For a more extensive discussion of the meaning of statistics in taxonomic work, see the last section of this chapter.

SAMPLES AND SAMPLING METHODS

The taxonomist attempts to study the properties of natural populations. However, an entire population cannot be brought into the laboratory or studied in the field. The specimens actually available to the taxonomist are usually only a small fraction of the individuals of which the population in nature is composed. Such a portion of the true population is called a *sample*. From the study of such a relatively small sample, we attempt to reconstruct the properties of the population from which it was drawn. We also seek to determine how different other samples drawn from the same population might be.

What qualities should a sample have in order to be a sound basis for taxonomic work? "The ideal representative of a population is a sample that is homogeneous, adequate and unbiased" (Simpson and Roe, 1939; see this work for a detailed discussion of these three properties of samples).

The taxonomist is only rarely in the position to obtain collections that are perfect in respect to these three qualifications. This is inevitable and not too serious, but the worker should be aware of the possible short-comings of his material.

Homogeneity. A large heterogeneous sample can often be segregated into several smaller homogeneous samples by separating the specimens according to age, sex, and locality. Season and habitat differences are additional factors which often introduce heterogeneity. If, for example, in a species of birds, samples from various localities are compared, conspicuous differences may exist when adult males are compared with adult males but may not be apparent when females and immatures are grouped in a single sample with the adult males. Homogeneity may occasionally be ignored in a qualitative analysis, as, for instance, in the selection of a diagnostic character that is equally valid for males and females, immature forms and adults. Great care must be taken when segregating a homogeneous sample to avoid bias (see below). Sometimes, as, for instance, in a growth series, heterogeneity cannot be eliminated. In other cases, *e.g.*, in fossil material, sufficient information may not be available to segregate the material according to sex or age. Indeed, it is sometimes the very object of the statistical analysis to facilitate such a segregation of the material into homogeneous components. A number of techniques have been described to achieve this, such as analyses of bimodal curves, plotting of regression lines of tentative segregates, etc.

Adequacy. The question of adequacy will have a different answer according to whether we are dealing with a variable character (such as size) which is present in all members of the population or a polymorphic character which has a given frequency within a population. Different statistical techniques must be employed for the two kinds of characters.

It was believed at one time that statistical analysis was possible only with large samples. It is now known that valuable information can also be obtained from small samples, in fact, even from single specimens (Simpson and Roe, 1939). Small size of samples is no excuse for failing to treat them statistically. On the other hand, it is axiomatic that the larger the sample, the more precise the inference that can be made from it (in regard to the characters of the population).

With polymorphic characters, which are present only in part of the population, the question is, How large must a sample be to include a specimen with a character that occurs in the population at a known frequency? Or, reciprocally, between what limits can the frequency of a given character fluctuate in a sample of a given size? We refer to Simpson and Roe (1939) for a discussion of the sampling limits and reproduce here a table (Table 9). In a sample of 30 specimens, for example, a character that occurs in 60 per cent of the population can be expected to be found in at least 10 but not more than 26 specimens. If a character occurs in 20 per cent of the population, a sample of 50 specimens is necessary to be virtually certain that it will include one with this character. Most likely it will be represented in a sample of 5 specimens. Cazier and Bacon (1949) state that in taxonomic statistics, "for all practical purposes samples of at least 15 to 25 specimens may be used with good results, but samples of 50 to 100 specimens are more desirable."

TABLE 9. SAMPLING LIMITS
(From Simpson and Roe, 1939)

Size of sample	Percentage of occurrence in population								
N	10%	20%	30%	40%	50%	60%	70%	80%	90%
5	0 3	0 4	0 5	0 5	0 5	0 5	0 5	1 5	2 5
10	0 4	0 6	0 8	0 9	0 10	1 10	2 10	4 10	6 10
15	0 5	0 8	0 10	0 12	1 14	3 15	5 15	7 15	10 15
20	0 6	0 9	0 12	1 15	3 17	5 19	8 20	10 20	14 20
25	0 7	0 11	0 15	3 18	5 20	7 23	10 25	14 25	18 25
30	0 8	0 13	1 18	4 20	6 23	10 26	13 29	17 30	22 30
40	0 10	0 16	3 21	6 25	10 30	14 34	19 37	24 40	30 40
50	0 12	1 19	5 25	9 31	14 36	19 41	25 45	31 49	38 50
75	0 16	4 26	10 35	17 43	24 51	32 58	40 65	49 71	60 75
100	1 19	8 32	16 44	25 55	35 65	45 75	56 84	68 92	81 99

Bias. The sample should be unbiased, that is, the method of getting the sample should be such that the variations of the pertinent characters occur in the sample at the same frequency as in the population. A sample is unbiased when every member of the population has an equal chance of being drawn. In order to approach this goal the specimens should be collected completely at random. In taxonomic work this ideal is rarely achieved. Collections are usually made at particular seasons and times of the day. Most of the early locality records of wild species of western North American *Drosophila* show them to be from national parks. A certain amount of bias is unavoidable, but it should be recognized and recorded. Never should part of a collection be discarded and only those specimens kept that are considered either typical or particularly interesting for being atypical. Nor should large specimens be favored over small ones. In polymorphic populations especially, great effort should be made to collect specimens in the true population frequency. In order to reduce collecting bias, it is often advisable to employ different collecting techniques at the same locality.

MEASUREMENTS AND OTHER VARIATES

Only quantitative data can be subjected to a statistical analysis. In this fact lies the importance of characters that can be counted or measured. Meristic (= countable) characters permit greater accuracy than measurements and are therefore favored wherever possible as, for instance, by students of echinoderms, fishes, and reptiles. Simpson and Roe (1939) give nine criteria of good numerical observations. Most important for measurements is that they be standardized (applying to a specified distance) and accurate. For instance, the length of the bill in birds may be measured in several ways: (1) from the nostril to the tip, (2) from the beginning of the feathering to the tip, or (3) from the beginning of the bony forehead to the tip. Observations have shown that the first can be measured very accurately but does not give the full length of the bill; the third can be measured fairly accurately in all birds with a steep forehead; and the second can rarely be measured with any accuracy. Consequently, in some genera of birds the third is the preferred measurement, in others the first. In this, as well as in all similar cases, the record should show which of several possible measurements was actually taken.

It is only rarely possible to predict which of a set of possible measurements will be most important in the comparison of several samples. It is therefore advisable to measure all variates that may possibly be of importance. Subsequent analysis will show that many of these measurements either fail to show significant differences or are merely duplications of other data. In view of the high costs of printing, such superfluous data should not be published. They may be placed in the archives of a public institution (museum or library) where they are available to other students.

When one is measuring an important lot of specimens or measuring specimens before one's method has been completely standardized, it is strongly advisable to measure each variate repeatedly. The duplicate sets of measurements should be taken on different days and on new record sheets. When completed, the various sets of measurements should be compared and averaged. Particularly deviating measurements should be checked for possible errors in the measuring technique.

Measurable Characteristics. Total length is usually a very important measurement, particularly when it is used as the yardstick for ratios and proportional measurements. In each case it should be specified what is meant by *total length*. Is it taken before or after preservation? Does it include or exclude appendages on the head and the tail? Total length is most satisfactory in beetles and other rather rigid, hard-shelled animals. In birds the wing length (= actually the length of the longest primary) is a much less variable quantity than total length measured in the flesh. The cube root of the weight may under certain conditions replace the total length in calculations of allometric ratios. Body length, *i.e.*, total length minus tail length, is usually a more accurate measure of size than total length.

Different measurements are used for nearly every category of animal. In mammals, for instance, body and tail length are measured, as well as length of the hind foot and ear and the various dimensions of the skull. In birds, wing, tail, bill, and tarsus are the most commonly measured variates. In most groups of insects not only length should be given but also width and antennal and tarsal formulas. These data should be given as a routine matter regardless of their immediate diagnostic value. Special measurements are traditionally given in particular taxonomic groups, such as the length of the rostrum in Hemiptera, length of the wings in some Diptera, etc. It is important for comparative purposes to give measurements that conform with the system which is customary in the group under study.

Technical Aspects of Measuring. Zoological measurements are now universally given in terms of the metric system. However, many descriptions written in the nineteenth century use inches and lines (1 line = $\frac{1}{12}$ in.) (Table 10).

TABLE 10. CONVERSION OF LINES INTO MILLIMETERS

1 line	= 2.11⅔ mm.	7 lines	= 14.81⅔ mm.
2 lines	= 4.23⅓ mm.	8 lines	= 16.93⅓ mm.
3 lines	= 6.35 mm.	9 lines	= 19.05 mm.
4 lines	= 8.46⅔ mm.	10 lines	= 21.16⅔ mm.
5 lines	= 10.58⅓ mm.	11 lines	= 23.28⅓ mm.
6 lines	= 12.7 mm.	12 lines	= 25.4 mm.

Various measuring tools are used for different groups of animals. A millimeter rule (often with a "zero stop") and dividers (calipers) are used for most larger animals. The eyepiece micrometer is used to measure microscopic objects. It may be divided into small or large units and may be arranged as a linear scale or in squares. The individual units must be translated into the metric system by calibration with a stage micrometer.

Projection devices, such as microscopic projectors, are sometimes useful. By means of such devices, the specimens can be drawn from a projected outline, and the various parts can then be measured, enlarged on a table. This method is particularly useful when relative sizes and angles are to be measured.

As far as refinement is concerned, it is important to carry measurements out to whatever decimal point may be necessary, but not to waste

A. M. N. H.
Dept. of Birds

Prunella immaculata

India, Burma, China

Catalogue No. Collector	Date	Locality	Altitude and Habitat	Sex	Plumage	Wing	Tail	Bill	
1 Koelz	Dec.23, 1936	N.Bengal,Darjeeling District,Tiger Hill	ca. 17,000'	♀	Fresh	80.5	58	14	
2 Koelz	Dec.23, 1936	"　　"　　"		♀	Fresh	80	56	13.5	
A.M.N.H. 584801 Osmaston	Nov.13, 1903	N. Bengal Darjeeling District	7,000'	♀	Slightly worn	80	59	14	
A.M.N.H. 307283 Vernay	Dec.1, 1938	N. Burma, Pyepat Ridge	5,000'	♀	Fresh	77.5	56	13.5	
A.M.N.H. 307284 Vernay	Dec.21, 1938	"　　"		♀	Fresh	79	57	13.5	
A.M.N.H. 307289 Vernay	Nov.12, 1939	N. Burma, nr. Hpawte	6,500'	♀	Slightly worn	76	58	14.5	
A.M.N.H. 307291 Vernay	Nov.28, 1939	N. Burma, Hpimaw		♀	"	77	55	13	
A.M.N.H. 307292 Vernay	Nov.24, 1939	N. Burma, Htawgaw		♀	"	78	59	14	
A.M.N.H. 307794 Berezowsky	Dec.15, 1893	Szechuan, China Mu-kua-chi		♀	Fresh	78	55.5	14	

Fig. 19. Filled-out data sheet as used in the American Museum of Natural History.

effort by an unreasonable accuracy. It would be useless to give the height of a person as 176.583 cm.

How, then, shall the proper degree of refinement be decided? Simpson and Roe (1939) recommended as the unit of measurement one-twentieth of the difference between the largest and the smallest specimen, if an adequate series is available. Thus if the measurements range from 10 to 12 mm., one should measure to $\frac{1}{10}$ mm.; if they range from 40 to 50 mm., to ½ mm.   If they range from 70 to 90 mm., no decimal places need be recorded.   If fractions are rounded up, they should consistently be rounded to the nearest full number, halves to the nearest even number. When fractions are measured, a bias in favor of integral numbers should be avoided.

Recording of Measurements.   It is advisable whenever large numbers of measurements are taken to enter them on special data sheets.   If adequate samples are available, each sample should be recorded on a separate sheet.   Each specimen should be entered separately, its museum number, age, and sex recorded, and then the various measurements recorded in separate columns.   If there is room, the calculated ratios between measurements can be entered on the same sheets (Fig. 19).

THE ELEMENTARY STATISTICS

Mean.   The most commonly used statistic is the *average*, or arithmetic mean (M).   It is calculated by dividing the sum of the measurements $(x_1 + x_2 + x_3 + x_4 + \cdots)$ by the total number of specimens (N).   The mean thus obtained is the mean of the sample, not of the total population.

Range.   By determining the smallest and the largest specimens of a sample, we obtain the *observed sample range, e.g.,* wing 72 to 83 mm.   It is evident that with an increase in the size of the sample, very soon specimens will be found that are smaller (70, 71) or larger (84, 85).   The larger the sample, the larger will be the range between the smallest and the largest specimens.   This dependence of the observed range on the size of the sample is one of the reasons why range is usually not considered a very useful statistic unless the size of the sample is stated exactly.

Normal Curve.   By arranging numerically all the measurements within a sample, one finds that not all measurements are equally frequent. Most frequent are specimens close to the arithmetic mean (M) of the sample, while specimens near the minimum and maximum are rare.

If a sufficiently large number of measurements is plotted, it is found that the resulting frequency curve usually corresponds to the so-called "normal curve."   The theory and properties of the normal curve are described in every textbook of statistics.   This curve is based on the laws of probability when the chances of an event occurring or not occurring are equal.   For example, when a coin is tossed once, there is a fifty-fifty chance that a head will turn up.   When a coin is tossed 10 times, a total of 5 heads and 5 tails will occur most frequently; other combinations, such as 6 heads and 4 tails, 7 heads and 3 tails, or 8 heads and 2 tails, with decreasing frequency; and a series of 10 heads or 10 tails will occur only rarely.   The normal curve is a graphic representation (plotting) of an infinite number of such trials.

The reason why most biological characters seem to show the pattern of variation of a normal curve is that they depend on a great number of genetic factors, which have either a positive or a negative effect on the character. Literally hundreds of genes, for instance, tend to increase body size, a similar number to decrease it. Many individuals of a population will have an approximately equal number of size-increasing and size-decreasing factors. Many fewer will have largely plus or largely minus factors. As a result, the population as a whole will show a variation pattern corresponding to the normal curve.

The normal curve is taken as the distributional pattern of the total population from which a given sample is drawn. By means of this curve one can determine the chances that a particular observation or measurement will fall within a given range of variation or the chances that a given character will appear in samples of 10 or 100 specimens. The statistics which determine the position, height, and spread of the normal curve are

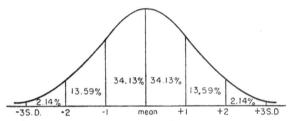

FIG. 20. Areas of the normal curve (*after Cazier and Bacon*, 1949).

the *mean*, which determines the center of the curve; the *frequency*, which determines its height; and the *standard deviation*, which shows how rapidly the curve falls off on each side of the mid-point.

Figure 20 gives an illustration of the normal curve. It can be seen that the curve is convex near the mean and becomes concave "less than one-third"[1] of the distance away from the mean. The point where the curve changes from convex to concave is one *standard deviation* (see below) distant from the mean. This convex center portion of the curve includes 68.27 per cent of the area under the curve. In other words, 68.27 per cent of the individuals of the population have values within this range. It is thus evident that the great majority of values occur near the mean, and that increasingly fewer measurements are found the farther away from the mean one moves. We shall return to a discussion of the concave

[1] The expression *less than one-third* is mathematically meaningless, because in theory the normal curve does not meet the base line (zero) until infinity. However, the term is used here because in practice, in biological populations, certain upper and lower extremes do not occur. There is no bee as large as an elephant or as small as a bacterium, no matter how many billions of bees are examined. Even though a finite linear range of a population does not exist mathematically, the part of the curve beyond three and one-half or four standard deviations is of negligible practical importance in work with natural populations.

"tails" of the curve in connection with the treatment of the overlap of two distribution curves.

Non-normal Curves. The curves describing biological populations are almost never completely normal. The most frequent deviation from normality is skewness. A skewed curve is a curve in which the mode (the highest point of the curve) is above or below the mean. Another deviation occurs when a curve is flatter (platykurtic) or steeper (leptokurtic) than the normal curve. Standard books on statistics may be consulted for the properties of such curves. The departures from normality are usually greatest in the "tails" of curves.

Standard Deviation. The standard deviation is a measure of variability. The broader the scattering of values around the mean, the "flatter" the curve, the greater the standard deviation.

Standard deviation (S.D.), also designated as sigma (σ), is defined as the square root of the sum (Σ) of the squared deviations (d) from the mean, divided by N. In other words, it is a measure of the deviations from the mean. The formula thus reads,

$$\text{S.D.} = \sqrt{\frac{\Sigma d^2}{N}}$$

The square of the S.D. is called the *variance*. The calculation of the S.D. is not very laborious (Simpson and Roe, 1939; Cazier and Bacon, 1949; or any textbook on statistics). In small samples (less than 15 specimens) the sum of squares is divided by (N-1) instead of by N. Some statisticians prefer this for samples of all sizes. If the exact value is not required, but only a rough approximation, an estimated S.D. can be read from a table (Simpson, 1941) if one knows N, M, and the observed range. This is one additional reason why the size of the sample (N) should always be given. The S.D. here defined is the sample S.D., which constitutes an estimate of the corresponding S.D. of the population.

Knowledge of the S.D. of the population permits predictions as to the range because

$M \pm 1$ S.D. includes 68.27 per cent of the population
$M \pm 2$ S.D. includes 95.45 per cent of the population
$M \pm 3$ S.D. includes 99.73 per cent of the population

For instance, if the mean of the sample is 70 mm. and its S.D. is 2 mm., less than 5 individuals among 100 of the population may be expected to have values outside the range 66 to 74 mm. ($M \pm 2$ S.D.).

Coefficient of Variability. The numerical value of the S.D. is closely correlated with the value of the mean. An S.D. of 2 indicates extremely low variability if the mean is 120, but very high variability if the mean is 8. In order to make the variability of different characteristics in different kinds of animals more directly comparable, it is advisable to calculate the coefficient of variability (C.V.).   C.V. = (S.D. × 100)/M, in other words, the S.D. as percentage of the mean.   To use the abbreviation V instead of C.V. is undesirable, since V is frequently used for variance.

Certain minor objections against this statistic have been raised by biometricians, but no better measure to compare variabilities has been proposed so far.

What is a small C.V.?   The numerical value of the C.V. depends on the measured character and on the particular taxonomic group.   There are different coefficients of variability for meristic quantities, linear measurements, and ratios.   The number of eyes (a meristic quantity) in the human species has a C.V. that is virtually zero; the height of the human body (even in a sample as homogeneous as a local population of adult males) has a C.V. exceeding 4.

The C.V. is often a sensitive indicator of the homogeneity of samples. If, for instance, the C.V. of a certain statistic fluctuates around 2.2 in samples of a series of populations, but is 4.5 in one sample, such a sample should be reinvestigated.   It may include an additional sibling species, wrongly sexed specimens, or some other alien component.   Zones of secondary intergradation are often characterized by an increased C.V.

Variability is the tendency of individuals of a population to differ from one another.   It finds its numerical expression in the coefficient of variability.   The calculation of C.V. is particularly useful when comparable samples of the same species from different localities are investigated, or when the variability of different variates is compared.

Linear Measurements.   Absolute size is extremely variable in most animals that continue to grow throughout life, such as fishes, snakes, and snails, not to mention such forms as corals and Bryozoa.   It is, however, fairly constant for certain measurements of adult mammals and even more so in adult birds.

A series of 49 adult males and 29 adult females of the kingfisher, *Halcyon chloris pealei* Finsch and Hartlaub, from Tutuila Island, Samoa, had the measurements and coefficients of variability shown in Table 11, below.

In carefully measured homogeneous samples of adult birds, the C.V. of wing length is usually between 1 and 2.5, rarely above 3.   In mammals, the C.V. for linear dimensions is usually between 4 and 10, occasionally between 3 and 4.

In insects which reach the imago stage through molt or metamorphosis, a small C.V. of linear measurements might be expected, since there is no further growth after the sclerotic exoskeleton has hardened.   However, it is actually rather large, since the final size of the imago depends a great deal on the feeding conditions of the larvae or nymphs.

The proportions of body parts are usually much more stable than the linear measurements, and ratios (see below) are therefore commonly studied in variable animals.

Meristic Quantities.   If the number of discrete, countable characters, such as the number of segments, scales, or chaetae, varies, we speak of *meristic variation*.   Some meristic characters may be exceedingly constant, as the number of eyes or legs in man; others may have a characteristic variability, as scales in lizards or fin rays in fishes.

TABLE 11.   MEASUREMENTS OF SERIES OF *Halcyon chloris pealei* FINSCH AND HARTLAUB FROM TUTUILA, SAMOA

	N	Range	Mean	S.D.	C.V.
Adult males:					
Wing.........	49	94.0–101.0	97.48	1.71	1.75
Tail.........	49	63.5– 69.5	66.44	1.32	1.98
Bill.........	49	31.0– 39.0	34.46	1.56	4.54
Adult females:					
Wing.........	29	95.5–102.5	98.86	0.88	0.90
Tail.........	29	64.0– 72.0	67.62	1.56	2.29
Bill.........	28	33.5– 37.5	35.20	0.98	2.63

The C.V. of most meristic characters is smaller than that of linear measurements, and it is not permissible to compare the coefficients of variability of the two kinds of characters.   If one wants to compare the C.V. of different groups of animals, one should compare relatively equivalent sets of data, such as linear measurements with linear measurements, ratios with ratios, etc.

Ratios and Indices.   While over-all length may be very variable in a population, particularly in species that continue to grow as adults, the proportions of the various body parts to each other may remain rather constant.   For comparisons between populations, taxonomists therefore often use ratios rather than linear measurements.   They are usually expressed in the formula

$$R \text{ (ratio)} = \frac{s \times 100}{l}$$

where s = the smaller of the two values, l = the larger.   This expresses the size of the smaller value as the percentage of the larger.   For example, if we want to determine the relative size of the head in a species of fish, we calculate (length of head $\times$ 100)/length of body (without head). Such a ratio is very quickly calculated with the help of a slide rule.   If R is near 100, it may happen that s is larger than l in some samples. It is obvious that the positions of s and l cannot be reversed in such cases, even when R becomes larger than 100.

If we want to tell how much larger the large measurement is than the small one, we can express the ratio as $R = l/s$. Ratios are best demonstrated visually in the form of scatter diagrams in which one value is plotted on the abscissa, the other on the ordinate (Fig. 21). By using different symbols for different populations, the presence or absence of overlaps between populations can be detected quickly. It can also be detected whether or not a straight-line correlation exists between the values. If one wants to determine the relative size of an organ or appendage, it is important that the proper standard of comparison be chosen. For instance, relative head width in insects is calculated against head length (without rostrum). Relative tail length in birds is usually calculated against wing length (as standard of general size). However, the wing is not an accurate yardstick for general size in migratory and high-altitude birds, nor in some birds in which the wing is used in courtship. The cube root ($\sqrt[3]{}$) of the weight might be a better measure in such species (Amadon, 1943). If an appendage is calculated against the whole, as tail against body, the appendage should not be included in the whole; the trunk without the tail should be used as standard of the "whole."

As mentioned above, ratios are more useful as taxonomic characters than direct measurements, because the variable factor of size is minimized (see below for change of ratios with size). Thus the head width of a small specimen of *Cimex lectularius* Linnaeus from Ain Sefra is 5.30, and that of a large specimen from Burkham, 6.30 (Johnson, 1939). Jenyns type of *C. columbarius* has a head width of 5.80. At first glance it would appear from these data that head width is of no value as a taxonomic character for the separation of *lectularius* and *columbarius*. However, the ratio of head width to length of third antennal segment is 1.43 for both the small and the large specimens of *lectularius* and 1.81 for *columbarius*. This difference was borne out by measurements of large numbers of individuals throughout the range of the bugs, the average ratio for 1,723 specimens of *lectularius* being 1.45 and the standard deviation 0.079, whereas the comparable figures for 409 specimens of *columbarius* were 1.78 and 0.096. Specimens of *lectularius* from animal and fowl houses tended more toward *columbarius* (ratio of head width to length of third antennal segment, 1.52; S.D., 0.079) but fell completely within the range of *lectularius* (after Johnson, 1939).

Care should be taken to check the rate of increase of each of the measurements used in a ratio, because different parts of the body of an animal commonly grow allometrically. Thus in the genus *Cimex*, the percentage increase with age is greater for length of the third antennal segment than for head width in *lectularius*, whereas the opposite is true in *columbarius* (Fig. 22). In this example allometry is so slight that it does not affect the validity of the conclusions for taxonomic purposes. In some

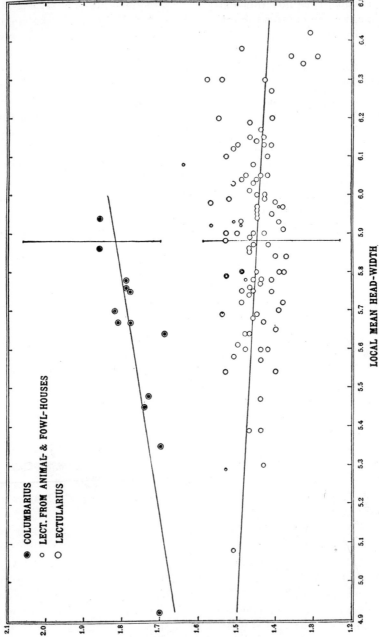

Fig. 21. Scatter diagram, showing the ratio of local mean head width to third antennal segment (ordinate) plotted against local mean head width (abscissa) in *Cimex lectularius* Linnaeus and *Cimex columbarius* Jenyns (*after Johnson*, 1939).

cases, however, allometry renders a particular pair of characters completely useless for taxonomic purposes. Parr (1949) describes a method of regression analysis dealing with a pair of characters showing allometric growth, a method which he found useful in fish taxonomy.

Qualitative Characters. When comparing two samples, one often finds that they differ merely by the degree of expression of a qualitative character. For example, birds from one region may be more brownish, from another more grayish, with some overlap. There are various ways

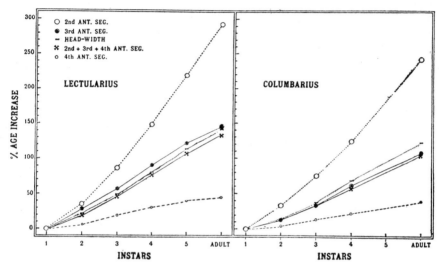

FIG. 22. Percentage increase with age in head width and antennal length for *Cimex lectularius* Linnaeus and *Cimex columbarius* Jenyns, showing allometric growth in *columbarius* (after *Johnson*, 1939).

of translating this qualitative difference into quantitative terms if it is desirable to determine the zone of overlap more accurately.

For instance, all the specimens of the various samples can be arranged in a single series, ranging from one extreme (numbered 1) to the other (numbered n). As an example, the 23 adult specimens of the thrush *Brachypteryx leucophrys* Temminck from the Malayan islands, which are in the collections of the American Museum of Natural History, can be arranged in a single series. Listing the most rufous bird first and the most olive bird last, we find the following sequence: $S, S, Sb, S, B, Sb, Sb, S, T, T, T, T, J, T, J, Sb, Sb, L, L, J, L, L, L$ (B = Bali, J = Java, L = Lombok, S = Sumatra, Sb = Sumbawa, and T = Timor). The average rank of these populations is then as follows: Sumatra, 1, 2, 4, 8 (3.75); Bali, 5; Sumbawa, 3, 6, 7, 16, 17 (9.8); Timor, 9, 10, 11, 12, 14, (11.2); Java, 13, 15, 20 (16.0); Lombok, 18, 19, 21, 22, 23 (20.6). There is much overlap in the characters of the populations, even though the Lombok birds are strikingly more olive than the Sumatra birds (Mayr, 1944).

A more accurate method, which is definitely to be preferred whenever large samples are available, is to establish a number of "classes." For these *Brachypteryx* specimens one might choose the following classes: class 1 (rufous), class 2 (fairly rufous), class 3 (rufous olive), class 4 (olive), class 5 (very olive); and select as standard of comparison that specimen that is closest to the mid-point of each class. If material is plentiful and greater accuracy is desired, the differences between the mid-points can again be divided into decimals that can be estimated.

Differences in pattern, such as degrees of spotting or banding, can also often be expressed in quantitative terms. Students of small mammals measure color differences quantitatively with the aid of a photovolt reflection meter (Blair, 1947).

ANALYSIS OF DIFFERENCES BETWEEN POPULATIONS

When two populations are compared (or, more accurately, samples from two populations), the taxonomist usually wants to know one of these three things:

1. If they are polymorphic, whether or not the frequencies of the two forms are the same in the two populations. This is achieved by the chi-square test (comparison of frequencies).

2. If they differ only slightly by a quantitative difference, whether or not the difference is statistically significant. This is determined by a statistical comparison of the means.

3. If they are clearly different, how much the population curves overlap (determination of overlap).

Comparison of Frequencies: Chi-square (χ^2) Test. A taxonomist is often confronted with the problem of having to determine whether two variants occur in two or more populations at the same frequency. These variants may be color forms or even the two sexes. The conventional way is to express the frequencies in percentages. But the calculation of a percentage does not tell us whether the populations are actually different or whether the observed difference between the samples is merely due to accidents of sampling. This can be determined by the chi-square test.

Let us consider a specific example. Among 80 specimens from locality *A* there are 58 of type 1 and 22 of type 2; among 43 specimens from locality *B* there are 24 specimens of type 1 and 19 specimens of type 2. Type 1 is therefore represented at locality *A* by 72.5 per cent of the specimens and at locality *B* by 55.8 per cent. Is this difference indicative of a population difference?

To test it, we set up a four-square table,

	Type 1	Type 2		Type 1	Type 2
Locality A	a	b	A	58	22
Locality B	c	d	B	24	19

and solve the equation:

$$\chi^2 = \frac{(ad - bc)^2(a + b + c + d)}{(a + b)(c + d)(a + c)(b + d)} = 3.65$$

Significance. What does this chi-square value of 3.65 mean? It has to be checked for "significance." It would lead us too far here to explain the statistical theory of significance, and we refer to textbooks of statistics (Simpson and Roe, 1939; Snedecor, 1946). When the difference between samples is "significant," it indicates that they were presumably not drawn from the same population. Significance is something relative; it indicates a deviation from expectation.

Significance is expressed in P (= probability) values. If an event is expected to occur in 1 out of 20 tries, this would indicate a P value of $\frac{1}{20} = 0.05$ (= 5 per cent level of significance). If it is expected to occur in less than 1 in 100 tries, the P value is less than 0.01 (below the 1 per cent level of significance).

P tables can be found in all standard statistical texts. By reference to a P table it is found that a chi-square value of 3.84 or larger is considered significant ($P = 0.05$). Thus the above-calculated figure of 3.65 does not quite reach the 5 per cent level of significance. If the samples (N) are small, Yates's correction must be made (see statistics textbooks). Some statisticians recommend this as a routine procedure in all cases.

Comparison of Means. The simplest solution of the problem of whether or not samples from two (biological) populations are taxonomically identical is to compare their means. If the two sample means do not differ significantly, it indicates that the samples could have been drawn from the same (statistical) population. The closeness of the sample mean to the real but unknown mean of the population is indicated by the standard error (σ_M or S.E.$_M$), which obviously depends on the size of the sample (N) and is therefore expressed as follows:

$$\text{S.E.}_M = \frac{\text{S.D.}}{\sqrt{N}}$$

(standard deviation divided by the square root of N, or sample size). The standard error is the same kind of probability estimate as the standard deviation and has the same distribution characteristics (*i.e.*, those of a normal curve): 68.27 per cent of the observed sample means will fall within ± 1 S.E., 95.45 per cent within ± 2 S.E., 99.73 per cent within ± 3 S.E., etc.

As a simple rule it can be stated that two samples are probably different if the difference between the means $(M_1 - M_2)$ is more than twice the sum of the standard errors $(\text{S.E.}_{M_1} + \text{S.E.}_{M_2})$ and almost certainly different if it is more than three times the sum of the standard errors.

If one wants to know whether the difference between the two sample means is statistically significant, it is necessary to calculate the standard error of the difference (S.E._d) between the two means, which is the square root of the sums of the squared standard errors:

$$\text{S.E.}_d = \sqrt{(\text{S.E.}_{M_1})^2 + (\text{S.E.}_{M_2})^2}$$

In this case we assume that the means of the two populations from which the samples were taken are equal (*i.e.*, we assume that the two samples were taken from the same population). Then if the difference between the means is over 3 times the S.E.$_d$, the hypothesis is incorrect, and the two samples were drawn from different populations.

If the number of specimens (N) is very different in the two samples, a more elaborate formula is advisable (Simpson and Roe, 1939):

$$\text{S.E.}_d = \sqrt{\frac{N_1}{N_2}(\text{S.E.}_{M_1})^2 + \frac{N_2}{N_1}(\text{S.E.}_{M_2})^2}$$

However, Hubbs and Perlmutter (1942) have shown that the simpler form is adequate in most cases, and that it leads only rarely to serious error. They also give a table of t values for these statistics.

Overlap between Populations. The simplest case is that every specimen of population A is different from every specimen of population B. More difficult are the cases where there is an overlap in characters. For instance, in the Polynesian honey-eater, *Foulehaio carunculata* (Gmelin), adult males from the Manua Islands have wing measurements of 99 to 106 (average 104.7) mm., from Tonga 104 to 114 (average 108.3) mm. How great is the overlap?

The coarsest way of testing overlap would be to plot the linear overlap of the observed samples (Fig. 23).

The figure shows that 2 of the 7 mm. (= 28.5 per cent) of the observed range of sample A (Manua) are overlapped by sample B (Tonga). This method of linear overlap is misleading in two ways: it gives only the overlap of the samples (which is much smaller than the overlap of the populations); and it exaggerates the importance of the end points of the range (while one glance at a pair of overlapping population curves shows that the "hump" of population curves is much more important than the "tails"). The calculation of linear overlap is obviously unsatisfactory. Before presenting a more adequate method, a few words need to be said on the aims of these methods.

The object of the taxonomist when comparing allopatric populations is most frequently to determine whether or not they belong to different subspecies. How different do two populations have to be to be recognized as two different subspecies? There is no general agreement on this point. Some splitters recognize populations as subspecies even if only the means differ "significantly" (in the statistical sense). Reasons against a sub-

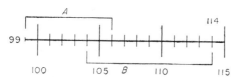

Fig. 23. Linear overlap of observed samples.

species criterion of such low significance have been stated in Chap. 2. Some lumpers, on the other hand, go to the opposite extreme and insist that populations are not worthy of subspecific separation unless *all* individuals are different. The most frequently proposed convention is the so-called "75 per cent rule."

This rule is subject to various interpretations. For instance, some taxonomists are satisfied if 75 per cent of all the specimens before them can be placed as one subspecies or the other. Most taxonomists accept, however, an interpretation of the rule according to which population A can be considered subspecifically distinct from population B if 75 per cent of the individuals of A are different from "all" the individuals of population B.

Unfortunately, this approach does not eliminate all the weaknesses of linear overlap, because again the end points of the range of variation are given crucial importance. How many standard deviations on either side of the mean should one include in a curve which theoretically reaches infinity? The tail of the curve attains such a flat slope beyond about 2 S.D. from the mean (Fig. 20) that little is added to the population by extending it. If we cut off the "tail" at 2.06 S.D. from the mean, we lose only 1.97 per cent of the population. By adding 1.18 S.D. (extending it to 3.24 S.D. from mean), we add only 1.91 per cent, which would give us 99.94 per cent of the population. This is the standard accepted by Amadon (1949), who proposes the following interpretation of the 75 per cent rule: A population A is subspecifically distinct if 75 per cent of its individuals differ from a "standard population" (Simpson, 1941) of

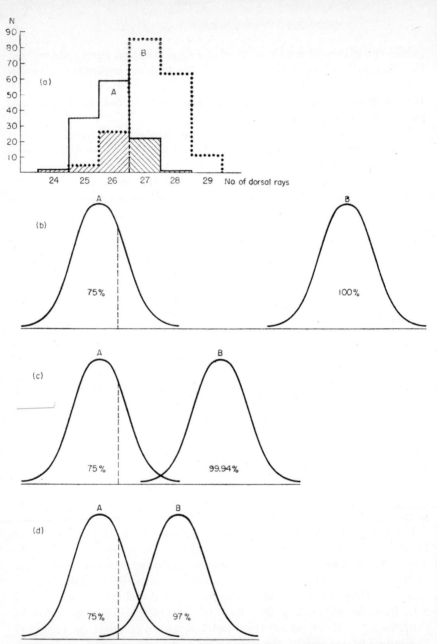

Fig. 24. Various interpretations of the 75 per cent rule for subspecies discrimination. (a) More than 75 per cent of the available sample will be correctly identified by placing the dividing line arbitrarily at a stated point. Illustrated by the number of dorsal rays in *Cynoscion regalis*, (A) subsp. *arenarius* (Gulf Coast) (usually 26 or less) and (B) subsp. *regalis* (Atlantic Coast) (usually 27 or more) (*from Ginsburg*, 1938). (b) 75 per cent of A differ from 100 per cent of B. (c) 75 per cent of A differ from all (= 99.94 per cent) of a standard population of B. (d) 75 per cent of A differ from all (= 1.881 S.D. = 97 per cent) of B.

1,000 individuals (= 99.94 per cent of the theoretical range of variability) of B (which corresponds to 3.24 S.D. on either side of the mean).

At this standard, more than 97 per cent of the individuals of A are different from more than 97 per cent of B, assuming the two standard deviations to be roughly alike. This would amount to no overlap at all in most of the relatively small samples usually available to taxonomists. Such a standard appears unnecessarily high. Current taxonomic practices permit greater overlap, although there is no agreement as to how much (Rand and Traylor, 1950). We suggest accepting as a standard of subspecific separation that 75 per cent of population A be different from 97 per cent of population B. Then about 90 per cent of the individuals of A are different from about 90 per cent of the individuals of B. How can this be expressed in terms of standard deviations?

When calculating overlaps, we are interested only in the part of the two population curves which is between the two means. In order to calculate the standard deviations that concern us, we must divide each population into that portion which lies between the means and that which lies outside. Of the 75 per cent of A, we find 50 per cent below the mean (M_1) and 25 per cent (= 0.674 S.D.) in the zone of overlap. Of the 97 per cent of B, we find 50 per cent above the mean (M_2) and 47 per cent (= 1.881 S.D.) in the zone of overlap. It is then evident, on the basis of the 75 and 97 per cent standard adopted by us, that two populations are subspecifically different if the difference of the means ($M_2 - M_1$) exceeds the sum of 0.674 S.D. + 1.881 S.D. = 2.56 S.D.

This simplified statement ignores the fact that the standard deviations of A and B are usually different. Even using the formula,

$$0.674 \text{ S.D.}_A + 1.881 \text{ S.D.}_B = 2.56 \text{ S.D.},$$

is only a slight improvement, since the solution is asymmetrical, and we shall get different results when determining subspecific difference by calculating 75 per cent of B differing from 97 per cent of A, that is,

$$0.674 \text{ S.D.}_B + 1.881 \text{ S.D.}_A = 2.56 \text{ S.D.}$$

It is evident that we should look for a symmetrical solution. The ideal solution would be to determine the point of intersection (I) of the two curves.

Unfortunately, the calculation of this point is very laborious and not suitable for routine taxonomic work. However, an approximation method exists, the error of which is small compared with the various other inaccuracies of the determination and comparison of subspecies differences. It is possible to calculate very simply a point which is close to the point of intersection, provided that the larger of the two standard deviations is not much greater than one and a half times the smaller. We obtain this approximated point by dividing the difference between the means by the sum of standard deviations. Let us call this figure the *coefficient of difference* (C.D.).

$$\text{C.D.} = \frac{M_B - M_A}{\text{S.D.}_A + \text{S.D.}_B}$$

The value which corresponds to our standard of subspecific difference (75 per cent *A* from 97 per cent *B*) = 2.56/2 = 1.28. Then, if the C.D. exceeds 1.28, it seems probable that it will be advisable to separate the two populations subspecifically. At this value about 90 per cent of *A* is different from about 90 per cent of *B*.

It is perhaps advisable to express the difference of two populations in terms of the magnitude of equal nonoverlap, *e.g.*, 90 per cent of *A* not overlapped by 90 per cent of *B*. In view of the importance of this standard, we add a table of the percentages of symmetrical nonoverlap associated with various C.D. values (Table 12). This will permit a quick

TABLE 12. PERCENTAGE OF NONOVERLAP OF PARTIALLY OVERLAPPING CURVES ASSOCIATED WITH STATED VALUES OF THE COEFFICIENT OF DIFFERENCE (C.D.)

Values	C.D.	Joint nonoverlap, per cent
Below the level of conventional subspecific distinctness	0.675	75
	0.84	80
	0.915	82
	0.995	84
	1.04	85
	1.08	86
	1.13	87
	1.175	88
	1.23	89
Conventional level of subspecific difference	1.28	90
Above the level of conventional subspecific difference	1.34	91
	1.405	92
	1.48	93
	1.555	94
	1.645	95
	1.75	96

check on whether or not a population difference is presumably of the level of subspecific distinctness. Only values of C.D. near 1.28 are given. Obvious subspecific identity is indicated by values much lower than 1.28; obvious subspecific difference is indicated by values that are much higher.

The method will be illustrated by an example. Oliver (1943) attempted to determine whether lizards of the species *Uta ornata* from northern Sonora (Pilares) and southern Sonora (Guirocoba), Mexico, are subspecifically distinct. The chief differentiating character between the two populations is the number of the enlarged dorsals of the primary row of scales. Means and S.D. of the two populations are as follows:

	Guirocoba	Pilares
Mean	27.76	34.60
S.D.	1.92	2.07

$$\text{C.D.} = \frac{M_B - M_A}{\text{S.D.}_A + \text{S.D.}_B} = \frac{34.60 - 27.76}{1.92 + 2.07} = \frac{6.84}{3.99} = 1.71$$

The C.D. of 1.71 indicates that more than 95 per cent of the Guirocoba population is different from more than 95 per cent of the Pilares population, in other words, that the two populations deserve to be separated subspecifically.

It must be understood that this method is only a rough approximation. It makes various assumptions that are not necessarily correct, *e.g.*, that the distribution curves are normal and that the sample mean is the population mean. The evaluation of the confidence limits is laborious and has not been attempted here. Nor has any attempt been made to extend this rather coarse method to multiple characters.

What is an even greater shortcoming is that such an arbitrary method does not allow for the many biological and biogeographical considerations of subspecies recognition. A yardstick such as the coefficient of difference is a useful guide and a help toward more uniform standards, but all borderline cases should be evaluated in the light of additional information. A well-isolated population may be worthy of subspecific recognition with a C.D. as low as 1.28, while a population that is part of a cline or of a checkerboard pattern may not be worth naming even though the C.D. exceeds 1.5. In a Polynesian honeyeater, *Foulehaio carunculata* (Gmelin), for example, adult males from Tonga have a wing length of 104 to 114 (average 108.3) mm., those from Fotuna Island of only 93 to 98 (average 95.9) mm. This would seem like a difference more than sufficient for subspecific recognition. However, not only do additional populations on some thirty other islands bridge the gap between these two extremes, but the populations of large-sized and small-sized forms are distributed in such an irregular manner as to make an intelligible delimitation of subspecies impossible (Mayr, 1932).

Multiple Character Analysis. Two populations that cannot be distinguished unequivocally by a single character can often be separated by using in the analysis simultaneously two or more characters. There are several methods available that permit such multivariate analysis. They are based on the observation that two characters are usually only incompletely correlated.   If, for instance, a bird population differs from another one by longer measurements of wing and of bill, and if we arrange all the specimens in a series from the smallest wing length up to the longest, it is very unlikely that they will fall into exactly the same series when arranged according to bill length.   If there is a slight overlap in the measurements of the two populations, it is sometimes possible to eliminate the overlap by adding (or multiplying) wing and bill length of each individual.

Much more reliable, but also more elaborate, are various other methods. Fisher (1938) gave a short review of the subject, and Burma (1949) has demonstrated one of the methods of multivariate analysis on a practical example.

Fisher's method of discriminant functions is probably the most useful of these methods; it is explained in detail in Mather's (1947) textbook. Recent applications of this method relate to differences of populations of fish (Stone, 1947), *Drosophila* (Carson and Stalker, 1947), and birds (Storer, 1950).

VISUAL PRESENTATION OF QUANTITATIVE DATA

It is often desirable to present numerical data visually.   Such a visual presentation not only permits a rapid survey of all the data, but actually often brings out fine points that are not apparent in the raw data.   A few simple methods may be described (see also Anderson, 1949, Chap. 6).

Histograms.   Unreduced samples are best shown as histograms.   A histogram consists of a set of rectangles in which the class means are plotted on the abscissa and the frequencies (usually number of specimens) on the ordinate.   This presentation has several advantages.   The principal one is that it presents the original data in minimum space. Whatever form of statistical analysis a subsequent author may want to apply, he will find the actual number of specimens given for each size class.   A quick comparison of different populations is made possible by arranging a series of histograms above one another (Fig. 25).

Population-range Diagrams.   Even more data can be compressed into minimum space by giving sample range, one or more standard deviations, and two standard errors.   This is the method of Hubbs and Perlmutter (1942), who plot one standard deviation (Fig. 26).   A better solution would probably be to plot one and one-half times the standard deviation. Nonoverlap of these plotted standard deviations ($1\frac{1}{2} + 1\frac{1}{2} = 3$) would at once indicate probable subspecific difference.   (For a discussion of the significance of the difference of means, see above.)

Scatter Diagrams.   The difference between two or more populations in respect to two characters is best illustrated by a scatter diagram. Each individual is indicated by a spot or other symbol which is placed where the value for one character (read off the ordinate) intersects the value for the other character (read off the abscissa); each population is indicated by a different symbol (circles, squares, triangles, solid or empty, etc.) (Fig. 21). Scatter diagrams have many advantages. They help to visualize allometric relationships and facilitate the plotting of regression lines. They also sometimes disclose errors of measurement or sexing that might otherwise go undiscovered.

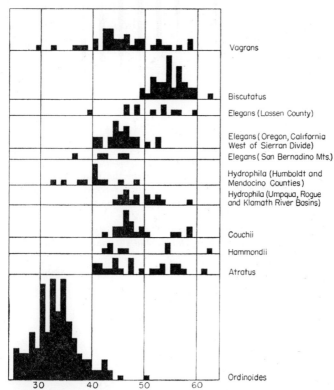

FIG. 25. Histograms showing head and body length in centimeters of adult males of *Thamnophis ordinoides*. Each square represents a specimen (*Fitch*, 1940).

If three characters are involved, triangular charts can be employed. In this case the actual values are not plotted, but rather their percentage contribution to the sum of the characters. For example, if character $a = 80$ mm., $b = 32$ mm., and $c = 48$ mm., then

$$a + b + c = 160 \text{ mm.} = 100 \text{ per cent.}$$

Then $a = 50$ per cent, $b = 20$ per cent, and $c = 30$ per cent of the whole. These percentages are plotted on the graph, which thus shows proportions rather than absolute sizes. In each individual case the triangular

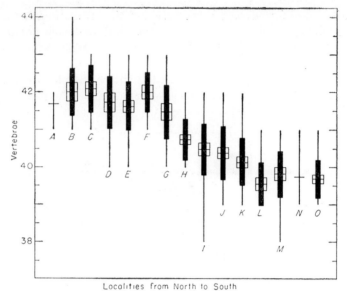

FIG. 26. Population-range diagram. Variation in the number of vertebrae of the anchovy, *Anchoviella mitchilli*. The letters *A* to *O* refer to 15 population samples, arranged from north (*A*) to south (*O*). In each sample the vertical line indicates the total variation of the sample; the broad portion of the line, one standard deviation on each side of the mean; the hollow rectangle, twice the standard error on each side of the mean; and the crossbar, the mean (*Hubbs and Perlmutter*, 1942).

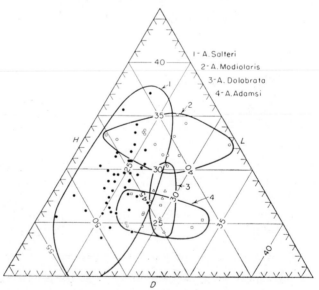

FIG. 27. Triangular graph of the length (*L*), height (*H*), and distance to maximum down-bulge (*D*) of four species of *Anthracomys* (*Burma*, 1948).

graph is scaled in such a way as to produce a maximum spread of the points. As an illustration we reproduce such a triangular chart from a recent paper by Burma (1948) (Fig. 27).

Mapping of Quantitative Data. It is often desirable to illustrate the geographical relationships of various populations with different quantitative characters. In the case of continuous characters (size, etc.), the simplest method is to record the means of the various populations on a base map, and if there is regularity to draw in the isophenes (= lines connecting points of equal expression of a character). For instance, if the means of a series of populations in a species vary from 142 to 187, it is helpful to draw in the isophenes of 140, 150, 160, 170, 180, and 190.

If qualitative or semiqualitative characters are to be plotted, it is sometimes helpful to choose a different symbol for each class of characters. The relative size of the symbol can be used to indicate sample size (Fig. 5).

To present frequencies of polymorph characters on a map, the "pie graph" is the most convenient method. The percentage occurrence within the population is indicated by the size of the segments (Fig. 28).

APPLICATION OF STATISTICAL METHODS

Comparison of populations is an important task of the taxonomist, and it is the principal object of an accurate quantitative description of a population to characterize it in such a way as to facilitate such comparisons.

In experimental sciences the investigator usually wants to know whether there is a significant difference between two sets of experiments. This significance is usually expressed as the probability that the various samples were drawn from the same "population" (in the special statistical sense of this word). Most experiments are designed to test whether a stated change in the experimental conditions produces a "significant" change in the experimental results. The experimenter is interested primarily in knowing whether or not a change has occurred and only secondarily in measuring its quantity.

The taxonomist, when comparing (allopatric) populations of the same species, knows before he starts that they are not completely identical. Population geneticists have demonstrated conclusively that in sexually reproducing animals no two natural populations are ever exactly alike. In fact, even populations from the same locality may be slightly different at different seasons of the year. The mere fact of a (statistically provable) difference between several populations of a species is therefore of no special interest to the taxonomist; he takes it for granted. Even the lowest recognizable taxonomic category (the subspecies) is normally composed of numerous populations that differ "significantly" in gene frequencies and in the means of certain variates. What the taxonomist

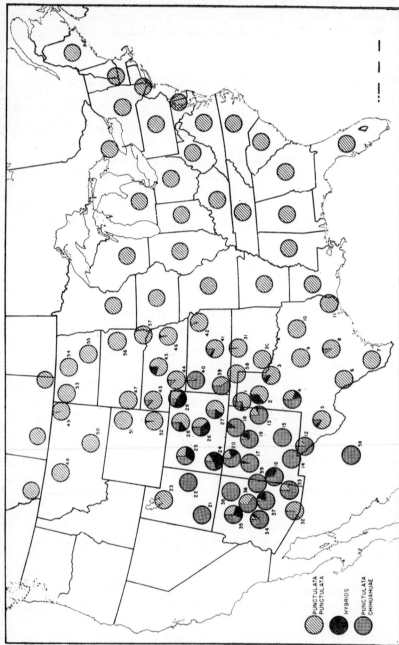

FIG. 28. Map of the distribution of the tiger beetle *Cicindela punctulata*, illustrating the pie-graph method. The size of each circle indicates the relative frequency in the collected samples of three variants: *punctulata*, *chihuahuae*, and intermediates. Many populations are pure *punctulata*, others are pure *chihuahuae* (*unpublished, courtesy of Dr. M. A. Cazier*).

wants to know is whether these differences between populations are large enough to justify classification in different taxonomic categories. The animal taxonomist is thus principally interested in the quantity of difference.

On the other hand, statistical methods do not usually reveal much about the quality of a difference. They do not permit a decision as to whether or not two allopatric populations belong to the same species, or whether two sympatric variants are individual variants or sympatric species. Reproductive isolation (the species criterion) and morphological differences are not necessarily closely correlated. Sibling species may be almost identical morphologically, while subspecies are often (*e.g.*, birds of paradise) strikingly different. Presence of intergradation between populations proves conspecificity; absence of intergradation between spatially isolated populations is ambiguous evidence—it does not prove reproductive isolation. Even with respect to the recognition of subspecies, statistical methods provide only one line of evidence.

There are thus many limitations to the information that statistical methods can yield. This still leaves a wide scope for the application of statistics to taxonomy. The particular method that needs to be applied depends on the taxonomic group and on the particular problem. For instance, species of birds are well known and well defined, and the most frequent problem with which the student of living birds is faced is whether two allopatric populations are sufficiently distinct to be considered different subspecies. Occasionally he has to analyze a sample of migrants and allocate them to one of the breeding populations. A paleontologist has to deal with many additional problems. If he has a secondary deposit, he wants to know whether the sample is homogeneous enough to have been derived from a single population. A study of the variability of the sample will yield clues useful in answering this question.

In the last analysis, statistics is merely an extension of ordinary reasoning as applied especially to numbers. Hence the statistical treatment of a problem is no better than the facts and judgments upon which it is based. Statistics should never be used to impart a false sense of precision. As applied to the comparison of populations by means of the normal curve, statistics deals with probabilities, not with certainties.

In practice, taxonomists should realize that there is no particular virtue in statistics per se. Statistical analysis is one of several tools which are available and which may or may not be used to advantage in a particular problem. Taxonomic studies at the alpha level utilize in general only the simplest statistics, *e.g.*, size, including range, if several specimens are available, and simple proportions or ratios. Population analyses are impossible because of the small numbers involved, and because there is no uniformity of sampling. Furthermore, comparisons between intraspecific populations to determine overlap cannot be made as long as the diagnostic differences of the species and their delimitation are still uncertain.

Gamma taxonomy, on the other hand, focuses on the population rather than the individual. The polytypic species is of paramount interest, and a study of quantitative characters is the rule. Taxonomists who study groups of organisms whose study has advanced to this level will find that statistical methods are an indispensable tool.

CHAPTER 8

PRESENTATION OF THE FINDINGS (DESCRIPTIONS, KEYS, PHYLOGENIES)

After taxonomic characters have been studied and analyzed, there remains the important task of recording the findings and presenting them in a useful manner. This is achieved in systematic zoology by means of descriptions, keys, and classifications. Depending on the immediate objective of the taxonomist, any or all of these methods of presentation may enter into the final published work (Chap. 9).

DESCRIPTIONS

The chief objective of a description is to facilitate subsequent recognition of the category involved. It was realized at an early date that different kinds of descriptions approach this goal in a different manner. Linnaeus distinguished clearly between the general *descriptio* (*character naturalis*) on one hand and the polynominal *differentia specifica* (*character essentialis*) on the other (Svenson, 1945). The latter contains "the essential characters by which the species is distinguished from its congeners." It corresponds to what is nowadays called a *diagnosis*.

The functions of the two kinds of description, the general description and the diagnosis, are by no means identical. The diagnosis serves to distinguish the species (or whatever taxon is involved) from other *known* similar or closely related ones. The general description has a broader function. It should present a general picture of the described taxon. It should give information not only on characters that are diagnostic with relation to previously described species, but also characters that may distinguish the species from yet unknown species. It should also provide information that may be of interest to others besides taxonomists.

Linnaeus and many taxonomists since have stressed the extreme practical importance of a short, unambiguous diagnosis. It can only rarely be combined successfully with the general description. The latter, in turn, no matter how exhaustive it is, cannot always provide a substitute for a type specimen (see Chap. 12) or, in many cases, for illustrations.

There is still considerable confusion in the literature concerning the meaning and usage of the terms *description* and *diagnosis*. Simpson (1945) states that in describing animals the taxonomist should achieve two objects, that of diagnosis and that of definition: "Diagnosis* is the art and practice of distinguishing between things. Definition† is the art and practice of setting limits to things. Both enter into taxonomy and . . . they are essentially different and their complementary roles should be clearly understood." Although the formal diagnosis in taxonomic work sometimes assists in the definition of a category, this function is mainly performed by the general description. The two terms, *diagnosis* and *description*, may then be used as follows:

Description. A more or less complete statement of the morphological characters of a taxon without special emphasis on those characters that distinguish it from coordinate units.

Diagnosis. A brief listing of the most important characters or character combinations that are peculiar to the given unit and by which it can be differentiated from other similar or closely related ones. The direct comparison of a species (or other taxon) with other specifically mentioned species (or other taxa) is usually called a *differential diagnosis*.

Such a comparison with other species is of great practical help to students who have no material of the newly described form. It also forces the author of a new form to review all the evidence for and against the publication of the description. (Rensch, 1934). Such a comparison ensures also that the diagnostic characters of the new form are mentioned and is therefore recommended by the International Commission on Zoological Nomenclature (Paris, 1948). If the nearest relatives are rare or poorly known, it is also helpful to make a comparison with a well-known, if not so closely related, species.

The Original Description. The description given at the time of proposal of a name for a new species, genus, or other category is called the *original description*. It has two primary functions. The first, as stated above, is to facilitate subsequent recognition and identification; the second is to make the new name available by fulfilling the requirements of Art. 25 of the International Rules of Zoological Nomenclature (Chap. 11).

The preparation of a proper description is a task the importance of which cannot be overemphasized. The describer is forced to rely on words to convey his meaning. Yet words, no matter how carefully chosen, are rarely adequate to give an accurate mental picture of the appearance of an organism. Nevertheless, it is the function of the description to enable a subsequent worker to identify specimens without reference to the type. This goal can be achieved in most cases by the careful worker, particularly when the description is properly coordinated with illustrative material.

---

* Ultimately from the Greek διαγιγνωσκω, to distinguish between two (things).

† Ultimately from the Latin *definio*, to enclose within limits.

The good description requires on the part of its author (1) a thorough knowledge of the group of organisms concerned, (2) a knowledge of structure and terminology, (3) an ability to evaluate differences and similarities, (4) an ability to select and emphasize the important, (5) a full understanding of the precise meaning of the words and the correct usage of the grammar of the language employed, and (6) a concern for the future worker. Ferris (1928) has stated, "If [the describer's] work of recording the data has been properly done those data are available for re-examination and re-evaluation. His conclusions can be checked, they can be extended or modified or rejected as appears desirable, all without the necessity of recourse to his types."

A brief review of the literature is sufficient to reveal that the form and style of descriptions are as individual as their authors, and that many authors are inconsistent in their choice of form and style. As we have previously emphasized, originality is an asset in approaching a problem but becomes a liability when carried over to the recording of data. In the lesser known groups much of the taxonomist's time is spent in comparing and contrasting one description with another. This task is difficult under any circumstances but is easier when the descriptions approximate one another in style, arrangement, and form. This does not mean that a completely standardized description is always possible or even desirable. The factors which influence the order of presentation, form, and style are factors which vary from group to group. Within a particular group, however, much can be done to standardize descriptions and thus increase their effectiveness and utility.

Style. The style generally used in descriptions as well as in diagnoses is telegraphic and concise. It is usually characterized by elimination of articles and verbs and by selection of adjectives and nouns of explicit meaning. It further involves proper use of capitals and punctuation and adherence to a logical sequence of presentation. Thus the telephonic-style statement, "The head is one-third longer than it is wide, the antennae are shorter than the body, and the outer segments are serrate" becomes simply "Head one-third longer than wide, antennae shorter than body, outer segments serrate." The descriptive style of the second statement has lost none of the preciseness or clarity of the first, yet is only one-half as long and may be both read and understood more quickly.

Sequence of Characters. The recommended sequence of characters depends on the form of the description. It is customary in a diagnosis to present characters in the order of their diagnostic importance (or what the author regards as the order of importance). This will facilitate rapid recognition. In the full description the material should be arranged in a standardized natural order, as, for instance, describing the body parts from anterior to the posterior, first on the dorsal and then on the ventral surface. The details may be varied to fit the group, yet still maintain a natural and readily comparable order. For instance, the sequence of presentation for a dorsoventrally flattened animal group would be different from that for either a laterally compressed or a robust group because of the different methods of orientation during study. The standardized sequence of characters helps assure that nothing important is being overlooked and that the description is comparative. It is very frustrating to try to use a taxonomic paper in which half a dozen species are described independently of one another, details being given, for example, of the antennae of one species, the pronotum of a second, and the elytra of a third. Such a procedure makes comparison quite impossible. Authoritative monographs usually adopt a standardized sequence of characters, and subsequent describers should follow it as far as possible.

The utility of a description may be increased by the use of devices which enable the reader to locate quickly the particular characters for which he may be looking. One such device is the use of paragraphs to break up the description according to main body divisions (*e.g.*, in insects: head, thorax, abdomen, wings, genitalia, etc.). Where paragraphing is undesirable, the same effect may be gained by italicizing these same key words. If the author has followed a natural sequence of presentation, either method will permit the reader to orient himself quickly at some particular point in the description without the necessity of reading the whole description.

What to Include in a Description. An exhaustive description of an organism would fill many volumes, as may readily be seen from a perusal of volumes on the morphology (physical anthropology) and anatomy of the human species. It is, therefore, obvious that even the so-called "detailed description" of a taxonomic species is highly selective and in the nature of an expanded diagnosis. How much subject matter should be included in a description depends on the group concerned and the state of knowledge of that group. Excessively long descriptions obscure the essential points; excessively short descriptions omit pertinent data. While the diagnosis serves to distinguish a species from other known species, the description should be detailed enough to anticipate possible differences from as yet undescribed species. The description should therefore be very detailed in poorly known groups, because it is impossible to predict which characters will distinguish a new species from those that are still undiscovered. On the other hand, the subspecies in a well-known species of birds may differ from one another so little in detail that an extensive description would be a repetition of the species description. In such a case the description may not differ from a diagnosis as, for instance, "Like subspecies *alba* but larger, upper parts blackish gray, not ash gray" (followed by a tabulation of the measurements).

Descriptions should include, in so far as practicable, all characters, both positive and negative, which are known to be useful or potentially useful in distinguishing other units in the same category. However, characters of higher categories should be omitted except where they are anomalous or where the assignment of the unit to the higher category is in doubt. For example, the description of a subspecies of song sparrow should not include reference to characters that are typical for all song sparrows (or worse, for all sparrows!). Violation of this rule is not only uneconomical but distracts attention from the essential features of the category concerned.

Beyond the above generalizations, there is little to guide the describer other than his own good judgment. The description, more than almost any other aspect of taxonomy, provides a permanent record of the author's ability to observe accurately, record precisely, select and interpret intelligently, and express clearly and concisely the facts which are before him.

The description should include a statement of the differences between the sexes and, if only one sex is available, a frank statement of the fact (*e.g.*, "female unknown"). Likewise the characters of immaturity should be discussed as well as larval stages. Available biological and ecological data should be presented. Such information is, in the case of sibling species, often more important than morphological characters.

Whether or not the description should be based exclusively on the type is a much disputed point. Those who favor this method argue that all too often it has eventually turned out that the original material and consequently also the description were a composite of several species. This makes it very difficult to disentangle the characters of the various species. They argue that it is much safer to restrict the description to the type and have it followed by a discussion of the variability of the rest of the material.

Others believe that such treatment favors the erroneous typological view that the type has a special significance as far as the characters of the species are concerned. They prefer the description to be a composite drawn from a consideration of the entire material and propose to mention at the end by what characters (if any) the type specimen differs from the rest of the material.

Actually both methods agree that (1) the entire variability of the species material should be described and (2) that it is advisable to mention the special features of the type specimen. Different authors may use different methods to achieve these objectives.

Description of Coloration. Differences in coloration are among the most important diagnostic characters in many groups of animals. A detailed description of the general pattern of coloration and of the precise tones of the various colors is therefore essential in many taxonomic groups. Subspecific differences in birds, mammals, and butterflies are often largely a matter of coloration. Many attempts have therefore been made to standardize color descriptions, since *rufous* or *tawny* do not necessarily suggest the same shade of color to every taxonomist. It is for this reason that color keys are widely used in taxonomy. Those of Ridgway (1912), Maerz and Paul (1950), and Villalobos-Dominguez and Villalobos (1947) are specially recommended. When fine shades of color are involved, a direct comparison with topotypical material is advisable. Even here the color keys are useful for standardization of terminologies.

Numerical Data. The recording of a set of precise measurements is an integral part of a well-rounded description. If the new form differs from its relatives in its proportions, such proportions should be recorded (see Chap. 7). Exact data should be given of numerically variable features of structure or pattern, such as numbers of spots, spines, scales, tail feathers, and so forth. The reasons for including such data are stated in Chap. 7.

Descriptive Treatment. A full descriptive treatment of a species may take the following form:

Scientific name

Taxonomic references and synonymy (if any)
Type (including type locality and repository)
Diagnosis and differential diagnosis (brief statement of essential differences from nearest relatives, see above)
Description
Measurements and other numerical data
Discussion
Range (geographical)
Habitat (ecological notes) and horizon (in fossils)
List of material examined

Illustrations. Illustrations are in most instances vastly superior to a verbal description. Anything that can be made clearly and sufficiently visible in a picture should be illustrated. The value of illustrations is recognized in the International Rules, since a scientific name given to a published illustration (prior to Jan. 1, 1931) is valid even if not accompanied by a single word of description. Such a naming of illustrations was quite customary in the days of Linnaeus. In our day, however, sound taxonomists always present a diagnosis and full description together with the illustrations. See Chap. 9 for a discussion of illustrations.

Redescriptions. The redescription of hitherto poorly described forms is an extremely important element of revisional and taxonomic work. In the present state of our knowledge of many animal groups, it is of greater importance than the description of new forms. Ferris (1928), in commenting on this phase of systematic entomology, has stated that

. . . a distressingly large percentage of the named species, in almost every group of the insects, cannot be recognized positively or even at all, on the basis of the existing literature. It is more important, for the advancement of our study, to redescribe such forms than it is to describe new species. The redescription of such forms should be regarded by the student as an essential part of his work upon any group which he may elect to study. The fact that a species has been named should make no essential difference in the way in which it is treated. . . . The proper aim is not to name species but to know them. The writer who contributes to the genuine knowledge of species is accomplishing far more than one who merely names them. The fact that the author's name accompanies the names of the new species which he describes should not be allowed to influence his activities.

With this view the authors heartily concur. On the other hand, if a good description is readily available in the literature, it is wasteful to publish copies of it again and again.

The specimen or specimens on which a redescription or illustration are based should be clearly indicated (the term *plesiotype* may be used) because, in the event that the species has been misidentified, a new species may be proposed for *X-us albus* Jones, not Smith. In such a case the type specimen of the new species is the specimen, or is selected from the specimens, on which the redescription or illustration was based.

Summary. Recommendations on the preparation of descriptions may be summarized as follows:

1. The taxonomic characters should be treated in a standardized sequence.

2. The most easily visible characters should be featured.

3. A direct diagnostic comparison with the nearest relative or relatives should supplement the description.

4. Since words alone can seldom give an adequate picture of the diagnostic characters of a form, appropriate illustrations should be provided whenever possible.

5. The description should provide quantitative data, supplemented with information on geographical range, ecology, habits, and similar data.

6. Species in poorly known genera should be very fully described.

7. The formal description should be followed by an informal discussion of the variable characters.

8. The description should be accompanied by full information on the type specimen (see Chap. 12) and other material before the author.

9. Characters that are common to all members of the next higher category should be omitted from the description.

KEYS

The object of keys is to separate and segregate characters in such a way as to provide, by means of a series of alternative choices, a safe road to identification. The ultimate goal of a key is the identification of taxa (species, genera, etc.). The procedure involved is somewhat analogous to that of the physician who, by means of a series of questions and examinations, arrives, by a process of elimination and confirmation, at the diagnosis of the ills of a patient, or to the elimination method in culture identification of bacteria.

Keys are also a tool for taxonomic analysis, since in their preparation one must select, evaluate, and arrange taxonomic characters. In this sense keys are an integral part of taxonomic procedure, as well as a means of presenting findings.

The construction of keys is a laborious and time-consuming task, involving the selection and sifting of the most useful and most clearly diagnostic characters. Ideal key characters apply equally to all individuals of the population (regardless of age and sex); are absolute (two scutellar bristles vs. one scutellar bristle); are external, so that they can be observed directly and without special equipment; and are relatively constant (without excessive individual variation). Unsuitable key characters include those that require a knowledge of all ages and stages of a species (*e.g.*, "sexual dimorphism present" vs. "sexual dimorphism absent"; "male larger than female" vs. "male smaller than female"; "fall molt complete" vs. "fall molt partial"; etc.), relative characters without absolute standard (*e.g.*, "darker" vs. "lighter," "larger" vs. "smaller," etc.), and overlapping characters ("larger, wing 152 to 162" vs. "smaller, wing 148 to 158"). In most cases the data will permit the choice of several characters for the various primary and secondary divisions of the key. It is here that the writer is called upon to exercise his best judgment in order to select the most satisfactory characters at the various levels. Frequently he is torn between a phylogenetic and utilitarian approach to the problem. The primary purpose of a key is utilitarian; diagrams, lists, numbers, or order of subsequent treatment will take care of phylogeny. However, when making a key in a poorly known group (with many undescribed species) it is useful to arrange the key in such a manner that closely related species key out near one another. This facilitates the subsequent insertion of new species, as well as the decision as to whether or not a species is new. The worker is indeed fortunate whose material will permit the construction of a key which will permit presentation of a phylogenetic arrangement without interfering with the main function, that of ensuring identification.

A good key is strictly dichotomous, not offering more than two alternatives at any point.[1] Alternatives should be precise. Ideally the statements should be sufficiently definite to permit identification of a single specimen without reference to other species. In any event, identification should be possible without reference to the opposite sex or to immature stages. These should be treated in different keys when dimorphism is exhibited. Ordinarily new species should not be designated as such in a key. Also, it is usually customary to omit authorities from specific names in keys unless these are not mentioned elsewhere in the article.

The style of keys is telegraphic, like that of descriptions, and the phrases are usually separated by semicolons. Even though the primary contrasting characters of each couplet may be diagnostic and definitive, supplemental characters are desirable in the event that the primary character may not be clearly discerned or the specimen may be injured or mounted in an unsatisfactory manner. One of the most satisfactory methods for assembling data for the construction of a key is shown in an example of the method and the subsequent analysis given in Table 13.

TABLE 13. ARRANGEMENT OF KEY CHARACTERS*

Name of species	Wings	Antennae	Antennal color	Eyes	Tarsal segments	Leg color
smithi . . . . . . *clear*		filiform	*black*	entire	*linear*	black
completa . . . . *opaque*		*serrate*	black	*entire*	linear	black
emarginata . . *opaque*		*serrate*	black	*emarginate*	linear	black
rufipes . . . . . . *opaque*		*filiform*	black	entire	linear	*red*
nigripes . . . . . *opaque*		*filiform*	black	entire	linear	*black*
flavicornis . . . *clear*		filiform	*yellow*	entire	*bilobed*	black
ruficornis . . . *clear*		filiform	*red*	entire	*linear*	black
californica . . *clear*		filiform	*black*	entire	*bilobed*	black

* Characters used in examples are italicized.

[1] If it is impossible to work out a key that permits the identification of all species, it is advisable to indicate this clearly and to key out as groups any species that cannot be diagnosed by key characters.

This example is oversimplified in order to demonstrate the method more clearly.

Several types of key are used in taxonomic papers, but those most frequently used fall into two classes, each of which is subject to considerable modification, although all are dichotomous and based on a series of choices. One of these is typified by the dichotomous bracket key. The other is the indented key. The latter type of key has the advantage that the relationship of the various divisions is apparent to the eye. It has the disadvantages, especially in a long key, that the alternatives may be widely separated and that it is wasteful of space. For these reasons the best uses of this type are for short keys, keys to higher categories, or comparative keys (keys which not only serve the purposes of identification but also treat the same comparative characters at each level for each group). An indented key based on the hypothetical data given in Table 13 might be as follows:

A. Wings opaque
   B. Antennae serrate
      C. Eyes entire..*completa*
      CC. Eyes emarginate................................*emarginata*
   BB. Antennae filiform
      C. Legs red...*rufipes*
      CC. Legs black..*nigripes*
AA. Wings clear
   B. Tarsal segments linear
      C. Antennae black.....................................*smithi*
      CC. Antennae red....................................*ruficornis*
   BB. Tarsal segments bilobed
      C. Antennae black..................................*californica*
      CC. Antennae yellow................................*flavicornis*

The second type of key, and the one in most common use today, is the bracket key. This key has the advantages that the couplets are composed of alternatives which are side by side for ready comparison, and that it is more economical of space because it is unindented. When properly constructed it may be run forward or backward with equal facility by following the numbers, which indicate the path that the various choices follow. This is the type which best fulfills the diagnostic purpose of a key. Its main disadvantage is that the relationship of the divisions is not apparent to the eye. An example based on the same data previously used is as follows:

1.   Wings opaque...2
        Wings clear..5
2 (1). Antennae serrate..3
        Antennae filiform..4
3 (2). Eyes entire...*completa*
        Eyes emarginate..*emarginata*

4 (2). Legs red...*rufipes*
      Legs black..*nigripes*
5 (1). Tarsal segments linear...6
      Tarsal segments bilobed...7
6 (5). Antennae black...*smithi*
      Antennae red...*ruficornis*
7 (5). Antennae black...*californica*
      Antennae yellow...*flavicornis*

A third type of key (serial key) combines certain features of the bracket key and the indented key. It shares with the indented key the advantage that the species are arranged according to the criterion of number of key characters in common, but it is more saving of space and therefore more satisfactory for long keys. Its main disadvantage is that the alternatives are widely separated. Thus in the choice of a key for a particular purpose, the advantages and disadvantages must be weighed against the objectives of the moment. No key can serve all purposes simultaneously. The following is an example of the third type of key:

1 (8). Wings opaque
2 (5). Antennae serrate
3 (4). Eyes entire...*completa*
4 (3). Eyes emarginate...*emarginata*
5 (2). Antennae filiform
6 (7). Legs red...*rufipes*
7 (6). Legs black...*nigripes*
8 (1). Wings clear
9 (12). Tarsal segments linear
10 (11). Antennae black...*smithi*
11 (10). Antennae red...*ruficornis*
12 (9). Tarsal segments bilobed
13 (14). Antennae black...*californica*
14 (13). Antennae yellow...*flavicornis*

Among the keys designed for special purposes may be mentioned pictorial keys, branching keys, box-type keys, and circular keys. The pictorial key is of value for field identification by nonscientists. During the Second World War, for example, malaria crews based their control operations on the results of field identifications of anopheline mosquito larvae (Fig. 29). The fact that critical characters were illustrated as well as described made the keys usable by such persons as medical corpsmen and engineers as well as by entomologists. Pictorial keys have been employed also in field guides to vertebrates and flowering plants.

Other types of key have been devised from time to time in an effort to convey a mental picture of the interrelationships of a group of organisms. Failure to impart such a picture at a glance is the chief defect of the traditional dichotomous key. This is not a serious defect for the specialist who is accustomed to using and interpreting keys, but it is a shortcoming from the viewpoint of the nonspecialist. To overcome this difficulty, three different types of key have been devised: the branching type (Fig. 30), the box type (Fig. 32), and the circular type (Fig. 31).

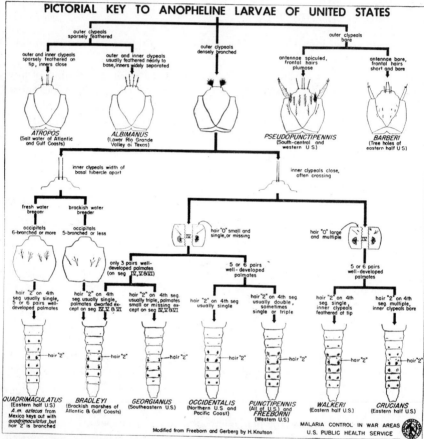

Fig. 29. Pictorial key to larvae of anopheline mosquitoes of the United States (*U.S. Public Health Service*).

The data of Table 13 are used in each case, so that the types are comparable.

Certain keys such as the indented (also the box-type and circular type) are sometimes referred to as *phylogenetic* keys. Such an appellation makes the silent assumption that the series of dichotomies chosen parallels the phylogenetic history. The taxonomic record in well-known groups has shown how easy it is to make mistakes in the interpretation of the phylogenetic value of characters. For instance, although in the groups listed in Table 13, *smithi-ruficornis-flavicornis-californica* may be a group that splits off very early from the other four species (*completa, emarginata, rufipes,* and *nigripes*), the visible difference between the groups may be ill defined (wings clear vs. opaque). To use such an

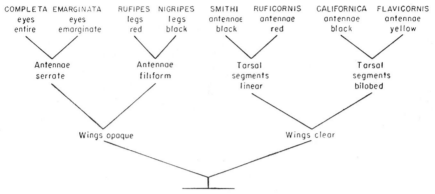

FIG. 30. Example of branching key based on analysis of characters in Table 13.

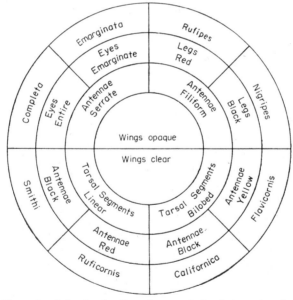

FIG. 31. Example of circular key based on analysis of characters in Table 13.

unreliable character as the very first bracket might lead to many misidentifications. Furthermore, subsequent discovery of additional characters may show that actually the form of the antennae is a more deepseated character than the wings, and this would lead to a different interpretation of the phylogeny. Finally, even the bracket-type key can be constructed in such a way as to group together the most closely related forms, except that monotypic dichotomies sometimes have to be placed out of order.

The Presentation of Phylogeny.   Natural classifications are based on phylogeny, although they can represent phylogeny only imperfectly (Chap. 3).   The great interest in phylogeny goes back to the early Darwinian days.   Darwin (1859) stated that all animals and plants were derived from common ancestors, but he made no attempt to reconstruct the genealogy of species and higher categories.   It was Haeckel (1866) who made a first attempt at presenting the relationships of all animals phylogenetically.   A phylogeny is traditionally represented by a branch-

Completa	*Emarginata*	*Rufipes*	*Nigripes*	*Smithi*	*Ruficornis*	*Californica*	*Flavicornis*
Eyes entire	Eyes emargi- nate	Legs red	Legs black	Antennae black	Antennae red	Antennae black	Antennae yellow
Antennae serrate		Antennae filiform		Tarsal segments linear		Tarsal segments bilobed	
Wings opaque				Wings clear			

FIG. 32. Example of box-type key based on analysis of characters in Table 13.

ing tree, somewhat as in human genealogies.   Ever since the invention of the phylogenetic tree by Haeckel, it has been customary among taxon-omists to express phylogenetic conclusions in the form of diagrams (Jepsen, 1944).   In spite of their numerous shortcomings, such diagrams are useful summarizations of taxonomic knowledge and provide a pictorial representation of the author's concept of the evolutionary history of a group.   Often a simple diagram shows more than many pages of detailed discussion or description.   Some of the more useful kinds of diagram are discussed below.

Phylogenetic Evidence.   Before diagramming can be attempted, an interpretation of the probable phylogeny must be reached on the basis of the taxonomic data.   It is here that the systematist must muster all his judgment and experience.   Because of the subjective nature of the problem, it is difficult to lay down any hard and fast procedures for attaining satisfactory results.   As has been remarked by Simpson (1945), "Phylogeny cannot be observed.   It is necessarily an inference from observations that bear on it, sometimes rather distantly, and that can usually be interpreted in more than one way."

One of the first steps in a phylogenetic study is usually the tabulation of the characters shared by the groups concerned. Not only structural features should be tabulated, but also biological, embryological, physiological, and geographical data to the extent to which they are available.

The second step consists in determining which of the tabulated characters are primitive and which specialized. This often requires reference to characters in related groups which fall outside of the study. Reduction (*e.g.*, loss of wings, fewer segments in appendages, etc.) is normally, but not always, an indication of specialization. Narrowly adaptive characters which restrict or limit the habits of a species or group are usually specializations.

Since the more primitive species or groups are likely to retain the most primitive characters, it is important to know where the most primitive forms are apt to be found. Here geographical distribution and habits aid greatly. New Zealand and Australia, and to a lesser degree South America, are great reservoirs of primitive types. Outside of these areas primitive groups may be widely but discontinuously distributed, frequently with highly localized, only distantly related, species. When the primitive groups have been located and the primitive characters recognized, a rough approximation of the relative ages of the groups concerned is possible. Fossil evidence, when available, may aid greatly in confirming such conclusions. With many animal groups, however, only limited help is normally available from this source.

Phylogenetic reasoning on the basis of degree of resemblance is confused by several natural consequences of evolution. The first is convergence due to adaptations to similar environmental conditions. Familiar examples are the distantly related but similar-appearing families of water beetles, which possess a common streamlined form; the strikingly similar structure of the forelegs in mantids (Mantodea) and mantispids (Neuroptera); and the superficially similar ectoparasites of vertebrates, which belong to at least six different orders of insects.

Second, phylogeny may be obscured by parallelism. The various species of *Drosophila*, for example, show similar mutations, such as orange eye. Consequently, orange-eye variants in *Drosophila* are not monophyletic but cut across phylogenetic lines. They are part of the genetic pattern of the group as a whole. The same phenomenon is evident in the white females of the various species of *Colias*. Mayr and Vaurie (1948) have given examples of such characters in certain birds, and Michener (1949) in saturniid moths. Michener concluded that in the Saturniidae a hind tibial spur has been independently lost at least 10 times in one subfamily, the epiphyses of the female at least 10 times in the family, and the articulation of the male genital harpes 7 times. He found that reduction of the labial palpi has occurred at least 9 times, and of the eyes and structures of the head capsule at least 14 times. Finally, front tibial spines have been acquired independently at least 10 times. It is obvious that any phylogenetic scheme utilizing these as primary characters indicative of close affinity would provide highly erroneous conclusions.

Traditional lines of relationship may be confused still further by the shuffling of characters seen in some closely related species. In these cases it would appear that all possible combinations of a given set of characters have been tried and are preserved to confuse the evolutionary picture. This seems to be true in various genera of bees.

Still another source of confusion is the reversal of evolutionary trends. It happens not infrequently in evolutionary lines that a specialization is

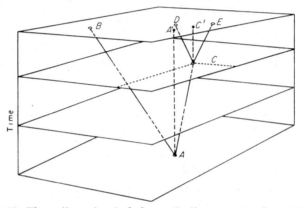

FIG. 33. Three-dimensional phylogenetic diagram (*after Lam*, 1936).

lost and that the descendants of specialized forms become secondarily "primitive." It is sometimes very difficult to distinguish between secondarily "primitive" forms and really primitive ones, unless there is supplementary evidence from the fossil record. On the subspecies level, the distribution pattern sometimes yields valuable clues. For instance, the rosy finches (*Leucosticte tephrocotis*) are descendants of the Asiatic *L. brandti*—*arctoa* group and entered North America via Bering Straits. The southernmost American form (*L. tephrocotis australis*, southern Rocky Mountains) has lost much of the bright coloration and sexual dimorphism of its species and has become secondarily similar to its primitive relatives in Central Asia. Similar secondarily "primitive" conditions of peripheral subspecies have been described in many species of birds (*e.g.*, in the genera *Pachycephala*, *Lalage*, and *Junco*).

The preservation of annectent types leads us to another kind of phylogenetic problem. In phylogeny the survival of relic types is particularly difficult to evaluate. Here we are dealing with the problem of differential rates of evolution. It appears that each group of organisms has evolved at varying speeds at various periods in its history and in various parts of the world. The reasons for this are discussed by Simpson (1944). Suffice it to say here that the possibility of relic forms must always be kept in mind, especially when phylogenetic reasoning is based solely on the present-day fauna.

Phylogenetic Diagrams. Phylogenetic diagrams are symbols designed to represent an author's interpretation of the evolutionary history of a group.

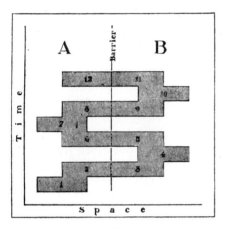 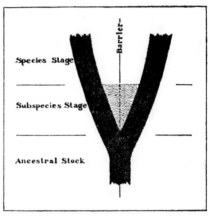

a   *b*

Fig. 34. (*a*) Diagram illustrating how geographical fragmentation of successive populations (the numbered rectangles) may accompany vertical differentiation of a phyletic line. The populations rarely remain in one locality for long but migrate. Some migrants become isolated from the parent stock by barriers, becoming ultimately differentiated into geographical races. The faunal succession in any locality (*A* or *B*) is never absolutely continuous, even though gaps may be obscure. The gaps may be produced by migrations, by depositional hiatus, and by local extermination. (*b*) A population becomes divided by a barrier causing partial isolation with limited gene flow for a time—the subspecies stage in speciation. After sufficient genetic differentiation has been reached, interbreeding ceases, gene flow is stopped, and the two branches become separate species (*Newell*, 1947).

The phylogeny of a group may be depicted as a three-dimensional figure (Fig. 33), with time as the ordinate, differentiation as the abscissae, and the angles (slopes of ascending branches from the vertical) indicating rate of divergence or velocity. Thus *A* represents an ancestral population which diverged from the vertical axis *A-A′* into the branches *B* and *C*. Line *B* diverged more rapidly (angle *B-A-A′*) and hence shows greater differentiation at the present time (top level). Line *C*, although less differentiated from the ancestral type, split again into *D* and *E*.

The actual split of a phyletic line is called *speciation* and is visualized as in Fig. 34*b* (Newell, 1947). Here "a population becomes divided by a barrier causing partial isolation with limited gene flow for a time—the subspecies state in speciation. After sufficient genetic differentiation has been reached interbreeding ceases, gene flow is stopped, and the two branches become separate species."

Actually the course of evolution is more involved than this, because subspecies are not always separated by barriers, and horizontal differentiation and vertical differentiation are simultaneous processes. Thus Fig. 34*a* illustrates (Newell, 1947)

. . . how geographic fragmentation of successive populations (the numbered rectangles) may accompany vertical differentiation of a phyletic line. The populations rarely remain in one locality for long, but migrate. Some migrants become isolated from the parent stock by barriers, becoming ultimately differentiated into geographic races. The faunal succession in any locality (*A* or *B*) is never absolutely continuous, even though gaps may be obscure. These gaps may be produced by migrations, by depositional hiatus, and by local extermination.

The foregoing diagrams are theoretical and therefore relatively simple. However, the application of the phylogentic concept to the classification of a group of organisms is not a simple matter. One of the best examples of such application is the phylogeny of the Equidae (Fig. 35). Here the fossil record is more complete than in most groups, so the pictorial diagram is based on actual specimens at numerous points along each of the evolutionary lines.

Unfortunately in most groups the fossil record is so incomplete that most phylogenetic diagrams cannot be based on historical data at all. In the absence of adequate paleontological evidence, it is necessary to resort to degree of differentiation and to geographical distribution of present-day forms as criteria for phylogenetic classification. In other words, we can arrive at a phylogenetic picture only indirectly from what amounts to an aerial view of the phylogenetic tree, the position of the main limbs or branches being inferred from the arrangement of the terminal twigs. This results, even under the most favorable circumstances, in only a rough approximation of the actual course of evolution in a group, because the relative rates of evolution are unknown, convergence of various lines is usually obscured, and extinct lines are lost.

Horizontal classification differs from *vertical* classification by the emphasis placed on direct descent: "Horizontal classification separates ancestral from descendent groups and unites contemporaneous groups, or those in a similar stage of evolution, if they are derived from a common ancestry. Vertical classification unites ancestral and descendent groups and separates contemporaneous groups that are diverging from a common ancestry" (Simpson, 1945). The relationships of these two types of classifica-

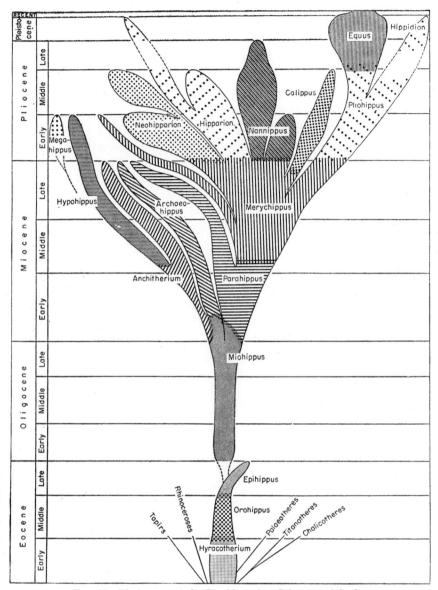

FIG. 35. Phylogeny of the Equidae after Stirton (original).

tion are shown in the accompanying diagrams (Figs. 36 and 37). In Fig. 36, which is deliberately drawn so as to be comparable to Fig. 33, group *B* is a large and diverse taxon. It is connected to the smaller group, *D*, by two attributes which, on the basis of experience, are considered to be fundamental or significant characters (*i.e.*, characters which, when used in a classification, make possible a large number of inferences). *E* is connected to *B* by one character and to *D* by four characters. The resulting diagram indicates, on the level or place of the present day, (1) size and diversity of the groups and (2) degree of differentiation of the groups.

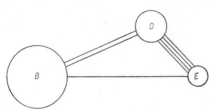

If the same data are projected on a three-dimensional figure (Fig. 37) we arrive at a purely hypothetical but nevertheless useful phylogenetic picture. The chief advantages of the tree-like representation over the simple line diagram are that relative sizes of groups can be indicated, and the perspective aids in comprehending the third dimension.

FIG. 36. Diagram of horizontal classification (*modified after Lam*, 1936).

As mentioned in the discussion of categories and concepts (Chap. 3), no design has yet been devised which will fully reflect all the data and conclusions regarding the history of any moderately complex and reasonably large group.   At best, with a relatively complete fossil record, *e.g.*, the phylogeny of the horse, it is possible to give only a rough approximation of the probable course of evolution.

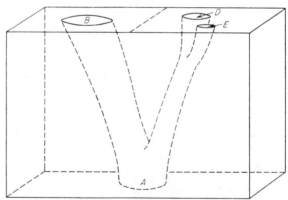

FIG. 37. Diagram of vertical classification (*modified after Lam*, 1936).

By far the majority of phylogenetic diagrams are made without any fossil evidence at all.   This involves the basic but unproved assumption that degree of resemblance of recent organisms is a direct function of their respective ages, the most divergent forms having branched off earlier than more closely related groups.   Based upon this axiom, various types of phylogenetic diagrams have been prepared and are in current use.   The simplest of these is a two-dimensional diagram with a hypothetical ancestor and branches indicating the supposed points of divergence.   The degree of departure from the vertical, *i.e.*, the angle, may or may not be used to indicate the supposed rate of evolution as compared with another angle on the same diagram (Osborn, 1895) (Fig. 38). This type of diagram is applicable to any level in the taxonomic hierarchy. It is usually schematic, *i.e.*, designed to fit the dimensions of a page rather than to indicate spatial interrelationships of the groups.

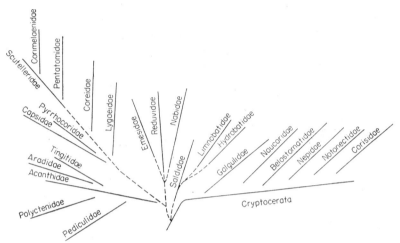

FIG. 38. Phylogeny of the Hemiptera (*Osborn*, 1895).

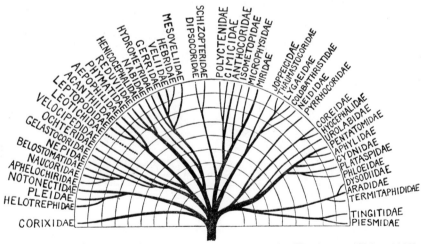

FIG. 39. Diagram showing relationships and origin of the Hemiptera (*China*, 1933).

Dendrograms. A tree-like modification, known as a "dendrogram," embodies the same principles but is slightly more adaptable to large groups. In this type of diagram great liberties are taken in bending "branches" to fit the space on a page, and angles are of no importance; but point of origin of branches is very important, and the most closely related forms are in proximity to one another (China, 1933) (Fig. 39). An example of a clear three-dimensional dendrogram is the representation of the evolution of the caddisworm case construction (Trichoptera) by Milne and Milne (1939) (Fig. 40).

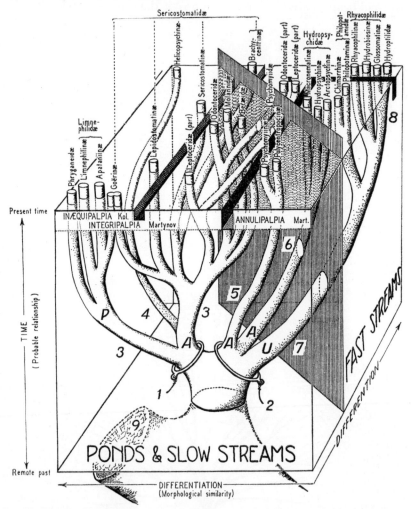

Fig. 40. A three-dimensional dendrogram representing the evolution of caddisworm case construction (*Milne and Milne, 1939*).

The actual steps in preparing a phylogenetic diagram or dendrogram are difficult to pin down, because so much depends on the breadth of vision and judgment of the taxonomist. Lam (1936) has analyzed the various types of diagram and has suggested a method by which characters can be tabulated for each species and then used quantitatively to arrange the branches of the phylogenetic tree. This is a laudable attempt to reduce the procedure of making phylogenetic diagrams to certain mechanical steps, and as a matter of fact, most taxonomists consciously or unconsciously go through these steps. However, the suggested procedure imparts a false sense of precision to a method which is very largely subjective, and which, in the last analysis, depends not on the number or degree of affinities but on the relative importance to be attached to the various resemblances and differences. Here judgment reigns supreme. Consequently no phylogenetic diagram is better than the taxonomic concepts on which it is based.

Linear Arrangement. Phylogeny can best be expressed in three dimensions. However, degrees of relationship can be expressed in two dimensions, and, as stated above, this is often done.

The most universally used expression of relationships is the linear arrangement. Because of our system of printing and binding books in a sequence of pages, some order of treatment is necessary. One species has to be treated first and one last. In common practice, species are arranged as nearly as possible according to degree of relationship with one another. Thus two species appearing on the same page are presumably more closely related to each other than either is to any other species. This scheme is of some value, presuming that the group is reasonably well known and that the classification includes all the species known and not just a restricted fauna. However, it should be remembered that the forms in a given group can almost never be arranged really "naturally" in a single linear sequence, and that in reality no arrangement of contemporaneous forms is directly phylogenetic.

But what of the over-all sequence? Here it is necessary to understand enough of the phylogeny of the group to decide which characters are "primitive" or generalized and which are specialized. Then the sequence may proceed in either direction, though commonly from generalized to specialized.

Since, as shown above, the actual phylogenetic history of animal groups is unknown, most linear arrangements of species, genera, and higher categories in catalogues and check lists are very dubious indeed. Some cataloguers have rebelled against the whole system and utilize a strict alphabetical arrangement. This may be more intellectually honest but is less satisfying to the student of evolution, let alone the curators who wish to arrange their collections in as nearly a natural order as our knowledge will permit.

A phylogenetic arrangement has numerous obvious advantages. It calls attention to possible synonyms; it prepares the way for the combining of allopatric forms into polytypic species; it often points to zoogeographical conclusions. By listing primitive species first and the more specialized ones later, it permits the working out of evolutionary trends.

CHAPTER 9

PREPARATION OF TAXONOMIC PAPERS

No taxonomic study is complete until the results have been published. Each worker owes to his science a report on the ground that he has covered. The fact that his predecessors have published the results of their investigations has made his own studies possible. Further, the field of systematic zoology is so great and the workers so few that significant progress will be impossible unless each systematist contributes his bit. This is, however, no justification for the publication of hasty or slipshod work or for flooding the literature with trivia.

Even when the worker has accomplished something worth while, he may fail in his duty to science by inadequate attention to the details of preparing his report for publication. The following suggestions, by no means exhaustive, are designed to provide a guide to some of the more important problems encountered in connection with the preparation of taxonomic articles for publication. The serious student will wish to pursue this subject further and consult authoritative sources (Trelease, 1951; Hurt, 1949; also *A Manual of Style* of the University of Chicago Press, the *U.S. Government Printing Office Style Manual*, and various style manuals or pamphlets designed for specialized fields or particular journals).

There are various kinds of taxonomic paper. Descriptions of new subspecies, species, and genera are forms of taxonomic presentation which may be published separately in short papers but are most useful when incorporated into larger, more comprehensive studies. Except in well-known groups, the isolated description, divorced from revisional or monographic work, is the least important form of taxonomic contribution and often a handicap rather than a help to subsequent workers. In the lesser known groups isolated descriptions are justified when names are needed in connection with biological or economic work, or in faunal works, or when a group has been recently revised and the new species can be readily fitted into the classification. Theoretically, except in the last case, in order to provide an adequate description the author must undertake much of the work basic to the preparation of a synopsis or revision anyway and with a little extra effort can carry it to that point. All too frequently, however, the isolated description results from but a cursory familiarity with previous work, and a greater percentage of synonyms is created through isolated descriptions than through revisional works.

Size and Number of Publications. Some authors apparently pride themselves on the number of titles in their bibliography. This leads to the publication of each new species or subspecies description as a separate article. As previously mentioned, there are times when the publication of separate descriptions is justified. As a general rule, however, material that belongs together should be published together, and in the final analysis the author is judged not by the number but by the quality of his publications.

Other authors go to the opposite extreme and include the most heterogeneous material in a single publication. This is particularly apt to be true for taxonomic monographs. It is a fact that taxonomic monographs are rarely read by general biologists; in fact, many of them are read by only a few specialists. If the author of a taxonomic revision has made interesting ecological, evolutionary, or zoogeographical discoveries, he should not conceal these findings in the introduction of the monograph (where they may remain forever buried) but should publish them in a general journal like *Ecology* or *Evolution* where the articles will, in turn, draw attention to the monograph. Many highly interesting and significant findings of the taxonomist will be overlooked by the general biologist if they are not brought to his attention by publication in a suitable journal.

Among the more comprehensive types of taxonomic publication, the following broad classes may be recognized. Many published works will be found which combine features of more than one of these classes.

Synopses and Reviews. Synopses and reviews are brief summaries of current knowledge of a group, and the inclusion of new material or new interpretations is not necessarily implied. They serve the utilitarian purpose of bringing scattered information on a group together in one place, perhaps as a basis for some future revisional or monographic study. Examples of taxonomic synopses and reviews are as follows:

La Rivers, Ira. 1947. A synopsis of the genus Endrodes (Coleoptera: Tenebrionidae). *Ann. Ent. Soc. Amer.*, **40**:318–328.

Ross, H. H. 1946. A review of the Nearctic Lepidostomatidae (Trichoptera). *Ann. Ent. Soc. Amer.*, **39**:265–291, 37 figs.

Revisions. Revisions are presentations of new material or new interpretations, integrated with previous knowledge through summary and reevaluation. They vary greatly in completeness of treatment. Some revisions are monographic in approach but fall short of a monograph because of inadequate material. Others are limited to a new arrangement of a group. Most of the important current taxonomic contributions in groups where new species are still constantly being discovered fall in this category. Such revisions may deal with a whole family (or part of one), with a genus, or with a species group. Generic revisions, illustrated by the following example, are the most common type of such work.

Sommerman, K. M. 1946. A revision of the genus Lachesilla north of Mexico (Corrodentia: Caeciliidae). *Ann. Ent. Soc. Amer.*, **39**:627–657, 4 plates.

Monographs. Monographs are complete systematic publications. They involve full systematic treatment of all species, subspecies, and other taxonomic units and a thorough knowledge on the author's part of the comparative anatomy of the group, the biology of the species and subspecies included, the immature stages in groups exhibiting metamorphosis, and detailed distributional data. For the student of evolution such monographic treatises are the most rewarding type of taxonomic publication. They permit a detailed treatment of geographic variation, of relationships, and of distributional history. Generalizations on the structure of species, modes of speciation, nature of taxonomic categories, and the like are based on such monographs. They have the disadvantage that they require more complete material than other kinds of taxonomic papers. However, with the growth of the collections in the museums of the world, it is becoming more frequently possible to prepare monographs. Some papers which fully qualify as monographs are published as revisions or under some other title. Unfortunately, in the present state of our knowledge of many groups, especially among the invertebrates, few taxonomic papers can justify the title, monograph. Monographs are more frequently possible among vertebrates. Two fairly typical examples of monographs are

Felt, E. P., and L. H. Joutel. 1904. Monograph of the genus Saperda. *N.Y. State Mus. Bul.* 74 (Ent. 20), 81 pp., 14 plates.
Hubbell, T. H. 1936. A monographic revision of the genus Ceuthophilus (Orthoptera, Gryllacrididae, Rhaphidophorinae). *Fla. Univ. Pub., Biol. Sci. Ser.*, Vol. II, No. 1, 551 pp., 38 plates.

Faunal Works. The faunal work is a method of presenting taxonomic material defined by a geographical area rather than by a taxonomic unit. Its objects are to make possible identifications in a particular area and to report detailed geographical distribution, rather than to clarify problems in general systematics. If the fauna involved is that of a very limited region, the report may consist of a "local list." Such a list is often the work of a local resident who has collected the area intensively. It can be exceedingly useful if based on adequate and carefully identified collections and if accompanied by quantitative data and ecological comments. The reports of expeditions and voyages also belong to the category of faunistic papers. They offer a convenient opportunity to describe new species and genera and to lay foundations for future work.

In order to prepare a faunal work in most of the lesser known groups, the taxonomist usually finds it necessary to delve deeply into problems of classification and general systematics. Thus most faunal works of this type make contributions to systematic zoology over and above their immediate objectives. However, although faunistic papers may be a mine of information for the biogeographer and the ecologist, they are usually not designed to provide data for the evolutionist; and in better known groups the preparation of faunal lists rarely permits the accurate determination of subspecies.

Examples of faunal works are

Fauna of British India. Taylor and Francis, London. Many volumes covering most groups of animals, published over the past half-century.

Biologia Centrali-Americana, 1879–1915, Parts 1–215. Dulau and Co., London.

Faune de France. 1921–1950 et seq., Vols. 1–53. Office Centrale de Faunistique Paris.

Faune de l'U.R.S.S. Institut Zoologique de l'Académie de U.R.S.S. (some 30 volumes published).

An example of a local list is

Brown, H. E. 1939. An annotated list of the species of Jassinae known to occur in Indiana (Homoptera, Cicadellidae). *Amer. Midland Nat.*, **21**:663–673.

Atlases. In recent times the need has been felt for complete illustrations of the species of various taxonomic groups. This is a reflection of the inadequacy of the printed word as a means of conveying a mental picture of the general facies of an animal. The idea of an atlas grew also out of the need for taxonomic data which are strictly comparable from one species to another. Since the purpose of an atlas is purely taxonomic, semidiagrammatic drawings are commonly used, though full halftones or colored plates have been employed when dealing with such groups as butterflies and birds.

Examples of this type of treatment are as follows:

Ferris, G. F. 1937–1950. Atlas of the scale insects of North America. Stanford University Press, Stanford University, Calif., 5 vols.

Ross, E. S., and H. R. Roberts. 1943. Mosquito atlas. American Entomological Society, Philadelphia, pt. I, 44 pp., pt. II, 44 pp.

Handbooks and Manuals. Certain works, although taxonomic, are designed primarily or exclusively for field identification. In such cases new species are expressly excluded, and emphasis is placed on clear-cut key characters or recognition characters. Examples of this type of publication are

Needham, J. G. 1929. A handbook of the dragonflies of North America. Charles C Thomas, Publisher, Springfield, Ill.

Hoffman, R. 1927. Birds of the Pacific states containing brief biographies and descriptions of about 400 species with especial reference to their appearance in the field. Houghton Mifflin Company, Boston.

Mayr, E. 1945. Birds of the Southwest Pacific. The Macmillan Company, New York, 316 pp.

Bond, J. 1947. Field guide to birds of the West Indies. The Macmillan Company, New York, 257 pp.

Klots, A. B. 1951. A field guide to the butterflies of North America east of the Great Plains. Houghton Mifflin Company, Boston, 349 pp.

Catalogues and Check Lists. Catalogues and check lists, although designed for very different purposes from the above-mentioned types of taxonomic publication, are among the most useful aids to the taxonomist. Catalogues are essentially indexes to taxonomic papers, arranged in such a manner as to provide a complete series of references for both zoological and nomenclatural purposes, according to taxonomic categories. Their preparation is a highly technical task requiring infinite patience, meticulous care, and an intimate knowledge of bibliographical sources and methods. Check lists, on the other hand, are designed to provide a skeleton classification of a group and a convenient and quick method for reference and arrangement of collections. They frequently contain little more than a list of valid names and synonyms, with a broad indication of the geographical area occupied by the species included. Check lists complement, but are not substitutes for, catalogues. They are most useful in the better known animal groups. The style of check lists depends on the group. In ornithology usually a complete reference to the valid names and synonyms is given, together with a detailed description of the range.

Typical examples of each of these are

Van Duzee, E. P. 1917. Catalogue of the Hemiptera of America north of Mexico. *Calif. Univ. Pub. Ent.*, no. 2, XIV + 902 pp.

McDunnough, J. 1938–1939. Check list of the Lepidoptera of Canada and the United States of America. Part I. Macrolepidoptera. Part II. Microlepidoptera. *South. Calif. Acad. Sci. Mem.*, **1**, 1–275; **2**(1), 1–171.

Mayr, E. 1941. List of New Guinea birds. American Museum of Natural History, New York, 260 pp.

FORM OF THE TAXONOMIC ARTICLE

Title. The title is the first part of the paper encountered by the reader, although it is often the last item to be added in the preparation of the paper. Its bibliographical prominence and significance warrant much care in its selection. The title should be long enough to be specific as to the contents of the paper but brief enough for easy indexing. Short words are preferable to polysyllabic terms. The most important nouns should be near the beginning of each series of words. The title should contain key words which in indexing will classify the article. Punctuation should be avoided unless essential to meaning. Among the essential elements of a title are (1) a clear indication of the field involved (taxonomy, morphology, ecology, etc.), (2) the scientific name of the category treated, (3) indications of the order and family either by means of scientific names (which may be in parentheses) or, rarely, by a well-known common name, and (4) the geographical area, fauna, or locality. The following are examples of good titles:

"A Taxonomic Revision of American Leafhoppers (Homoptera, Cicadellidae)"
"A Check List of the Birds of Alabama"
"Geographical Variation of Hippodamia convergens in Southern California (Coleoptera, Coccinellidae)"
"Two New Species of Wood Rats (Neotoma) from the Rocky Mountain Region"

The following are a few examples of poor titles for taxonomic papers. On the basis of the above-enumerated principles the objections to these are obvious.

"New Hymenoptera"
"Notes on Mammals"
"The Western Biota"
"A Collecting Trip to Texas"
"Additions to the Fauna of Nebraska"
"Studies in the Mollusca"
"A New Acanthiza"

Titles need not be as bad as these, however, to cause difficulties for cataloguers, abstracters, reviewers, and other bibliographers. No author has cause for complaint of his work being overlooked if it masquerades under an incomplete, ambiguous, or misleading title.

Author's Name. The author's name follows the title. Bibliographical problems are simplified if an author always uses the same form of his name. The entomologist Laporte sometimes published under the name, Laporte, sometimes under le Comte de Castelnau. The bibliographical confusion which resulted still persists in modern literature. Women taxonomists who begin publication before marriage frequently avoid similar confusion by continuing to publish under their maiden names or by a system of hyphenation, *e.g.*, Dorothy McKey-Fender. It is customary in America to omit degrees and titles from the author's name, although these are used in many European journals. The author's address should follow his name in order to facilitate correspondence and should be precise so that postal authorities can recognize it.

When more than one author is involved, the order of names is determined by the nature of the contribution each has made. When the work has been rather equally shared, the problem is solved by a coauthorship, in which case the names are usually arranged in alphabetical order. When the work has been disproportionately divided or there is a marked discrepancy in age or experience, a senior and junior authorship may result. In such cases the name of the senior author appears first.

Introduction. Every taxonomic paper should include an introductory paragraph stating the scope of the paper and, where pertinent, the reasons for the study, as well as the nature of the studied material. Frequently a brief historical review is appropriate. These features serve to orient the casual reader and the new student of the group, as well as to refresh the minds of other workers in the field.

Acknowledgments. Acknowledgments may be included in the introduction when they can be treated as part of the natural sequence of exposition. Some authors place them in a footnote appended to the author's name. This system is in regular use by the *Annals of the Entomological Society of America* and certain other journals which are primarily taxonomic in content. Sometimes the acknowledgments precede the summary.

Methods Used and Materials Studied. In a revisional or monographic work it is desirable to include a statement on methods utilized and collections, specimens, or other materials studied. This enables the reader to evaluate conclusions and to judge the thoroughness of the work. Standard methods for measuring, mounting, staining, special preparations, etc., may be referred to by name and reference. Only new methods need to be described in detail.

Body of the Text. The material comprising the body of the text will, of course, depend on the scope and objectives of the particular paper. It is perhaps sufficient to mention that a complete systematic paper includes (1) a definition of the highest category included (family, tribe, etc.), (2) a key (or keys) to all intermediate categories treated (genera), (3) synonymies and descriptions of the intermediate categories (genera), (4) statement of the generic types, (5) comparisons with other genera, (6) keys to the species of each genus, (7) synonymies and descriptions of each species, and (8) statements as to type localities and to location of types, general distribution, hosts and other significant biological data, comparisons with other species, etc. (for details on preparation of descriptions and keys see Chap. 8).

Synonymy. In monographs, revisions, and catalogues it is customary and advisable to give the complete synonymy of every species. During the earlier stages of the development of our taxonomic literature it was customary to give not only the synonyms but also a more or less complete list of all references to the species, with the names and combinations used in previous publications. In the better-known groups of animals this is both unnecessary and uneconomical, and this function is reserved for bibliographical catalogues.[1] Unfortunately, some groups of animals (*e.g.*, insects) have been so incompletely catalogued, or existing catalogues are so out-of-date, that bibliographical synonymies are still an essential element of the full taxonomic treatment. This is especially true when much of the literature prior to 1900 is more significant nomenclaturally than zoologically, and the later publications are more significant zoologically than nomenclaturally. An understanding of both is required by the modern working taxonomist in such groups.

New synonymy can most usefully be cited with the following sequence of data: (1) scientific name (in its original form), (2) author, (3) date of publication, (4) reference, (5) type locality, (6) present location of type (optional). For example,

Oncideres rhodostictus Bates

Oncideres rhodosticta Bates, 1885, *Biol. Cent.-Amer., Coleopt.,* **5**:367. [Lerdo, Mex.; British Mus. (Nat. Hist.)].

Oncideres trinodatus Casey, 1913, *Mem. Coleopt.,* **4**:352. [El Paso, Tex.; U.S. Natl. Mus.]. *New synonymy.*[2]

The above form is sufficient for a revision of a well-catalogued group. In groups where the literature has not been summarized adequately and the nomenclature remains confused, a full synonymy (*i.e.*, a list of scientific names, incorrect and correct, specifying the books and authors employing them) may be required. This should include all references which have nomenclatural or zoological significance, arranged chronologically under the actual name (correct or incorrect) by which the author actually referred to them. Many authors here use the convenient device of a comma inserted between the specific name and the author [*X-us albus*, Smith (not Brown)] to distinguish between a misidentification which has no nomenclatural status, and a homonym [*X-us albus* Jones (not Brown)] which has. A widely used form for a full bibliographical synonymy is as follows:

Oncideres rhodostictus Bates

Oncideres rhodosticta Bates, 1885, *Biol. Cent.-Amer., Coleopt.,* **5**:367 [type: Lerdo, Mex.; British Mus. (Nat. Hist.)]; Linsley, 1940, *Jour. Econ. Ent.,* **33**:562 (synon.,

[1] For example, Peters, in his *Check-list of the Birds of the World* (1931 *et seq.*), does not list synonyms that can be found in the previous standard works: *Catalogue of Birds of the British Museum* (1873–1892) and the *Handlist of Birds* (1896–1910). More recent checklists of birds do not repeat synonyms correctly cited by Peters.

[2] This synonymy was published as new in the *Journal of Economic Entomology,* **33**:562, 1940. Its use as an example here and elsewhere in the present discussion is not to be interpreted as a nomenclatural change.

distr.); Linsley, 1942, *Proc. Calif. Acad. Sci.*, (4) **24**:76 (distr.); Dillon and Dillon, 1945, *Sci. Pub. Reading Mus.*, no. 5: xv (key); Dillon and Dillon, 1946, *l.c.*, **6**:313, 382 (revis.).

Oncideres putator, Horn (not Thomson, 1868), 1885, *Trans. Amer. Ent. Soc.*, **12**:195 (key, distr.); Schaeffer, 1906, *Can. Ent.*, **38**:19 (key).

Oncideres cingulatus, Hamilton (in part) (not Say, 1826), 1896, *Trans. Amer. Ent. Soc.*, **23**:141 (distr.).

Oncideres trinodatus Casey, 1913, *Mem. Coleopt.*, **4**:352, [type: El Paso, Tex.; U.S. Natl. Mus.].

Oncideres sp., Craighead, 1923, *Can. Dept. Agr. Bul.* 17 (n.s.), p. 132 (larva, hosts).

Oncideres pustulatus, Essig (not Le Conte, 1854), 1926, Insects of Western North America, p. 460, Fig. 368 (habits, distr.).

The above synonymy might appear in an abbreviated check list as follows:

Oncideres Serville, 1835

1. *rhodostictus* Bates, 1885   So. Calif. to Tex.
   trinodatus Casey, 1913   No. Mex.
                                L. Calif.

When a check list contains a terminal bibliography, the usefulness of the check list may be increased by giving page references which may then be located by author, date, and page in the bibliography. Thus, *rhodostictus* Bates, **1885**:367, or, more simply, **85**:367.

In a complete synonymy it is often desirable to indicate the various combinations under which each name has appeared. This may be conveniently accomplished by taking the oldest specific name and following it through its various combinations, then the next oldest, etc., as follows:

Megacyllene antennata (White)

Clytus antennatus White, 1855, *Cat. Coleopt. Brit. Mus.*, **8**:252 [type: "W. Coast of America"; British Mus. (Nat. Hist.)].

Cyllene antennatus, Horn, 1880, *Trans. Amer. Ent. Soc.*, **8**:135 (descr., syn., distr.); Craighead, 1923, *Can. Dept. Agr., Bul.* 27, p. 33 (larva, biol.); Hopping, 1937, *Ann. Ent. Soc. Amer.*, **30**: 441, pl. 1 (revis.).

Megacyllene antennata, Casey, 1912, *Mem. Coleopt.*, **3**:348, 351 (descr.).

Arhopalus eurystethus LeConte, 1858, *Proc. Acad. Nat. Sci. Phila.*, **1858**:82 [type: Sonora, Mex.; Mus. Comp. Zool., Harvard]; LeConte, 1859, in Thomson, Arcana Naturae, p. 127, pl. 13, Fig. 9.

In the above example, the comma between the specific combination and the author's name has again been used, this time to distinguish between a new combination (*Cyllene antennatus*, Horn, 1880) and an original combination (*Clytus antennatus* White, 1855).

Generic synonymy is handled in much the same way as a specific synonymy, except that in the case of new synonymy or full bibliographic treatment, the generic type (and its designator, if any) is cited in place of the type locality and type location. The synonymy of the genus *Dicrurus*, as cited in Vaurie's (1949) revision of the Dicruridae, may be listed as an example.

Genus *Dicrurus* Vieillot

Dicrurus Vieillot, April 14, 1816, Analyse d'une nouvelle ornithologie élémentaire, p. 41. Type, by subsequent designation, *Corvus balicassius* Linnaeus (G. R. Gray, 1841, A list of the genera of birds, ed. 2, p. 47).

Edolius Cuvier, Dec. 7, 1816, Le règne animal, vol. 1, p. 350. Type, by subsequent designation, *Lanius forficatus* Linnaeus (G. R. Gray, 1855, Catalogue of the genera and subgenera of birds, p. 58).

Drongo Tickell, 1833, Jour. Asiatic Soc. Bengal, vol. 2, p. 573. Type, by monotypy, *Drongo caerulescens* Tickell = *Lanius caerulescens* Linnaeus.

Chibia Hodgson, 1836, India Rev., vol. 1, p. 324. Type, by subsequent designation, *Edolius barbatus* J. E. Gray = *Corvus hottentottus* Linnaeus (G. R. Gray, 1841, A list of the genera of birds, ed. 2, p. 47).

Bhringa Hodgson, 1836, India Rev., vol. 1, p. 325. Type, by original designation and monotypy, *Bhringa tectirostris* Hodgson.

Bhuchanga Hodgson, 1836, India Rev., vol. 1, p. 326. Type, by subsequent designation, *Bhuchanga albirictus* Hodgson (Sharpe, 1877, Catalogue of birds in the British Museum, vol. 3, p. 245).

Chaptia Hodgson, 1836, India Rev., vol. 1, p. 326. Type, by monotypy, *Chaptia muscipetoides* Hodgson = *Dicrurus aeneus* Vieillot.

Dissemurus Gloger, 1841, Gemeinnütziges Hand- und Hilfsbuch der Naturgeschichte, p. 347. Type, by monotypy, *Cuculus paradiseus* Linnaeus.

Musicus Reichenbach, 1850, Avium systema naturale, pl. 88, fig. 9. Figure of generic details, no species included, cf. Bonaparte, 1854, Compt. Rendus Acad. Sci. Paris, vol. 38, p. 540. Type, by tautonomy, *Dicrurus musicus* Vieillot = *Corvus adsimilis* Bechstein.

Dicranostreptus Reichenbach, 1850, Avium systema naturale, pl. 88, fig. 12. Figure of generic details, no species included. Type, by subsequent designation, *Edolius megarhynchus* Quoy and Gaimard (G. R. Gray, 1855, Catalogue of the genera and subgenera of birds, p. 58).

Summary. A summary is usually unnecessary in a strictly taxonomic paper. When required, it should be brief but should not be in telegraphic style. It should be written as a series of short paragraphs and should be specific, not in broad general terms.

References and Bibliography. References are generally treated either in footnotes, or in parentheses in the text, or in a terminal bibliography. Footnotes are useful when but a few references are involved and when repeated reference to the same bibliographical item is unnecessary. Since they are costly to handle in typesetting and printing, however, and may add materially to publishing costs, parenthetical references are to be preferred. When references are numerous, they are most frequently handled in a terminal bibliography. In most cases this bibliography should be as short as is consistent with its purpose, and the items included should be selected. Frequently the value of the terminal bibliography may be greatly increased by including parenthetical comments on the nature of the subject matter covered.   Unverified references may be included when necessary for completeness, but they should be marked with an asterisk or some other device to indicate the fact that the author has not seen them.

Bibliographical items should receive full citation, including author, title, publication, volume, pages, date, etc.   Text references to the terminal bibliography may be made by enclosing an author's name and date (sometimes also page) in parentheses.   Two or more references to publications by a single author in the same year may be designated by appended letters (Smith, 1940a; Smith, 1940b).   The author-date system of bibliographical reference is far more satisfactory than the straight numbering system which is sometimes used.   The number system tells nothing about the reference; moreover, the author-date system permits the addition of references during the preparation of the manuscript without the necessity of renumbering all references beyond the point of insertion.

A formal "Bibliography" implies completeness of coverage of the subject.   "Literature Cited" indicates restriction of references and is self-explanatory.

Examples of footnote entries and terminal bibliographies are given below.   Numerous exceptions will be encountered, especially various government documents, but a majority of literature citations will fit into one or another of the simple styles illustrated.   It is becoming standard practice to list the year of the publication immediately after the author's name, since this sequence agrees with that of the author-date system of reference.

Bibliography

Wheeler, William Morton
>   1889a. Homologues in embryo Hemiptera of the appendages to the first abdominal segment of other insect embryos. *American Naturalist*, Volume XXIII, pp. 644–645.
>
>   1889b. Über drüsenartige Gebilde im ersten Abdominalsegment der Hemipterenembryonen. *Zoologischer Anzeiger*, Band XII, pp. 500–504, 2 figs.
>
>   1910. Ants, their structure, development and behavior. New York. Columbia University Press, pp. xxvi + 664, front. 286 figs. 8vo (Columbia University Biological Series, IX).

Literature Cited

Wheeler, W. M.   1889a. Homologues in embryo Hemiptera of the appendages to the first abdominal segment of other insect embryos. *Amer. Nat.*, **23**:644–645.
>   1889b. Über drüsenartige Gebilde im ersten Abdominalsegment der Hemipterenembryonen. *Zool. Anz.*, **12**:500–504.
>   1910. Ants, their structure, development and behavior. Columbia University Press, New York. xxvi + 664 pp.

[Footnote]

---

* Wheeler, W. M.   1889.   *Amer. Nat.*, **23**:644–645.

In the typescript, footnotes are entered beneath a marginal line in the text (see example above) rather than at the bottom of the page, because in the final publication, pagination is entirely different from the original pagination.

If the work cited is by several authors, only the first need be reversed for alphabetical purposes.   Thus,

McAtee, W. L., and J. R. Malloch.   1922.   Changes in names of American Rhynchota, chiefly Emesinae.   *Proc. Biol. Soc. Wash.*, **35**:95–96.

The original style of capitalization and italics may be followed.   However, many titles are set entirely in capitals; others are set entirely in lower case, except that the first word and scientific and place names are capitalized.   The full title should be given in all but the briefest of footnotes, because readers obtain valuable leads in this way.

Abbreviations of journals should follow such standard works as the *World List of Scientific Periodicals* or the list of *Abbreviations used in the Department of Agriculture for Titles of Publications* (Whitlock, Carolyn, *U.S. Dept. Agr. Misc. Pub.* 337, pp. 1–278, 1939.   Price 30 cents).

The citation: (Wheeler, 1889*a*) is specific enough because it refers to a two-page paper.   On the other hand, it may be necessary to refer to a particular page of a larger work, thus: (Wheeler, 1910, p. 263).   In this case the page is indicated in the citation, and the complete work is listed in the bibliography.

PREPARATION OF THE MANUSCRIPT FOR PUBLICATION

Aside from matters involved in the actual organization and construction of a taxonomic paper, there are some points which should be kept in mind in order to facilitate editorial handling after the paper has been submitted for publication.   Editors are much more apt to accept readily and publish quickly papers which are in good form and require a minimum amount of editing.   Most publications have special form requirements, and much editorial time can be saved by careful advance reference to the journal in which the paper is to be published.

Typing.   All manuscript submitted for publication should be typed.   The original drafts may be on yellow paper, but the final copy should be on standard (8½ by 11 in. or 8 by 10 ½ in.) white paper, entirely double-spaced (some publications require triple spacing), and with a wide margin for adding proof marks and for editing.   If approximately the same number of lines is typed on each page, the editor can conveniently estimate the size of the final printed paper.   However, some editors require that pages end with completed paragraphs.   Pages should be numbered consecutively in the upper right-hand corner.   Inserted pages are numbered alphabetically (*e.g.*, 65*a*).   Whole sheets should be used for insertions, regardless of length of inserted matter. When it becomes necessary to cut and rearrange, sheets should be assembled by pasting, not by pinning. All tabular material should be typed on separate sheets, since it is usually set in a different type from the text.

Underlining. Underlining indicates that the material so marked is to be printed in italics. In a taxonomic manuscript submitted for publication, underlining should be limited to scientific names of genera and species which appear in the text. New names should not be underlined, because the editor will usually mark these with a wavy line to indicate boldface. Indications of style or sizes of type for titles, headings, subheadings, sideheadings, and the like should be left to the editor. In general, marks which the author makes merely interfere with the editor's work, though marginal notes as to the relative rank of headings may be helpful.

Legends and Text Citations to Illustrations. Titles and legends should be self-explanatory. The manuscript of these titles should be typewritten, double-spaced on separate sheets (several titles on a single sheet), and assembled in numerical order at the end of the manuscript following the bibliography. A short identifying title may be placed on each plate for purposes of identification, but this title will not be printed. Usually in the process of handling, titles and legends go to the typesetter with the rest of the manuscript, whereas illustrations are sent to the engraver. The printer may never see the original drawings.

The place of insertion of the illustrations should be marked in the manuscript and also in the galley proof. Illustrations are usually numbered starting with each article, but some journals number plates consecutively throughout a volume. In any event, a new series of figure numbers or letters should be used on each plate. Many journals designate figures with Arabic numbers, plates with Roman numerals. All figures should be referred to in the text by number.

Revision of the Manuscript. Some few authors have sufficient mastery of the English language so that they can write directly in final form for publication. Other equally competent scientists find it necessary to revise page after page not once but many times. T. D. A. Cockerell was an example of the former type of writer, whereas, by his own testimony, Charles Darwin was an inveterate reviser.

Trelease (1951) recommends careful reading of the manuscript 10 times, each time for one of the following: (1) consistency, (2) sentences, (3) clearness, (4) repetition, (5) connectives, (6) euphony, (7) punctuation, (8) style, (9) accuracy, and (10) length. Authors of taxonomic papers seldom follow the details of this recommendation, but most papers would benefit by more revisions than are usually given. It often helps to put a manuscript aside for a while before the final revision is made. It is always advisable to have other persons read a manuscript before it is submitted for publication. A fully corrected carbon copy of the manuscript should be kept by the author for use in case the original is lost.

Proofreading. Most scientific journals permit the author to read proof on his papers before publication. Some few journals place the entire burden of the proofreading on the author and hold him responsible for typographical or other errors which may pass undetected. In any event, where the author sees the proof, proofreading becomes a very important part of his scientific responsibility. The scientific value of his paper can be greatly lessened by unfortunate typographical errors. Such errors are sometimes obvious to the reader, but they may be insidious and wholly misleading.

In general, the submission of proof to the author is to permit the elimination of errors for which the printer is responsible. Author's errors are his own responsibility, and some publications charge authors for corrections other than printers' errors. Changes in proof are costly and therefore should not be made unless necessary or unless the author is willing to assume the cost of the change.

Proofreading cannot always be done satisfactorily by one person. It is advisable to supplement the personal reading by having someone else read slowly from the original manuscript, while the proofreader (preferably the author) carefully reads the proof. Special attention should be given to punctuation, spelling of scientific names, numbers, and dates of all kinds. When corrections are necessary, they should be made according to the standard system of proofreaders' marks (Fig. 41).

Most authors see only galley proofs of their papers. These are long sheets with the text continuous and not broken into pages. For most journals a galley is the equivalent of about three printed pages. Some publications also submit page proofs to the authors. In such cases proofreading cannot be restricted to individual words which were corrected in the galley proof but must include the whole line in which the word appeared. Modern linotype machines cannot change a single letter in a word but must reset the whole line. If a word was inserted, it may have been necessary to reset several lines or perhaps the remainder of the paragraph. The author should carefully check everything which has been reset. Corrected proof should be returned at once to the editor or printer in order to avoid delay in publication. The printing of an entire issue of a periodical may be held up by a single tardy author.

Illustrations. The object of illustrations in taxonomic papers is to present precise, comparative information which cannot be so well expressed in words or which is needed to elucidate the written text. Thus accuracy, simplicity, and intelligibility are prime considerations. In the preparation of illustrations, advance consideration should be given to the method of reproduction which will ultimately be utilized in publication, since this affects both the techniques to be followed and the cost of preparation and publication.

Technique in drawing is largely a personal matter, depending on the ability and training of the individual. A scientist is fortunate if he

ẽ	Delete and close up	em⏐	En dash
℗	Reverse	;⏐	Insert semicolon
◡	Close up	⊙	Insert colon
#	Insert space	⊙	Insert period
¶	Paragraph	?⏐	Insert interrogation point
☐	Indent one em	℗	Query to author
⊏	Move to left	⁀	Use ligature
⊐	Move to right	㏠	Spell out
⊔	Lower	tr	Transpose
⊓	Elevate	wf	Wrong font
∧	Insert marginal addition	bf	Set in **bold face type**
V∧	Even space	rom	Set in ⬭roman⬭ type
✕	Broken letter	ital	Set in *italic* type
↓	Push down space	caps	Set in <u>CAPITALS</u>
⸺	Straighten line	sc	Set in <u>SMALL CAPITALS</u>
‖	Align type	lc	Set in lower case
⋏	Insert comma	⅂	Lower-case letter
ⱽ	Insert apostrophe	stet	Let it stand
ⱽ⁾	Insert quotes	no ¶	Run in same paragraph
=⏐	Hyphen	ld⟩	Insert lead between lines
em⏐	Em dash	hr#	Hair space between letters

Fɪɢ. 41. Proofreaders' marks.

happens to be endowed with talent as an artist. However, the scientist who lacks artistic talent need not be discouraged, because clear-cut diagrammatic drawings are perfectly satisfactory and, in some cases, superior to artistic drawings for scientific purposes. Ferris (1928) has called this type of drawing *drafting* and expresses the opinion that any conscientious scientist can learn to make satisfactory drawings of this kind. Several books or manuals have been published on the subject, among which may be mentioned Ridgway (1938), Kuhl (1949), and Cannon (1936).

Pencil sketches should be made with a soft pencil, and bilaterally symmetrical animals should be "corrected" for symmetry by tracing one half on the other with thin semitransparent paper.

The original outline may be obtained by freehand sketching but, at least with microscopically small organisms, can be done more quickly and accurately by one or another mechanical means. Perhaps the most popular of these devices is the *camera lucida*, which, by means of prisms and a mirror, projects the microscope image on a piece of paper. With this

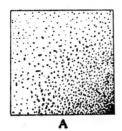 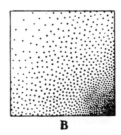 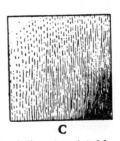

A   **B**   **C**

FIG. 42. Simple types of shading: *A*, pseudo stipple; *B*, stipple; *C*, lines (*reprinted from The Principles of Systematic Entomology, by Gordon Floyd Ferris, with permission of the author and the publishers, Stanford University Press*).

apparatus it is possible to look in the microscope and see the specimen superimposed on the reflection of the paper. By careful adjustment of the light, it is possible to draw an outline with the specimen and the pencil point both clearly in view. Another method of obtaining the outline is the direct projection of an image on a screen or paper by a microprojector attached to the microscope. Still another technique is to photograph the specimen and print an enlargement on a dull mat paper. The outline can be inked directly on the photograph, after which the photographic emulsion can be washed off. Some workers prefer to sketch freehand on a crosshatched paper, guided by a grid in the ocular of the microscope.

The preliminary sketches should be checked for accuracy of proportion and then transferred to the final drawing paper. A hard-surface white paper is best for black-and-white line drawings, but various surfaced papers may be used for special purposes. Chalk-surface "stipple boards" are especially useful when shading is desired, soft carbon pencils or black wax crayons being used to obtain the desired effects. High lights may be shown on chalk-surface papers by simply scraping an area.

Pens of various styles may be used, depending on the strength of line desired and on the preference of the illustrator.

Line drawings are made with black India ink. The lines should be firm and even—not scratched—and should be heavier on the lower right side of the drawing (assuming that the light source is from the upper left) to indicate depth and contour (Fig. 43). Convexity may also be indicated by short crosslines on the side away from the light (Fig. 44).

More elaborate shading may be rendered by stipple or parallel lines, but this requires more artistic ability and should not be attempted without considerable practice. If stippling is to be done, it should be even, not irregularly speckled, the variations in tone being due to spacing rather

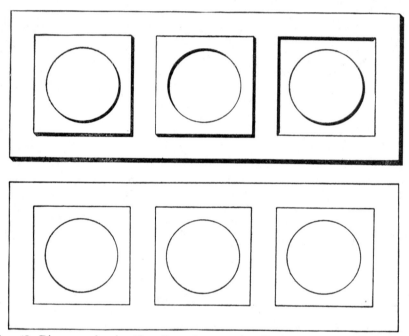

Fig. 43. Diagrams showing the effect of conventionalized shading as employed by mechanical draftsmen (*reprinted from The Principles of Systematic Entomology, by Gordon Floyd Ferris, with the permission of the author and of the publishers, Stanford University Press*).

than size of dots. Lines are also useful for shading but require great care. In every case, individual drawings should be made one and one half to two times larger than final size, because minor imperfections in line and stipple are deemphasized by reduction (Fig. 42).

Transparent stipple paper is available commercially with various sizes of dots, crosshatching, and lines. These papers may be pressed onto drawings and trimmed to fit a given space, thus automatically providing a uniform tone. This technique is especially useful for distribution maps, which, incidentally, are handled exactly like line drawings.

More delicate shading is accomplished by rubbing on tones of carbon pencil, using a soft stub, or by brushing on various dilutions of India ink. In either case a very different type of drawing results which must be reproduced as a halftone or fulltone, like a photograph. Details of mounting and labeling halftones will be given later.

Photographs are generally less effective than drawings because of lack of contrast and dimension. However, they do serve to portray general facies or habitus, and they are indispensable for portraying the habitat of a given species and other biological features. Photographs should be specific, *i.e.*, concentrated on the portrayal of one object. They should show as much contrast as possible, and they must not be dull or blurred.

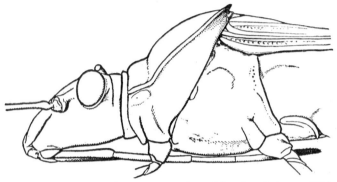

Fig. 44. *Riptortus tutuilensis* China; lateral view of head and thorax (*China*, 1930)

For best reproduction, photographs to be shown on the same plate should have similar backgrounds and should be similar in tone, both for esthetic reasons and because the engraver cannot make a satisfactory plate if the photographs are uneven in tone. If for any reason photographs are not up to standard, they may be improved somewhat by careful retouching. This is a delicate operation and should not be undertaken without considerable experience. A mat print is made, and soft pencil is employed to strengthen lines or emphasize certain points. Then the retouched photograph is rephotographed and printed on glossy paper or, in some cases, may be used directly.

Halftone drawings or retouched photographs should be protected by a tissue-paper cover to prevent rubbing.

Colored illustrations are strictly in the realm of works of art and, as such, should be left to the skilled artist or scientist-illustrator. No general rules are given here, because so much depends on the skill of the artist. A recent development along this line is the production of color prints by photography. In the future this method may be exploited more fully; it has already proved useful for illustrations of butterflies.

Drawings are most frequently reproduced either as zinc etchings or halftones or by photolithography. Zinc etchings are produced by photographing the illustration on zinc and etching away the background with acid. It is the least expensive method of reproduction and is especially satisfactory for line drawings, graphs, charts, etc. Halftones are screened and broken up into tiny dots, so that white areas appear gray. The method is more costly than zinc etchings but shows greater detail and more delicate shading. If desired, the background may be routed out, as in zinc etching, but this still further increases the cost. In photolithography the illustration is photographed on gelatine and is

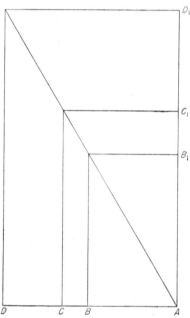

Fig. 45. Method of calculating proportions for enlargement or reduction of illustrations. If the side *AC* of an illustration is enlarged to *AD* or reduced to *AB*, the length of the other side (*AD'* or *AB'*) can be easily determined as the point of intersection with the diagonal.

not screened, thus becoming a fulltone process. It will therefore show even greater detail than a halftone but lacks some of the contrast. Halftones and photogelatin plates are often printed on glossy paper or at a different printing establishment, and for this reason it is frequently easiest to assemble them together at the end of an article. Zinc etchings are usually printed on the same paper as the text and may therefore more readily be distributed through the article as plates or text figures. The latter are most economical when printed the same width as the printed page.

Proper proportions for the original drawing may be obtained by expanding on a diagonal line through a rectangle drawn to page size (Fig. 45).

Room must be allowed at the bottom of the page for the legend.   Figure numbers, letters, abbreviations, etc., should be put on neatly.   In order to be legible, letters should be $1\frac{1}{2}$ or $2 \times \frac{1}{16}$ in. or $\frac{3}{32}$ in. high, depending on the amount of reduction.   Freehand lettering is rarely satisfactory. Numbers and letters may be clipped from old calenders or standard characters printed on gummed paper, or they may be made by various mechanical lettering guides.   The editor, when determining the amount of reduction, is limited by the size of the page, the need for captions, and other considerations and is therefore often not in a position to follow the instructions of the author.   This is particularly true in the case of large figures.   Magnification or reduction should therefore not be stated on the figures themselves, but rather in the captions.

Where many illustrations are to be utilized, grouping is often required for economical reproduction.   For zinc etchings, drawings may be assembled into plates by merely arranging and pasting on a cardboard sheet. Colorless paste or rubber cement should be used.   The paper edges of individual drawings will not show.   For halftones, however, trimmed edges will show, and when several drawings are to be fitted together for a plate, a mechanical paper cutter should be used for trimming.   Slight discolorations, especially when yellowish, also become conspicuous in reproduction. It is usually more satisfactory to draw numbers and letters directly on the original, rather than pasting them on.   However, characters printed on transparent gummed paper are also available for halftone.   Photographs should be mounted with smooth edges touching and symmetrical, so that the engraver can rout out neat, straight lines.

Curves and graphs are reproduced by zinc etchings and largely used as text figures.   In preparing them for publication, the same instructions as to size, proportions, and lettering apply as for drawings.   However, they should be made either on white paper or blue-lined coordinate paper, never on green-, black-, red-, or yellow-lined paper unless the coordinates are to be reproduced.

Colored illustrations are the most complicated and most expensive to reproduce.   A screen similar to halftone screens is used, and several separate colors are used in printing, each one superimposed on the previous impressions.

Some scientific journals charge the author for cuts (approximately $10 per page for zinc cuts and $15 per page for copper halftone plates).   An author may be billed for the glossy paper if halftones are to be printed in a journal which normally employs a rough eggshell-surface paper.   This extra cost may include not only the paper but the hand labor involved in tipping in or pasting in the extra pages.

Offset printing obviates most of these difficulties because the entire page, included printed (or typed) matter and line cuts, is photographed on a plate and then rolled onto a second roller before it is printed on the final paper. Photographs are made separately because of differences in contrast and then are "stripped in" on the negative of the photolithographed page. By this method illustrations cost no more than printed matter.

It is a wise precaution to retain good, clear, photographic copies of all illustrations in the event that they are lost in the mail. A good photograph of a drawing is only slightly inferior to an original as a basis for reproduction.

Reprints. Reprints must be ordered at the time the proof is returned to the editor. It is advisable to order a much larger number of reprints of all papers that deal with general principles.

PART 3

ZOOLOGICAL NOMENCLATURE

CHAPTER 10

HISTORICAL AND PHILOSOPHIC BASIS OF NOMENCLATURE

The respective roles of classification and nomenclature are often misunderstood. The identification, delimitation, and ranking of taxonomic categories are zoological tasks. The role of nomenclature is merely to provide labels for these taxonomic categories in order to facilitate communication among biologists. We cannot speak of objects if they do not have names. Nomenclature (nō-men-clā-tūr) means a system of names. The term is derived from the Latin *nomen*, name, and *calare*, to call, and means literally to call by name. Nomenclature thus is the "language" of zoology, and the rules of nomenclature are its grammar. Nomenclature is a means to an end, not an end in itself. Since all zoologists work with animals and use their names, it is essential that the general principles of zoological nomenclature be familiar to all zoologists, whether they are systematists or not.

Zoological nomenclature, as stated above, is the language of the zoologist. To be a useful means of communication a language must be widespread, and the same words must have the same meaning to everyone. Universality and stability are therefore the principal objects of any nomenclature. Unfortunately, complete stability is impossible, since nomenclature involves the naming of taxonomic categories, and new discoveries are bound to change the concepts and limits of these categories. Scientific progress is therefore bound to lead to some name changing. A second group of name changes, which we shall discuss in the next chapter, is, however, independent of scientific progress.

THE ORIGIN OF THE BINOMINAL SYSTEM

Vernacular Names. There are in most languages more or less elaborate systems of nomenclature for animals and plants. A primitive tribe of Papuans in the mountains of northwestern New Guinea has 137 different names for the 138 species of local birds. Hunting peoples usually have a better knowledge of nature and consequently a richer taxonomic nomenclature than agricultural or particularly, urban peoples. The more conspicuous species of mammals, fishes, birds, and insects have names in all the languages of Europe. They are an accepted part of German, French, Spanish, and other languages. In English many of our so-called "common names" are of Anglo-Saxon origin. Those applied to major

201

groups of animals are usually short, frequently monosyllabic, as bear, finch, frog, bee, etc. Common names for species are often formed by modifying these group names with a descriptive noun or adjective, thus polar bear, brown bear, etc. These double names are binominal. Many of the better known species, however, were always uninominal: for example, among British birds, raven, rook, jay, (mag)pie, (jack)daw, robin, redwing, twite, linnet, nightingale, hoopoe, lapwing, quail, partridge, and many others; and among the butterflies, monarch, grayling, ringlet, peacock, comma, swallowtail, etc. Others were polynominal, such as small pearl-bordered fritillary, dark green fritillary, etc.

Such common, or vernacular, names have proved inadequate for scientific purposes, because they are different in the thousands of languages and dialects of the world. The same name is often applied to different organisms in different regions (*e.g.*, *robin*), or the same organism is known under different names in different areas. It is evident that it would be difficult to base a universal nomenclature of scientific names on the vernacular names of one of the living languages.

Scientific Names. Latin was the international language of European scholars of the Middle Ages, and the majority of scientific treatises up to the eighteenth century were written in that language. Modern scientific nomenclature is a direct descendent of the terminologies of the naturalists of the sixteenth to eighteenth centuries, who wrote in Latin. Linnaeus is to be credited with having standardized the system of scientific nomenclature. Even before Linnaeus there was a recognition of the categories *genus* and *species*, which in part goes back to the nomenclature of primitive peoples (Bartlett, 1940). Linnaeus based his generic concept on the concepts of Tournefort and Plumier, who in turn reformed the less rigid generic concepts of Brunfels and Bauhin. The generic names themselves often went back to names used by the Romans or Greeks.

Plato definitely recognized two categories, the genus ($\gamma\epsilon\nu\sigma$) and the species ($\epsilon\iota\delta\sigma$), and so did his pupil Aristotle (Chap. 1). The naturalists of the pre-Linnaean era were not consistent in the Latin names they gave to plants and animals. These names ranged all the way from uninominals (a generic name only) and binominals (a generic and a single trivial name) to polynominals (a generic name with several trivial epithets). The reason for this confusion was that they tried to combine two different functions in the name: naming (in the restricted sense of the word) and describing. A unique type of animal they might refer to with a uninominal (*Cantharis*). A species with relatives they might refer to with a qualifying adjective: *Musca carnivora, M. canum, M. equina* (Moufet, 1634). If they found that the original *M. carnivora* actually consisted of two species, a later author would refer to them as *M. carnivora major* and

M. carnivora minor. The specific name, whose function was diagnostic, evolved into a specific phrase. Eventually these phrase names became so elaborate and changed so often that the need arose for a simple "label" for each species. To satisfy this need, Linnaeus introduced a single "catchword" for each species, the *nomen triviale*. For instance, for the honey bee, *Apis pubescens, thorace subgriseo, abdomine fusco, pedibus posticis glabris utrinque margine ciliatis*, he introduced the trivial name *mellifera*; for other bees of the genus *Apis*, the names *surinamensis, longicornis*, and so forth. This simple system of a unique combination of two names for every species, often called the binominal system, was quickly accepted by zoologists. Linnaeus applied this system for the first time consistently to animals in 1758 in the tenth edition of his *Systema naturae*. This work was therefore designated in the International Rules as the starting point of zoological nomenclature.

CODES OF NOMENCLATURE

The simplicity of the binominal system proved tremendously stimulating to taxonomy. It gave anyone the authority to apply Latin names to organisms, and these names automatically had permanent status, either as valid names or as synonyms. If an author in the post-Linnaean period described an apparently new animal in the vernacular or in polynominals, as was done, for instance, by Daubenton, Sonnerat, Buffon, Latham, Brisson, and many other naturalists of that period, other taxonomists would rename these species according to the Linnaean system, that is, with Latin binominals. When finally (after 1800) virtually all authors had adopted the Linnaean system, a new source of confusion appeared: many authors decided to change existing names if they had not been correctly formed according to Greek or Latin grammar, or if the old name proved to be inapplicable (*e.g., brunneus* was changed to *viridis* because it was found that in life the animal was green). Geographical names were often changed when they were found to be inaccurate (*e.g., capensis* was changed to *indicus* if it was found that the species came from India rather than from the Cape of Good Hope). The result was nomenclatural confusion, if not anarchy. The need for a set of definite rules of nomenclature became clear. As a matter of fact, the need for a nomenclatural procedure had already been recognized by Linnaeus (1751), who formulated a personal set of rules. Fabricius (1778) followed with another personal code for entomological nomenclature, and Rudolphi (1801) did likewise for the naming of parasites. Here the matter rested for nearly half a century, during which time a large amount of work was published with little uniformity as to procedure. It was, however, acknowledged by most authors even at that early period that a name that was in prior use was not to be arbitrarily replaced by a subsequently published name.   Otherwise there was little uniformity.

The taxonomist in the middle of the twentieth century can hardly realize the "confusion of tongues" in zoological nomenclature during the the first half of the nineteenth century.   Owing to the disturbances caused by the Napoleonic wars, there had been a drastic reduction— almost a standstill—in exchange of scientific publications and periodicals. This led to ignorance of the publications of other countries and to the development of many local scientific nomenclatures.   As Strickland said in 1842,

If an English zoologist, for example, visits the museums and converses with the professors of France, he finds that their *scientific* language is almost as foreign to him as their *vernacular*.   Almost every specimen which he examines is labelled by a title which is unknown to him, and he feels that nothing short of continued residence in that country can make him conversant with her science.   If he proceeds thence to Germany or Russia, he is again at a loss, bewildered everywhere amidst the confusion of nomenclature, he returns in despair to his own country and to the museums and books to which he is accustomed.

Eventually the situation became so critical that the British Association for the Advancement of Science appointed a committee to draw up a general set of rules for zoological nomenclature.   The resulting code (Strickland, 1842), often referred to as the "Strickland Code" from the name of one of the committee members, was a brilliant piece of work for its time and formed the basis of all future codes.   In 1843 the Strickland Code was republished in France, Italy, and the United States.   Although scarcely international in scope, these rules fully justified Strickland's expressed hope, "that they may lead to sufficient uniformity of method in the future to rescue science from becoming a mere chaos of words."

The American Association for the Advancement of Science, thirty years later, appointed W̊. H. Dall as a committee of one "to obtain an expression from the working naturalists of America, in regard to the nature of a set of rules for facilitating the decision of questions relating to nomenclature."   The so-called "Dall Code" (Dall, 1877) is still one of the best essays on zoological nomenclature.   However, it was never formally adopted by the Association.

During the next two decades national codes were adopted by the Société Zoologique de France (1881) and by the Deutsche Zoologische Gesellschaft (1894).   In 1885 an excellent code for bird nomenclature was prepared by the American Ornithologists' Union (revised, 1908), and the International Congress of Geology adopted the so-called "Douvillé Code" (Douvillé, 1881), which set the procedure for naming fossils.

By this time it had become evident that zoological nomenclature was an international matter and could be handled only by an international set of rules. Hence the First International Zoological Congress, Paris, 1889, adopted a code proposed by Raphael Blanchard. This was actually the beginning of our present International Rules. The Second International Congress, Moscow, 1892, readopted the Blanchard Code, but unfortunately it was not generally accepted outside of France and America for nationalistic and perhaps other reasons.

Thus, in the year 1895, according to Stiles (1905),

English systematists were following the Strickland Code; French systematists were following the International Code; German systematists were following the German Code; American systematists were divided between the Stricklandian, the A.O.U., the Dall, and the International Codes; systematists in special groups were in some cases following special or even personal codes; and systematists of Italy, Russia, and some other countries were following either the International or some other code.

In an attempt to resolve this apparently hopeless confusion, an international committee of five members—R. Blanchard (Paris), J. V. Carus (Leipzig), F. A. Jentink (Leyden), P. L. Sclater (London), and C. W. Stiles (Washington)—was appointed by the Third International Zoological Congress, Leyden, 1895. This committee made a careful study of all existing codes and, after being increased to 15 members at the Fourth International Congress, Cambridge, 1898, finally brought forth the *Règles Internationales de la Nomenclature Zoologique*. These rules were adopted by the Fifth International Zoological Congress, Berlin, 1901, and were edited in French by Blanchard, in English by Stiles, and in German by Maehrenthal. The French text is the definitive text (Règles, 1905). At the Sixth Congress, Berne, 1904, the committee of 15 was made a permanent commission (later increased to 18) and served with changing membership for nearly half a century. At the Paris Congress, 1948, the limit on membership was removed, and provision was made for revision and codification of the rules.

The Rules became the universal code of nomenclature. At no time since they were formally adopted has a nationally biased system of nomenclature been established. The International Rules have thus been truly international.

THE INTERNATIONAL RULES

The International Rules of Zoological Nomenclature (also called International Code or simply the Code), as adopted by the Fifth International Zoological Congress (Berlin, 1901), consisted of 41 articles and 20 recommendations, dealing with family, generic, specific, and subspecific names, with their validity, formation, and orthography.[1] Articles 33 to 41 dealt

---

[1] For a detailed presentation and interpretation of the Rules as they were prior to the Paris decisions, see Richter, 1948.

with priority, others with the designation of types and the rejection of names. Various provisions of the International Rules are explained in detail in Chaps. 12 to 16.

All good law is living law. It affects the surrounding situation and, in turn, is affected by it. This is true for all codes of law, including the International Rules of Zoological Nomenclature. The adoption of the International Rules has helped not only to produce stability in nomenclature, but also to standardize certain taxonomic procedures. However, during the fifty years in which the rules have been in force, a number of contradictions and omissions have been discovered.

Major changes have involved the revision of articles or the adoption of new articles. Most of the changes in the International Rules up to 1948 were in the form of Opinions of the International Commission.

The Opinions, of which 194 have been rendered by the International Commission, are of several kinds. In most cases they attempt to rephrase obscurely worded articles of the Rules more clearly or to interpret them as applied to particularly difficult cases. A second type of Opinion deals with nomenclatural situations that were not covered by the original articles. A third type of Opinion reports special acts of the Commission, particularly suspensions of the Rules in particular cases (see also Van Cleave, 1943).

More basic changes in the articles have been adopted by vote of the International Commission and, after approval by the Section on Nomenclature, by formal vote of the International Congress in plenary session. On four occasions major changes of the rules have been adopted since 1901. The first was the refinement of the type method adopted by the Seventh International Zoological Congress at Boston. The principles involved, according to which the names of all categories up to the family are based on a type, are explained in Chap. 12.

The second major change, which was the immediate result of the nomenclatural upheaval created by the retroactive adoption of the type method, was the Plenary Powers Resolution (Monaco, 1913). It permits the suspension of the rules in any case where "the strict application of the rules will clearly result in greater confusion than uniformity."

The third major change was the modification of Art. 25 as adopted by the Budapest Congress in 1927. The original version of the Rules failed to require a mentioning of the differentiating characters of the genus, species, or subspecies in the formal description and, in the case of a generic name, the definite unambiguous designation of a type species. At Budapest it was decided that it would be mandatory after Dec. 31, 1930, to include in the formal description "a summary of characters [seu diagnosis; seu definition; seu condensed description] which differentiate or distinguish the genus or the species from other genera or species" and in the case of a genus, the definite unambiguous designation of a type species. The Article was interpreted differently by various authors, and an attempt was therefore made at the Paris Congress (see Chap. 11) to clarify this Article.

During the 47 years prior to 1948 that the International Rules were in effect, so much poorly digested case law had accumulated that a complete revision of the Rules was authorized at the Paris Congress (1948). Specifically, all interpretations of the Rules contained in Opinions and Declarations were incorporated into the Revised Rules, after which the Opinions and Declarations were repealed and canceled for all except historical purposes; numerous amendments, additions, and clarifications were adopted; the meaning of the expression *binary nomenclature* was fixed as exactly equivalent to *binominal nomenclature;* the term *indication* as used in Art. 25 was defined; rules were adopted for the first time relating to secondary homonyms and names for forms of less than subspecific rank; the status of names on the Official List of Generic Names in Zoology was clarified; and an Official List of Specific Trivial Names in Zoology was established. In addition, the composition and bylaws of the Commission were changed, the most important changes being removal of the limit to the number of commissioners and liberalizing of the voting procedure of the Commission. Three important subjects were deferred for consideration at the next meeting of the International Commission. These questions which are *sub judice* are (1) emendations, (2) the names of families and higher categories, and (3) neotypes.

Some of the Paris procedures and decisions have been criticized, especially the temporary suspension of the bylaws and the decisions on names for categories of less than subspecific rank, the treatment of secondary homonyms and of *nomina nuda*, and the retroactive change from the right of the first reviser to strict page and line precedence in determining priority. Presumably any of these criticisms that are substantiated will be considered at future meetings of the International Commission and will result in continued improvement of the International Rules.

RANGE OF AUTHORITY OF THE RULES

The International Rules of Zoological Nomenclature apply to both neozoology and paleozoology. Since there is no separate code for paleontological nomenclature, no nomenclatural dualism can develop. If a living species was first named on the basis of fossil material, the name is also valid for the living species. If a generic name has been used for a fossil animal, it cannot be used for a different genus of living animals, and vice versa.

There is a separate code for plant names, the International Rules of Botanical Nomenclature, which applies equally to recent and to fossil plants. Also, an International Bacteriological Code of Nomenclature was adopted in 1947 (Buchanan *et al.*, 1948). There are so many differences between these codes that it is unlikely that a uniform biological code will be adopted in the foreseeable future.

FUNCTIONS AND POWERS OF THE INTERNATIONAL COMMISSION

The International Commission on Zoological Nomenclature derives its authority from the International Congresses of Zoology, reporting at each meeting of the Congress through the Section on Nomenclature of the Congress. Although the actions of the Commission are submitted for formal ratification at the plenary session of each congress, the Commission is virtually independent and self-perpetuating, in the sense that it has full power to proceed about its business in intercongress periods. Deliberations take place in open meetings (Paris, 1948) in conjunction with meetings of the Congress or by correspondence in the intervals between congresses. Results are published in the *Bulletin of Zoological Nomenclature* and in other official publications of the Commission. The financial affairs of the Commission are handled through the International Trust for Zoological Nomenclature, which is incorporated under British law.

The functions of the International Commission are (1) to recommend to the Congress amendments or additions to the Rules; (2) to render opinions as to the interpretations of questions of zoological nomenclature in the Rules; (3) to compile the official lists of generic and trivial names in zoology; and (4) to use the plenary powers to set aside the International Rules when it would appear that greater confusion than uniformity would result from a strict application of the Rules.

Thus the International Commission is an authoritative body with power to interpret, amend, or suspend provisions of the Rules. Questions of nomenclature submitted to the Commission must be accompanied by a full statement of the history of the case, since the Commission is a board of review, not a fact-finding board. A petition for setting aside the rules must contain proof that strict application of the rules would result in greater confusion than stability. Furthermore, a well-documented petition to the International Commission should preferably bear the endorsement of one or more national or specialist committees on nomenclature.

NOMENCLATURE COMMITTEES

The fourth part of the Plenary Powers Resolution (Monaco, 1913), which was made a separate section of the Rules (Paris, 1948) states, "That the Congress fully approves the plan that has been inaugurated by the Commission of conferring with special committees from the special group involved in any given case, and that it authorizes and instructs the Commission to continue and extend this policy."

The first international committee on entomological nomenclature was formed at the First International Congress of Entomology at Brussels in 1910. Specific powers were given to this committee at the Second Congress (Oxford, 1912) as follows: to elect, in conjunction with the executive committee and the national committees, additional members as necessity arises, such election to be subject to the approval of the Congress following, but the additional members meanwhile having full voting power; to enter into communication with the entomological societies of the world, with a view of forming national committees on entomological nomenclature; to collect, in cooperation with the national committees, the opinions of entomologists on questions of nomenclature as affecting entomology; to consider what elucidations, extensions, and emendations, if any, are required in the International Rules of Zoological Nomenclature; and to present a report on these points before the next Congress of Entomology. Finally, the International Entomological Committee on Nomenclature was commissioned to communicate the above resolutions, unanimously carried, to the secretary of the International Commission on Zoological Nomenclature and to take such action as would ensure the adequate representation of entomology on the International Commission on Zoological Nomenclature (*Proc. 2d Congress:* **1914**:120–121).

National Committees. Various national committees have functioned at one time or another in various parts of the world. At present the nomenclature committee of the Society of Systematic Zoology is the most representative committee in America.

Specialist Committees in America. The better known nomenclature committees in special fields in America are those of the American Ornithological Union, the American Society of Mammalogists, the American Malacological Union, the Entomological Society of America, and the Joint Committee on Zoological Nomenclature for Paleontology in America. The first of these was the pioneer in the field of specialist committees, having prepared a code for ornithological nomenclature in 1885 and revised it on several occasions. At the present time the A.O.U. committee regularly considers proposals for name changes in birds.

Local Committees. Local nomenclature committees of societies and museums are too numerous to list, but a few of the better known American committees are the Washington, D.C., Nomenclature Discussion Group (composed of taxonomists of the U.S. National Museum, Bureau of Entomology and Plant Quarantine, U.S. Geological Survey, Fish and Wildlife Service, U.S. Public Health Service, etc.) and the nomenclature committee of the American Museum of Natural History. These committees have varied objectives, but in general they provide a focal point for questions on nomenclature and, most important, an opportunity for individuals to share ideas and discuss problems in this field.

ALTERNATE SYSTEMS OF NOMENCLATURE

In spite of the obvious advantage of the binominal system of nomenclature in fulfilling simultaneously two functions in relation to the names of animals (discreteness in the specific trivial name and expression of relationship in the generic name), the binominal system has several weaknesses. The first one is that the scientific name changes every time the generic classification of a species is changed. The second is that with the ever-increasing number of genera (by 1950 over 220,000 generic names had been proposed for animals), the generic name alone is no longer able to express position in the system.

At the time of Linnaeus, when less than a thousand generic names were sufficient for all the known animals, the Linnaean nomenclature ideally fulfilled its two functions. Now no zoologist can memorize more than a fraction of the names of the more than 100,000 valid genera. If a generic name is mentioned somewhere in a biological treatise, it is often difficult to determine to what higher category it belongs. For this reason several authors have proposed modifications of the present system in order to express the higher categories by prefixes or suffixes attached to the generic names.

Harting, who was apparently the first to suggest such a system, proposed the use of class suffixes combined with ordinal prefixes. Herrera (1899) advocated a system similar to that of Harting. He proposed to prefix generic names with a syllable to indicate class (Ins = Insecta), to terminate them with us or s, and to place behind the specific name initials to further help in placing the genus. In his system $Apis\ mellifera$ is written $Insapis\ mellifera$ (I, HY, A).

More recently Rhumbler (1910) followed by Heikertinger (1916, 1918) and Felt and Bishop (1926) suggested modifying the generic name with initial letters indicating class and order and terminations indicating subkingdom (us = Vertebrata, a = Invertebrata, um = Protozoa). Thus $Papilio$ becomes $Ylpapilia$ (Y = Insecta, l = Lepidoptera, a = Invertebrata). Further, specific trivial names were modified to indicate distribution with vowels indicating continents (e = North America), consonants indicating oceans, and combinations used for wider distribution (ae = Asia and America). Thus the squash bug ($Anasa\ tristis$) would be written $Yranasa\ etrista$.

Systems for locating names in their proper phylogenetic position have been proposed by Tornier (1898) and Felt (1934). Both these are based on classifying symbols combined into formulae. Tornier advocated the use of letter formulae to indicate higher categories and numerical designations for species. Thus, VROCZ, 2 = $Zamenis\ arenarius$ Boulenger (V = Vertebrate, R = Reptiles, O = Ophidia, C = Colubriidae, Z =

Zamenis). Felt used four-letter combinations based on the same system. Thus Ilre = Geometridae (I = Insecta, l = Lepidoptera, re = arbitrary designation for Geometridae).

Needham (1910, 1911) suggested a return to the Linnaean concept of all-inclusive genera designated by *fit* names, with subgenera, species, and varieties designated by simple combinations of letters and figures.

That none of these systems has been seriously considered by most workers indicates either that the present system is more satisfactory or that scientists are inherently conservative. Probably both factors are at work in maintaining the *status quo*, and it seems certain that our present system will continue for many years to come. The International Commission has considered the system of Herrera (and also that of Rhumbler) and has ruled (Opinion 72) that "designations of animals, according to the system proposed by Herrera . . . are formulae and not names. Accordingly they have no status in nomenclature, and are therefore not subject to consideration under the Law of Priority. No author is under obligation to cite these designations in any table of synonymy, index, or other list of names." A similar ruling (Opinion 132) applied to the "Gattungsbezeichnungen" of Sololew.

Viewed in the light of centuries, however, and with unforeseen millions of possible forms remaining to be described and named, a more mechanical system may eventually become necessary. Recent advances in the cataloguing of books, fingerprints, card files, etc., by means of mechanical sorting devices suggest that, should it ever become necessary, it may be possible to deal with problems of animal classification in a similar manner. Such a system, however, would presumably be supplementary to the present system of scientific names rather than replacing it. A system of symbols consisting of letters and numerals might be a more logical way of designating organisms, particularly if all were known, but it would have the serious disadvantage that long series of numerals are very difficult to remember.

CHAPTER 11

THE PRINCIPLE OF PRIORITY

Of all the rules of zoological nomenclature, the most difficult to formulate was the one determining which of two or more competing names should be chosen. Since it is obvious from the continuing argument that final acceptance of a principle has not yet been agreed upon, this problem will be discussed in detail.

During the lifetime of Linnaeus there was a fair degree of stability in nomenclature, since the authority of Linnaeus led to the general acceptance of the names proposed by him. Some of his successors, such as Fabricius among the entomologists, exerted a similar authority, but a great deal of arbitrariness in nomenclature characterized the period from 1780 to 1850. Owing to the French Revolution and the Napoleonic wars, this was also a period of disturbed communications, and taxonomists in one country were often unaware of the new species and genera described by taxonomists in other countries. Each author used his own judgment as to which names to adopt. The need for a replacement of this subjective method by one which was more objective became increasingly acute. The nomenclatural chaos prevalent at that period is not appreciated by those contemporary authors who blame the rules of nomenclature for all the evils of name changing. A clear distinction must be made between the need for rules to stabilize names and the specific rules which may be adopted for this purpose. If the current rules are deficient, this does not prove that rules, as such, are unnecessary.

The fathers of modern nomenclature, from Fabricius, Rudolphi, and Strickland on, thought that the subjectivity and arbitrariness of personal nomenclature could be abolished if an objective criterion were adopted. They believed that the continuous changing of names could be prevented if priority were adopted as a basic principle of nomenclature. Under this principle it would not be possible to change or replace an earlier name merely because it was incorrectly formed or misleading or for other personal, esthetic, or even scientific reasons. It is evident from much of the earliest writings on the subject that the "priority" these authors had in mind was a *priority of usage* rather than a *priority of publication*. However, admirable though the principle of priority of usage is, it is subjective, and so an attempt was made to restore objectivity by

212

replacing priority of usage with priority of publication. Unfortunately, while gaining objectivity, the nomenclaturists abandoned one of the most important objects of nomenclature, namely, stability.

It is not enough that the zoologists of all nations agree to have a single nomenclature. Essential as stability in space may be, it should be supplemented by stability in time. Ideally, if an animal is called *Turdus musicus* in 1850, it should also be *Turdus musicus* in 1900, in 1950, and forever. Furthermore, the name should not be used for any other animal. This would seem axiomatic. Actually, this particular scientific name (*Turdus musicus*) was used for one hundred and fifty years for the common European song thrush but about 1910 was shifted to the redwing (as it later turned out, quite unnecessarily). This is by no means an exceptional case; in fact, thousands of familiar species of animals have had their names changed in the past fifty years owing to a strict interpretation of the rule of priority of publication. It would be unfair, however, to blame all name changes on the law of priority. There are various reasons for name changes, discussed below.

REASONS FOR NAME CHANGES

There has been much confusion in the literature on the reasons for name changes. Some zoologists seem to be under the impression that every change of names is indicative of scientific progress. Actually there are two classes of name changes: (1) changes necessitated by scientific progress and (2) changes dictated by rules of nomenclature.

I. **Changes Necessitated by Scientific Progress.** These changes are inevitable regardless of the kind of rules of nomenclature that is in force. Such changes may be referred to as "scientific changes of names." Examples of such are the following:

A. *Change of Generic Component of the Binominal Resulting from Transfer of a Species from One Genus to Another.* The scientific name of a species, being compounded of the generic and specific epithet, will change if a species is transferred to a different genus. Usually there is one of three reasons for such a transfer:

1. A genus may be found to be heterogeneous and to require division into several genera, some of which may be new.

2. A species may be erroneously allocated to a genus *A* and subsequent research shows that it requires transfer to a previously named genus *B*.

3. Genus A is found to be the same as a previously named genus *B*, so that it becomes a synonym of *B*.

The change of name under (1) is caused by the dividing of a genus, under (3) by the combining of two genera, and under (2) by the transfer of a species from one genus to another. A change of the generic component of the species binominal is involved in all three cases.

B. Change of Specific Trivial Name Resulting from Transfer of a Species to a Different Genus. In cases (2) and (3) above, it is possible that the specific trivial name of the transferred species is already in use in genus *B* and that it therefore becomes homonymous. Since it is not permissible to have identical names for two different species in a single genus, obviously one of the two names will have to be replaced.

C. Synonymizing of Two Currently Accepted Species Names. It happens not infrequently that more detailed researches prove that two currently listed species are merely stages or phases (see Chap. 5) of a single species. Or in groups that have not yet been monographed, it may be found that workers in different parts of the world use different names for the same species. It is evident that one of these names will have to be synonymized. The reduction in the number of names in this case indicates scientific progress and is independent of the kind of rules accepted. Which of the two names is to be synonymized is, however, very much a matter of rules.

D. Analysis of Species Complexes. Under a single scientific name there is sometimes concealed a whole group of sibling species. For instance, the three *Anopheles* mosquito species, *messeae* Falleroni, *atroparvus* van Thiel, and *labranchiae* Falleroni, were listed until recently as *Anopheles maculipennis* Meigen. As soon as it was realized that several species were involved, it was inevitable that the undescribed sibling species had to have a name.

In all four cases (I*A*, I*B*, I*C*, I*D*), the name changes are caused by scientific progress, regardless of the particular rules of nomenclature in force.

II. Changes Dictated by Rules of Nomenclature. The criticism of the nontaxonomists (medical researchers, parasitologists, physiologists, geneticists, etc.) is on the whole directed against name changes that are not caused by scientific progress but result from the application of rules of nomenclature. Critics of such changes point out that there were no rules of nomenclature for the early taxonomists to follow, and that conscientious taxonomists of that period should not be penalized by retroactive application of our modern rules, especially when such action results in more confusion than uniformity in nomenclature.

A. Discovery of an Earlier Synonym. The discovery of an earlier synonym is a frequent source of trouble. If the name with priority of publication was a forgotten name at the time of its discovery, or if its original description was so poor that the identity could be determined only by examination of the type, the use of such a name appears to be open to particular criticism.

B. Discovery of an Earlier Homonym. Occasionally it is found that an earlier primary homonym exists for a well-known name in current use.

A name change is particularly difficult to defend if the senior homonym is no longer in the same genus and thus the main source of confusion has been removed.

C. Discovery of an Earlier Genotype Fixation. It may be discovered that an earlier author has priority of genotype fixation, and that he has selected a species which has been transferred in the meantime to another genus or has been selected as type of yet another genus. By adhering to priority of type fixation, a wholesale shift of generic names may result, as has indeed happened in numerous instances.

D. Discovery of Inapplicable Type Specimens. When the original description is vague, short, or otherwise lacking in essential diagnostic features, it may happen that the name is eventually applied to some species other than the original one. When subsequent authors supply the diagnostic details, such a name may become standard for a well-known species, until the original type specimen is reexamined and it is found that the name does not apply. Misidentified species are particularly critical when they have been designated as types of genera.

All four of these changes (II*A*, II*B*, II*C*, II*D*) have several features in common. First of all, they do not result in scientific progress. Secondly, all are the result of bibliographical or historical searches and not of biological analysis.

Name changing for the sake of priority started in 1842 with the adoption of the Strickland Code. Few accurate figures are available on the percentage of names that have had to be changed owing to application of the law of priority. The figure of 90 per cent that has been quoted for birds is undoubtedly too high. Since 1885, 77 species (28 per cent) of Fenno-Scandian carabids have had their names changed; since 1896, 35 species (11 per cent); and since 1939, 6 species. Many more will have to have their names changed if the recent proposals of Csiki and Jeannel are considered (Lindroth, 1949). Old names are still being continuously discovered, even in the most thoroughly studied groups of animals. These discoveries involve names of some of our most familiar species.

PRIORITY VERSUS CONTINUITY

In view of the nomenclatural upheaval caused by the strict application of the principle of priority of publication, zoologists began to rebel against "priority" soon after the proposal of the Strickland Code. As early as 1849 Darwin wrote to Strickland with regard to cirriped nomenclature, ". . . I believe if I were to follow the strict rule of priority more harm would be done than good . . . ." and this conviction has been shared by an increasing number of zoologists down to the present time.

As early as 1858, at the annual meeting of the German entomologists at Dresden, H. R. Schaum proposed that "no name should be replaced, if it had been in general use for 30 years or longer, even if subsequently an older name was discovered." He warned that "perhaps one-third of the currently used names, including some of the best known, might have to be changed if this rule of superannuation was not accepted." However, his warning was not heeded. We now know that Schaum actually underestimated the eventual results.

Schaum was not a lone dissenter. Indeed, the evidence indicates that the majority of the zoologists is and always has been opposed to the rigid application of the laws of priority. In 1911 the invertebrate taxonomist T. Mortensen took an opinion poll among Scandinavian zoologists; only two were in favor of a strict interpretation of the rule of priority, 120 were against it (*Ann. Mag. Nat. Hist.*, **8**:770, 1911). The Zoological Section of the British Association for the Advancement of Science took a poll in Great Britain. Of 112 votes cast, 26 were in favor of, 86 against, strict application of the priority rule. S. W. Williston reported at the Monaco meeting, "I think I am safe in saying that the majority of American zoologists is opposed to the rigid application of the law of priority" *Internatl. Cong. Zool. Proc.*, p. 827, 1913).

At the Paris Congress (1948) (see *Bul. Zool. Nomencl.*, **5**:5–18, 1950) the question of priority came up again. On the one hand a petition had been received from a group of American zoologists favoring a relatively strict application of priority. As opposed to this the Scandinavian zoologists presented a petition in which 63 of 71 signers favored protection of names in general use since 1850, and Viennese zoologists sent a communication favoring restriction of priority: "*Jeder heute einheitlich gebrauchte, eingelebte wissenshaftliche Tiername ist ein unschätzbarer nomenklatorischer Wert, ein Verständigungsmittel, dessen Zerstörung den Zoologiebetrieb schwer schädigt. Bis zur endgültigen Regelung der Verhältnisse ist daher jede Aenderung eines einheitlich gebrauchten Namens zu unterlassen, wenn für die Aenderung nur formal-nomenklatorische (Prioritäts-) Gründe, aber keine systematischen Notwendigkeiten vorliegen*" (*Bul. Zool. Nomencl.*, **5**:78, 1950).

In the ensuing discussion it developed that there was a unanimous feeling that a provision should be adopted to prevent the upsetting of well-established names solely through the strict application of the law of priority. Accordingly the Commission was invited "to consider generally the problem of how to secure greater stability in Zoological Nomenclature and to submit a report thereon, with proposals, to the next (Fourteenth) International Congress of Zoology."

The Continuity Principle. What alternative is there to strict priority? Despairing that priority will ever lead to stability, some taxonomists have recently proposed to replace priority by "continuity" (Heikertinger, 1943). A group of prominent German entomologists proposed the resolution, "No zoologist shall change a currently used name merely for the sake of priority. No zoologist shall use a name changed contrary to this rule." As laudable as many may consider the sentiment expressed in this proposal, such a rule would have serious practical difficulties. In popular groups like birds or butterflies it is usually easy to determine the currently used name. The scientific name of a species may well be cited more than a thousand times in a twenty-year period (hence the utter confusion resulting from changing such a universally used name!). In an obscure family of invertebrates, a rare species may not be mentioned more than once in a generation. What shall be considered the currently used names in such a group?

Even if the continuity principle were adopted, it still would have to rely heavily on priority. There are many cases in which monographers do not agree on the choice of the currently used names. Some monographers do work that is notoriously poor. Shall their conclusions then become the standard of nomenclature? Furthermore, there are some cases in which it develops that two currently used names refer to the same zoological category (species or genus). One or the other must be synonymized. Most of these cases cannot be decided without resorting to priority.

The zoologist thus seems to be caught between Scylla and Charybdis. The believers in continuity favor currently used names but have no objective method for determining which names are currently used. On the other hand, the adherents of rigid priority have an objective method but sacrifice to it one of the main objects of nomenclature, namely, stability. Furthermore, this method allows no unequivocally final nomenclature, because there is no guarantee, except for the Linnaean names of 1758, that a hitherto overlooked older name does not exist.

THE PLENARY POWERS

The International Commission attempted to solve this dilemma by means of a compromise. At the Monaco meeting in 1913, the International Congress conferred on the Commission plenary powers to suspend the law of priority in cases where "the strict application of the Rules would clearly result in greater confusion than uniformity." Thus the law of priority was retained, but a loophole was provided for special cases.

Unfortunately the Monaco Resolution did not settle the matter, because the procedure for setting aside the rules was too cumbersome. Applications for suspension of the Rules were required to give not less than one year's notice in two or more of a specified list of scientific journals, so that zoologists could present arguments for or against sus-

pension in each case. It was further required that the Commission's
vote be unanimously in favor of suspension, or, if only a two-thirds
majority of the full Commission were in favor, then, at the next International Congress, the president of the Section on Nomenclature was
required to select a special board of three members, consisting of one
member of the Commission who voted on each side of the question and
one ex-member of the Commission who had not expressed any public
opinion on the case, this special board to review the evidence and, by
majority vote, decide the question without further reference to the
Congress.

It is not surprising, in view of these difficulties, that the Monaco
Resolution contributed little toward the stabilization of zoological
nomenclature. Thousands of names were changed, while only 53 were
conserved by the Commission in the 35 years from 1913 to the Paris
meeting of the Commission in 1948. These names were added to the
Official List as *nomina conservanda*. Most zoologists felt that there were
far too few of these stabilizing decisions, and all zoologists agreed that the
amount of time required to process a case (as many as 15 years and never
less than 5 years) was too long, especially since the status of the name
remained in doubt during this time. The *modus operandi* broke down
completely during the Second World War when, for 13 years, the Commission did not meet. At the first postwar meeting (Paris, 1948) there
was a strong element that favored liberalizing the restrictions on the use
of the plenary powers, although there was also a petition from the propo-
nents of strict priority advocating further restrictions on the use of the
plenary powers.

The views of the former group prevailed. As a result the Monaco
Resolution was modified (see below) and it was decided (*Bul. Zool.
Nomencl.*, **4**:234–235, 1950) that (1) where a worker discovers that a well-
known name in common use, particularly a name of importance in
medicine, agriculture, veterinary science, or other applied fields of
biology, is invalid under either the rule of priority or the rule of homonymy or, in the case of a generic name, has as its type a species not
commonly accepted as referable to the genus in question, that worker
should at once report the case to the International Commission on
Zoological Nomenclature for such action as the Commission may deem to
be proper; (2) *that in such cases neither the worker by whom the error is
discovered nor any other worker shall substitute some other name for that in
common use, until such time as the decision on the future status of the name in
question is made known by the Commission.* This settled the status of
names during the period when they are *sub judice* and also placed the onus
on individual taxonomists to submit cases involving well-known names
in common use, particularly in medicine, agriculture, etc., *at once*. The

actual procedure is outlined in the revised wording of the Plenary Powers Resolution, which is in part as follows:

PLENARY POWERS RESOLUTION

Article I. Plenary power is herewith conferred upon the International Commission on Zoological Nomenclature, acting for this Congress, to suspend the Rules as applied to any given case, where in its judgment the strict application of the Rules will clearly result in greater confusion than uniformity, *provided,* however, that not less than six months' notice from the date of publication in Bulletin of Zoological Nomenclature, shall be given that the question of a possible suspension of the Rules as applied to such a case is under consideration, thereby making it possible for zoologists, particularly specialists in the group in question, to present arguments for or against the suspension under consideration; the notice to be published in the Bulletin of Zoological Nomenclature and in two other serials, of which one is to be a serial published in Europe and the other a serial published in America, the serials in question to be selected on each occasion by the Secretary to the Commission as being, in his opinion, the serials in which publication of the notice is best calculated to bring the subject matter of the notice to the attention of interested specialists; and *provided,* also, that the vote in the Commission is either unanimous or, if by a majority, then by a majority of the whole Commission or, when after a period of six months calculated from the date of dispatch by the Secretary to the Commission of voting papers in regard to the proposed case, not less than one-fourth of the total number of members of the Commission, calculated by reference to the number of such members as at the date on which the voting papers were so dispatched, record their votes on the said proposal or, without voting, signify their willingness to support the view of other members of the Commission, provided that, where the voting is not unanimous, such proposal shall require to receive at least two affirmative votes out of every three votes cast, in order to secure its adoption by the Commission. A decision taken by the Commission under their plenary powers is final and not subject to appeal.

Article 2. The foregoing authority refers especially to cases of the names of larval stages; the transference of names from one genus or species to another; the suppression for nomenclatorial purposes of some old long-forgotten or long-ignored work containing new names, the introduction of which would sink in synonymy names that are well established in current use; the suppression of any long-ignored name, or in the case of a generic name, any long-ignored type designation or type selection where the acceptance of that name or, as the case might be, that type designation or type selection, would in the first case sink in synonymy, or in the second case, sink in synonymy or alter the meaning to be attached to, some well-known name in current use; cases where confusion exists and is likely to persist through the impossibility, in the absence of the use of such powers, of determining the species to which a given specific or subspecific trivial name should be applied.

It is doubtful if the liberalized procedures inaugurated at Paris will solve the problem. The fact is that zoological nomenclature has become so intricate that an ever-increasing number of cases need to be referred to the Commission. Thus from 1907 to 1936, 133 cases were dealt with by the Commission (less than 5 per year). From 1936 to 1950, 218 decisions were reached (14 per year). At the present time (1951), 268 cases await decision, and new applications are being received at the rate of 8 per month (96 per year)! When one considers the fact that the Commissioners are scattered all over the world, that they serve without compensation, and that only a small proportion of the regular commissioners are able to attend the meetings which take place at five-year intervals, it becomes evident that the situation is very serious.

THE LAW OF PRIORITY

The law of priority covers the period from Jan. 1, 1758, to the present. Its basis is to be found in Art. 25 of the Rules and, as amended at Paris (1948), its essential provisions are that *the valid name of a genus or species can be only that name under which it was first designated, on the conditions*

1. That (prior to Jan. 1, 1931) this name was published (see below) and accompanied by an indication (see below) or a definition or a description, and, in the case of a generic or subgeneric name, that the genus or subgenus was monotypical or a type species was designated or indicated by the original author when publishing the name, or that the name, on being first published, was accompanied by no verbal definition or description, the only indication given being that provided by the citation under the generic or subgeneric name concerned of the names of one or more previously published nominal species; and

2. That the author has applied the principles of binominal nomenclature (see below).

3. That no generic name nor specific trivial name published after Dec. 31, 1930, shall have any status of availability (hence also of validity) under the Rules, unless and until it is published either

a. With a statement in words indicating the characters of the genus, species, or subspecies concerned (see Statement of Characters, below)

b. In the case of a name proposed as a substitute for a name which is invalid by reason of being a homonym, with a reference to the name which is thereby replaced (see Replacement of Junior Homonyms, later in this chapter)

c. In the case of a generic name or subgeneric name, with a type species designated or, as the case may be, indicated in accordance with one or other of the rules prescribed for determining the type species of a genus or subgenus upon the basis of the original publication (*i.e.*, Rules (*a*) to (*d*) in Art. 30; see below)

4. That even if a name satisfies all the requirements specified above, that name is not a valid name if it is rejected under the law of homonymy.

On the following pages the more important rulings of the Commission with respect to the law of priority are summarized. Many of these were first promulgated in connection with Opinions of the International Commission, but most are interpretations or new rulings made by the Commission at its Paris meeting in 1948. In order not to complicate unduly the wording of the law of priority, numerous special cases have been omitted. A full account of these will be found in Vol. 4 of the *Bulletin of Zoological Nomenclature*, pp. 1 to 760, and also in the revised Rules, which are scheduled for publication at an early date.

Publication. A scientific name becomes available through publication. What constitutes publication was not clearly specified in the original Rules, but the Commission has elucidated the question in several Opinions (15, 87, and 191). At the Paris meeting (1948) the International Commission clarified the definition of publication further. The Commission decided that a name made public prior to Dec. 31, 1950, is regarded as published only if it complies with both the following conditions: (1) it must be included in a document reproduced either by printing or by some other mechanical method of reproduction which secures that every copy is identical with every other copy; (2) the document in which the name is included must be a document issued for purposes of record and of consultation by interested persons and must accordingly not be issued for consideration by special persons, or for particular purposes or for only a limited time.

Further, in order to be regarded as published, any name made public after Dec. 31, 1950, must comply with all the following conditions: (1) it must have been made public in conditions which satisfy the requirements above; (2) the document containing the new name must be reproduced on paper and with ink of quality and durability sufficient to offer a reasonable prospect of permanency; (3) where a document is distributed by (or on behalf of) its author to certain selected persons, at least some copies must also be placed on sale or made available for issue free of charge to any institution or person who may apply for a copy.

Furthermore, it was recommended that publications carry a clear statement of the name of the institution or individual responsible for publishing the work or journal concerned, of the address from which the work or journal may be purchased, and of the price for which a copy may be obtained.

It was further specified by the Commission that none of the following types of action constitute publication: the anonymous issue, or the issue over initials only, of a work or paper after Dec. 31, 1950; the deposit of a document, however reproduced, in a public library or in the library of a scientific institution; the distribution of printers' proof sheets; the presentation of a paper before a meeting of any kind; the distribution of *separata* (preprints, offprints, etc.) in advance of the appearance of the paper in question in the journal for inclusion in which it was printed; the affixing of labels or tags on museum specimens.

The date of publication is the date on which the publication was mailed to subscribers or placed on sale or, where the whole edition is distributed free of charge, mailed to institutions and individuals to whom such free copies are normally distributed. The May issue of a journal which is actually mailed on June 22 is considered as published on June 22. In the last century journals were sometimes as much as six to ten months late. This is particularly misleading when the December issue of a journal is not mailed until the next year.

Even more confusing are many serial publications, parts of which sometimes continue to be issued over a period of twenty or thirty years. In such publications each part has a separate publication date, namely, the date on which it was actually mailed.

Sherborn and other bibliographers have devoted much time to discovering actual dates of publication. Valuable records of the dates of publication of many periodicals and series are found in the *Journal of the Society for the Bibliography of Natural History*, 1936–1949, Vols. 1 to 2.

Simultaneously Published Names. The International Rules, in the version valid for the 33 years from 1905 to 1948, decreed that if two or more names for the same taxonomic unit were published in the same article, these names were to be considered as published simultaneously. In such a case it was the privilege of the first reviser (Art. 28) to select one of these names as the valid one and to place the others in synonymy. This ruling permitted adoption of the more suitable or better known of the available names and had a beneficial effect on nomenclatural stability.

At the Paris meeting (1948) this rule was revoked and the following ruling was adopted with retroactive effect:

(1) If two or more names are published for the same taxonomic unit, or if the same name was published for more than one taxonomic unit in the same book or serial, so that the names were in consequence of identical date, the name printed on the earlier of the pages concerned is to have precedence; (2) if two or more such names are published on the same page, the name which appears on the line nearest to the top of the page is to have precedence; and (3) if two or more such names are printed in the same line, a name appearing earlier is to have precedence over any name appearing later in the same line.

Official Languages. Languages recommended for use in describing new systematic units are German, English, French, Italian, and Latin.

Indication. The International Commission on Zoological Nomenclature has also ruled on how the word *indication* in the law of priority is to be construed. With regard to specific names, an indication is a bibliographic reference, or a published figure (illustration), or a definite citation of an earlier name for which a new name is proposed. With regard to generic names, it has been decided than an indication is a bibliographical reference, or a definite citation of an earlier name for which a new name is proposed, or the citation of the names of one or more previously published species (Opinion 1 as amended at Paris, 1948). A generic name is not to be treated as having been published with an indication by virtue only of its having been published as the generic component of a species name cited in a synonymy given for a nominal species.

Further, in no case is the word *indication* to be construed as including museum labels, museum specimens, or vernacular names. However, the description of the work of an animal constitutes an indication even if unaccompanied by a description of the animal itself, provided that it satisfies the other provisions of Art. 25.

Binary vs. Binominal. It was ruled at Paris (1948) that the expression *nomenclature binaire* is completely synonymous with the expression *nomenclature binominale*, and that in order to qualify as an author who has applied the principles of binominal nomenclature, an author must have consistently applied those principles in the book or paper in question and not merely in a particular section or passage thereof.

Statement of Characters. Authors were urged (Paris, 1948), when drawing up descriptions, to give not only a diagnosis, but also a differential diagnosis, indicating (1) *in the case of a generic or subgeneric name*, the characters which separate the new genus or subgenus from the previously described genus or subgenus to which it is considered most closely related; (2) *in the case of a specific name*, the characters which separate the new species from the previously described species to which it is considered to be most closely allied, and, if that is a little-known species, the characters which separate the new species from a well-known or common species included in the genus; (3) *in the case of a subspecific name*, the characters which distinguish the new subspecies from the subspecies to which it is considered to be most closely allied, and, if that is a little-known subspecies, the characters which distinguish the new subspecies from a well-known or common subspecies of the species concerned.

Designation of a Type Species. A recommendation was passed by the Commission (Paris, 1948) urging every author, when publishing a name for a new genus or subgenus, (1) expressly to designate by name the type species; (2) when designating as the type a species the name of which has already been published, to cite that species, first under the original binominal combination, with a bibliographical reference to the place where it was published, and second under its new binominal combination, consisting of the new generic (or generic and subgeneric) name and the specific trivial name.

Designation of New Names. It is recommended that an author who publishes a name as new state definitely that it is new, and that this statement be made only in the first publication, thus: new species (or *species nova, n. sp., sp. n.*). The date of publication should not be added to the name in this first publication. Subsequent references should add the name of the author and date of publication at least once and preferably the first time the name appears. To further facilitate the work of cataloguers, most editors of scientific journals now set new names in boldface type, while the setting of all textual scientific names in italics has long been an established rule of editorial style.

Specific Names. For a further discussion of the requirements for validation of specific trivial names, see Chap. 13.

Rejection of Names. Names proposed under the Rules are available, *e.g.*, have a status in nomenclature. If they do not conform to the rules, they are *nomina nuda* and are unavailable and without standing in nomenclature. Even though available a name may not be valid, because it may have been previously used for some other group of animals (homonym), or it may stand for an animal already described under another name (synonym). Thus invalid names are of two types, homonyms and synonyms, both resulting from application of the law of priority.[1]

Synonyms. Synonyms are different names for one and the same thing. The oldest available name is the valid name and may be referred to as the *senior synonym* (Blackwelder, 1949) in contrast to *junior synonyms,* which are more recent and therefore invalid names.

In biology there are two quite distinct kinds of junior synonym. There are some which are clearly proposed for the same thing (new names for supposedly preoccupied names, and names based on the same specimens or illustrations) and are therefore absolutely synonymous; they can never be separated by any means. These are called *absolute synonyms, objective synonyms,* or *nomenclatural synonyms.*

There are other synonyms that are synonyms only in the opinion of one or more students. One person may lump two genera together, making the names synonyms; another may recognize them as two separate genera, making both names valid. Synonyms that are based on opinion are called *conditional synonyms, subjective synonyms,* or *zoological synonyms* (Blackwelder, 1949).

Homonyms. Homonyms are one and the same name for two or more different things. In the case of genera these are always unavailable, because, as pointed out previously, all generic names of animals are on an

---

[1] The International Commission on Zoological Nomenclature has stated (Opinion 107, Summary, in part), " . . . a name in current use is not to be supplanted by an earlier but rarely adopted or unadopted name unless the argument is unambiguous and unless the premises are not subject to differences of opinion . . . ."

equal footing and must stand on their own. Two genera in the animal kingdom with the same name would cause continual confusion.[1] However, the same name may be used for both a genus of plants and a genus of animals. At the species level identical specific trivial names are permissible, provided that they are not referred to the same nominal genus. When two names are found to be homonymous, the more recent name is said to be preoccupied by the older name.

A primary homonym exists when two scientific names, at the time of their original publication, consisted of the same combination of generic and specific trivial names: thus *X-us albus* Smith, 1910 and *X-us albus* Jones, 1920. In this case the latter is renamed, and *X-us albus* Jones is rejected and can never be revived, even though *X-us albus* Smith be subsequently removed to another genus, thus eliminating the conflict. If the original author of the preoccupied name is deceased, a dedicatory replacement name is often proposed, such as *X-us jonesi* Brown. If he is still alive, the procedure outlined in the Code of Ethics is to be followed (Chap. 17).

Secondary homonyms result either from the combination of two genera (*e.g.*, when *X-us* with its species *albus* is combined with *Y-us*, which also has a species *albus*) or from reclassification or taxonomic transference (*X-us albus* Smith is transferred to *Y-us*, which also has a species *albus*).

Homonyms may be classified in much the same way as synonyms, the oldest name being the *senior homonym* and the more recent name the *junior homonym*. To carry the analogy still further, secondary specific homonyms are comparable to conditional synonyms, in the sense that both are the result of revised classification or transference of species and hence are matters of opinion.

A type of homonymy which is rarely encountered is specific homonymy in connection with generic homonymy. For example, *Noctua variegata* Jung, 1792, represents an insect, and *N. variegata* Quoy and Gaimard, 1830, a bird. The International Commission has ruled (Paris, 1948) that in such cases the later published of the two specific trivial names is not to be rejected on grounds of homonymy.

The distinction between primary and secondary homonyms is an important one but is an oversimplification. Actually nine types of homonymy may be recognized (Blackwelder, 1948) (Table 14). *A*, *B*, *C*, and *D* are primary homonyms, and *E*, *F*, *G*, *H*, and *I* are secondary homonyms. Still another classification of homonyms (Blackwelder, 1948) is based on the criterion of current use at the time of discovery, in contrast to historical homonyms, or names which are not homonyms at the

---

[1] The International Commission on Zoological Nomenclature has taken action to eliminate the concurrent use of certain similar but *not* identical names in allied genera where obvious confusion would result.

time of discovery. *A*, *E*, and *F* are present homonyms, in contrast to all the others, which are historical homonyms.

At Paris (1948) the International Commission decided on a method of dealing with homonyms which involves both the above criteria, *i.e.*, the permanent replacement of primary homonyms whenever discovered, combined with the permanent replacement of secondary homonyms only

TABLE 14. TYPES OF HOMONYMS

A			B			C		
	X-us	*Y-us*		*X-us*	*Y-us*		*X-us*	*Y-us*
1800	*albus* F.		1800	*albus* F.		1800	*albus* F.	
1880		*albus* Smith	1880		*albus* Smith	1880		*albus* Smith
1900			1900			1900		
Present			Present			Present		

D			E			F		
	X-us	*Y-us*		*X-us*	*Y-us*		*X-us*	*Y-us*
1800	*albus* F.		1800		*albus* F.	1800		*albus* F.
1880		*albus* Smith	1880			1880	*albus* Smith	
1900			1900	*albus* Smith		1900		
Present			Present			Present		

G			H			I		
	X-us	*Y-us*		*X-us*	*Y-us*		*X-us*	*Y-us*
1800		*albus* F.	1800		*albus* F.	1800		*albus* F.
1880			1880	*albus* Smith		1880		
1900	*albus* Smith		1900			1900	*albus* Smith	
Present			Present			Present		

if discovered where the condition of homonymy exists. Thus in Table 14, cases *A*, *B*, *C*, *D*, *E*, and *F* would require new names at the present time, whereas *G*, *H*, and *I* would not.

According to Art. 35 of the International Rules as amended at Paris,

Where it is evident that two generic names either (1) consist of the same Latin word or of the same Latinized word (including proper names other than modern patronymics), or (2) are based upon the same modern patronymic, or (3) are based upon the name of the same continent, country, district, town or other place or upon the name of the same geographical feature such as a mountain, island, sea, river or lake, and the said generic names are distinguished from one another only by one or more of the under-mentioned differences in spelling, the two names are to be treated as homonyms of one another.

It was further ruled that this is an exhaustive provision, and therefore that no generic name which differs from another generic name in any other way is to be rejected as a homonym of that generic name (Table 15).

TABLE 15. DIFFERENCES IN SPELLING THAT ARE CONSIDERED HOMONYMOUS
The use of *ae*, *oe*, and *e*
The use of *ei*, *i*, and *y*
The transcription of the semivowel or consonantal "i" as "y," "ei," "ej," or "ij"
The use of "f" and "ph"
The use of "c" and "k"
The aspiration or nonaspiration of a consonant
The presence or absence of a *c* before a *t*
The use of a single or double consonant

The same rules apply to specific trivial names, except that differences in the termination of adjectives are to be ignored.

Replacement of Junior Homonyms. The Commission at its meeting in Paris passed a recommendation urging authors, when publishing substitute names, to give a full bibliographical reference to the name itself, its author, the date on which it was published, the title of the book or serial in which it was published, and the volume number (if any) or letter or other mark distinguishing the portion in which the name was published.

It was ruled at Paris (1948) that after Dec. 31, 1950, no replacement name for a secondary junior homonym is to be accepted unless the author of the new name clearly indicates that he believes that the species involved are congeneric. Prior to this date no such limitation is imposed.

A specific junior homonym should be renamed as follows: *X-us niger* Smith, new name (or *nomen novum*) for *X-us fuscus* Jones, 1860, *Trans. Ent. Soc.*, **6**:42, not Brown, 1800, Insects, p. 63.

Although primary homonyms are "stillborn and cannot be brought to life" (Art. 36), it has not been the practice of zoologists to rename junior homonyms if a synonym is available. This is certainly sound practice in the case of objective synonyms, *e.g.*, two species based upon the same type specimen, but this is of rare occurrence. Usually the available synonym is a subjective synonym and therefore is open to question and may be subject to removal from the synonymy. This situation has been the excuse for the unnecessary creation of hundreds of replacement names which have never been removed from synonymy. It is therefore better to wait before renaming a homonym with an available subjective synonym, until it is certain that the subjective synonym is not applicable. An exception to this procedure might be made in the case of genera that serve as types of higher categories.

Secondary subjective homonyms are created by the transfer of specific trivial names from one genus to another or by the union of two genera. Confusion may be caused by careless or loose handling of such situations.

For example, it may be stated simply that *X-us albus* Smith, 1900, is transferred to the genus *Y-us*, where it becomes a secondary homonym of *Y-us albus* Jones, 1880. But it is the actual combination of generic and specific trivial names that makes homonymy, so it has been argued that technically the homonymy does not exist until *X-us albus* Smith is cited as *Y-us albus* (Smith, 1900, not Jones, 1880). Still more subject to confusion is the situation when two genera are united. If it is simply stated that the two genera are synonymous without citing any species, it may be assumed that the types of the two genera were meant to be regarded as congeneric. The status of the remaining species of the two genera and the existence of homonymy, if any, must be inferred.

To obviate the above difficulties, it has been recommended that when a reviser creates a secondary homonym, he should expressly cite the two species concerned in the same genus; expressly list the later published of the two specific trivial names as a homonym; and give a new name to or resurrect an available name for the species the specific trivial name of which has been rejected.

Before proposing a new name as a replacement for one which is preoccupied, an author must make sure of the following four points:

1. That there is no other name available for the species (or genus). There have been a few nomenclaturists, of whom Embrik Strand was the most notorious, who have provided alternative names for all junior homonyms whenever a catalogue or nomenclator was published. Since most of these homonyms were already known to specialists, such wholesale renaming has resulted in nothing but an added burden in synonymies.

2. That the original author of the preoccupied name is no longer alive. The Code of Ethics is very specific on the renaming of preoccupied homonyms:

When it is noticed by any zoölogist that the generic or trivial name published by any living author as new is in reality a homonym, and therefore unavailable under Articles 34 and 36 of the International Rules, the proper action, from a standpoint of professional etiquette, is for said person to notify said author of the facts of the case, and to give said author ample opportunity to propose a substitute name.

A name proposed in violation of the Code of Ethics (Chap. 17) is available under the Rules, but it does not enhance the prestige of its author.

3. That the new name is proposed in the form recommended in the Rules. A new name is invalid and unavailable unless proposed in accordance with the provisions of Arts. 25 and 34 to 36. In accordance with the Paris recommendations, it is well to provide a full bibliographical reference (not merely "Smith 1907") to the original citation of the

preoccupied name and to name the type species, in the case of preoccupied generic names.

4. That it is desirable to propose the new name. If a new name is proposed for a species, it takes automatically the same type and the type locality of the preoccupied name. However, there are occasions when it is preferable to describe a new species (or subspecies) rather than to replace a preoccupied name with a *nomen novum*. This is true particularly if the type of the preoccupied name is no longer in existence, or if there is the slightest doubt as to the identity of the species with the preoccupied name.

For example, there are two species of shrike-billed flycatchers (*Clytorhynchus*) on Taviuni in the Fiji Islands which differ mainly in size. A specimen of one of these species was described by Layard in 1875 as *Pachycephala macrorhyncha* and transferred in 1876 to the genus *Clytorhynchus*. The original description was poor, and since the type was lost, some subsequent authors referred *macrorhyncha* to the large species (*nigrogularis*) of *Clytorhynchus*, others to the small one (*vitiensis*). Although the latter disposition of the name is presumably correct, Mayr (1933) preferred to describe the Taviuni subspecies of *vitiensis* as new (with an existing type), rather than to make a *nomen novum*, when it was discovered that *P. macrorhyncha* Layard 1875 was preoccupied by *P. macrorhyncha* Strickland 1849.

Under exceptional circumstances a homonym may provide an opportunity to shift an originally ill-chosen type locality of a subspecies. For example, let us assume that there is a species with a northern and a a southern subspecies, meeting in a narrow zone of intergradation. The type locality of the southern subspecies is far in the south, but the type locality of the population the name of which had always been applied to the northern subspecies is actually located in the zone of intergradation. If it is found that this name is preoccupied, it is better not to replace it, but to redescribe the northern subspecies and select a new type locality in the middle of its range. The number of cases where such a shift of type localities is desirable is undoubtedly very small. In the majority of the cases it would only be confusing.

The Names of Combined or Divided Categories. The question of priority among names for combined categories is resolved as follows:

A genus formed by the union of two or more genera or subgenera takes the oldest valid generic or subgeneric name of its components.

The same rule obtains when two or more species or subspecies are united to form a single species or subspecies.

When two families (or higher categories) are combined, the name of the oldest family is usually considered as the valid name of the composite family, not the name of the family with the oldest type genus, or the largest family, or the family with the best known name (this subject is *sub judice* at the present time).

The division of a taxonomic category is governed by the provisions of Art. 29, which states, "If the genus is divided into two or more restricted genera, its valid name must be retained for one of the restricted genera. If a type was originally established for said genus, the generic name is retained for the restricted genus containing said type." When a species is divided into several subspecies, the subspecies which contains the topotypical population becomes the *nominate* subspecies, *i.e.*, its subspecific trivial name is the same as the specific trivial name.

Linnaeus described the red-winged blackbird (*Agelaius phoeniceus*) on the basis of Catesby's drawings and description from South Carolina. South Carolina has therefore been fixed as the type locality. When this species was divided into several subspecies, the subspecies of eastern North America (including the region of South Carolina) became automatically the nominate subspecies, namely, *Agelaius phoeniceus phoeniceus* Linnaeus.

Occasionally authors create synonyms by ignoring this rule. For instance, Thienemann (1938) found that the well-known turbellarian worm, *Planaria alpina*, consisted of two subspecies. The northern one (northern Germany, Scandinavia) he called *septentrionalis;* the southern one (Alps) he called *meridionalis*. Since the species had been described originally from Scandinavia and the Alps, it is obvious that either *meridionalis* or *septentrionalis* is a synonym of the nominate subspecies *P. alpina alpina*, the type locality of which needs to be restricted to one of the two areas.

Emendations. Article 19 of the Rules states that the original orthography of a name is to be preserved unless an error of transcription (actually, *transliteration*), a *lapsus calami*, or a typographical error is evident. Emendations are intentional changes in the original orthography of a name made to correct a *lapsus* or error. As a result of the indiscriminate use of emendations, particularly during the nineteenth century, taxonomists are frequently confronted with a choice of several names for an animal. Articles 19 and 20 and various Opinions were intended to clarify the treatment of emendations but unfortunately have failed to do so because of ambiguous wording (Kirby, 1944).

The International Commission at Paris (1948) set this matter aside for full consideration at its next meeting but, without prejudice, agreed to recommend that in determining whether an error is evident, particular attention should be paid to evidence contained in the book or paper in which the name was first published. The following examples were cited to illustrate cases where the original spelling of a name should be emended:

1. In the case of modern patronymics, where the spelling of the scientific name is different from that of the person to whom the genus or species is dedicated, the spelling of the scientific name is to be emended. Example: the names *Ruppelia* Swainson, 1839, and *Rupellia* Swainson, 1839, are to be emended to *Rüppellia*, in view of the fact that this genus was dedicated to a zoologist named Rüppell.

2. In cases where an author founds a new name upon one or more Greek words but inadvertently makes an error in transliterating the Greek letters into the Latin alphabet, the error is to be corrected. Example: the inadvertent mistransliteration of the Greek letter *zeta* committed in the spelling of *Pentoxocera*, a name formed from the Greek words πεντα (five), οζος (branch), and κερας (horn), is to be corrected, and the spelling of this name is to be emended to *Pentozocera*.

3. When an author founds a new name upon one or more Greek words cited in the original publication, and one of the words proves to be spelled incorrectly, thus causing an error in the spelling of the scientific name, the spelling of the name is to be emended. Example: the authors of the generic name which was originally published as *Athlennes* stated that the name was based on a Greek word of similar spelling (*i.e.*, a word having the Greek letter *theta* as its second letter). In fact, however, the Greek word concerned has as its second letter the Greek letter *beta*. The spelling of this generic name is therefore to be emended to *Ablennes*.

4. When an author founds a specific trivial name upon the locality or district from which the type specimen was obtained, but as a result of misreading or miscopying the name of the locality publishes a name with erroneous spelling, the name is to be emended. When Gunther gave to a new fish the name *Leuciscus hakuensis*, he selected that specific trivial name because he had misread as Lake Hakou the locality of the type specimen of this species. In fact, however, the name of the type locality was Lake Hakone. In these circumstances, the specific trivial name *hakuensis* is to be emended to *hakonensis*.

5. When an author, in naming a new species, selects for its specific trivial name a word which, though adjectival in form, is not a recognized Latin adjective, and where that author uses for the nominative singular of that word the termination *ius* (masculine) or *ia* (feminine), these terminations are to be corrected to *eus* and *ea*, respectively. Example: the word *iridia* (published by Gibbons in 1855 as a new specific trivial name in the combination *Salmo iridia*), though adjectival in form, is not a recognized Latin adjective. The specific trivial name is, therefore, to be emended to *irideus* (masculine) and *iridea* (feminine).

Article 20 states that in forming names derived from languages in which the Latin alphabet is used, the exact original spelling, including diacritical marks, is to be retained. Examples: *Stålia*, etc. However, it is recommended that in proposing new names based on personal names which are written sometimes with ä, ö, or ü, at other times with ae, oe, and ue, authors should adopt ae, oe, and ue. Example: *muelleri* in preference to *mülleri*.

Blackwelder, Knight, and Sabrosky (1948) differentiate between emendations and errors. Emendations are defined as intentional changes, whereas errors are any changes that are not emendations. As interpreted in Opinion 29, errors are correctable and are to be treated as if corrected wherever they occur. They have no separate status in nomenclature, do not preoccupy, are not available as replacement names, and never acquire validity by citation in synonymy. Blackwelder, Knight, and Sabrosky (1948) cite as an example the generic name *Oxytelus* (Coleoptera), which has been written erroneously as *Cxytelus*, *Otylelus*, *Orytelus*, *Oxitelus*, *Oxyletus*, *Oxyteles*, *Oxyteius*, *Oxytellus*, *Oxeotelus*, *Oxytetus*, and *Oyxtelus*. These are all to be corrected and have no separate status.

Emendations, on the other hand, do have separate status, even if invalid at the time they are proposed. This point was clarified by the International Commission (Paris, 1948) as follows: (1) a generic name published as an invalid emendation of an earlier name (an emendation made otherwise than in accordance with Art. 19) is to be rejected as a synonym of the earlier name where that name is an available name, the type species of the later published nominal genus being automatically the same species as the type species of the earlier published nominal genus; (2) where the name of a genus is rejected as an invalid homonym, and the next oldest name is a name published as an invalid emendation of that name, and that invalid emendation is sufficiently different in spelling from the original name not to be a homonym thereof under the conditions contained in the third paragraph of Art. 35 as applied to Art. 34 by Opinion 147, the generic name originally published as an invalid emendation becomes an available name for the genus in question and has priority as from the date on which it was first published as an invalid emendation and is to be attributed to the author by whom it was so published.

Authority Citation for Scientific Names. Article 21 of the Rules states, "The author of a scientific name is that person who first publishes the name in connection with an indication, a definition, or a description unless it is clear from the contents of the publication that some other person is responsible for said name and its indication, definition, or description."

The word *responsible* in the above statement is particularly significant. The author's name following a scientific name is not intended as a means of awarding credit to the worker, but rather serves to fix responsibility for the name and to assist in locating its original description and eventually placing the species accurately.[1] In this same connection it should be remembered that, once a name is published the original author has no more right to the name than anyone else.

It is not required by the Rules that the author's name be quoted every time a scientific name is used. But "if it is desired to cite the author's name, this should follow the scientific name without interposition of any mark of punctuation" (Art. 22). This practice has now become so general that Pearse (1933) made the statement, "The scientific name of an animal consists of the genus, species, *and the name of* the author." Such a statement is misleading, because the code specifies that scientific names shall be ". . . . uninominal for subgenera and all higher groups, binominal for species, and trinominal for subspecies" (Art. 2). Hence the author's name cannot be regarded as part of the scientific name. However, a recommendation was passed at the Paris (1948) meeting of the International Commission to the effect that the authority for a name should be cited at least on the occasion of its first appearance in any publication.

Because of frequent advances in knowledge of the classification, it often becomes necessary to change species from one genus to another. Without the name of the author it is quite impossible to tell whether *X-us albus* is the original *albus* described in this genus by Smith or *X-us albus* Brown, *Z-us albus* Jones, or any one of a host of other species with the same name which may subsequently have been referred, correctly or incorrectly, to the genus *X-us*. It is customary to place in parentheses the name of an author of a species which has been transferred from one genus to another. This was apparently first sanctioned by the Strickland Code (1842) and is officially approved in the present International Rules as follows: "When a species is transferred to another than the original genus or the specific name is combined with any other generic name than that with which it was originally published, the name of the author of the specific name is retained in the notation but placed in parentheses" (Art. 23). Thus *X-us albus* Smith, when referred to the genus *Y-us*, becomes *Y-us albus* (Smith).

The Rules state that "if it is desired to cite the author of the new combination, his name follows the parenthesis." Thus when Jones transfers *X-us albus* Smith to the genus *Y-us*, it is permissible to cite the name as *Y-us albus* (Smith) Jones. Although this method of two-man authority

---

[1] Opinion 30 (International Commission) states that ". . . *responsibility* takes precedence over *credit* in publishing new names" and Opinion 49, that ". . . it is the sense of the Commission that the fundamental idea in citing an author's name is not in order to give him credit, but (1) to hold him responsible, and (2) as a bibliographic aid."

has been widely used by botanists for the past half-century, it has had little use in zoology. When botanists cite only a single authority, the name retained is often that of the author of the new combination rather than the original describer.

The rule dealing with parentheses has become rather onerous in recent years. Many species have been transferred repeatedly from one genus to another, and it often requires much time-consuming research to determine in what genus a species was first described. Typists and editors also tend to insert parentheses where they are not required, in order to restore "consistency." In view of these difficulties it was proposed by Osgood (1939) that this rule be made optional. Many recent authors have followed this advice. In large genera with uncertain nomenclature, and particularly those in which homonyms occur, the use of parentheses is a necessity. The rule should, of course, be rigidly followed in a strictly nomenclatural work, such as a check list, catalogue, or monograph.

With the vast increase in number of names and the inevitable transfer of specific trivial names from one nominal genus to another, it has become increasingly difficult to trace the history of the name of a species of animal. In an effort to facilitate bibliographical work in the future, it is recommended that all nomenclatural changes be made in a formal manner. This is obvious when new synonymy or new homonymy is involved (see pp. 227 to 229), but it is not so obvious, and is often handled carelessly, in the case of new combinations. In addition to the authority citation *X-us albus* (Smith) Jones, therefore, it is recommended that the words *new combination* be added at the time the combination is first proposed.

One of the problems arising from authority citation has been that of abbreviating author's names. During the first half-century of operation of our nomenclatural system, the number of authors' names was small enough so that distinctive abbreviations could be utilized without duplication or confusion. Thus *L.* stood for Linnaeus, and *F.* or *Fab.* indicated that the species was described by Fabricius. As the number of workers increased, these abbreviations were expanded to *Linn.* and *Fabr.*, but thousands of other less prominent names severely taxed the inventive minds of abbreviators and the memory of scientists called on to keep the numerous combinations of letters in mind. Toward the end of the nineteenth century an attempt was made by the Museum für Naturkunde in Berlin to standardize abbreviations, and the International Rules recommended (Art. 22) that this list be followed if abbreviations are to be used. At Paris the International Commission withdrew this recommendation on the grounds that the above-mentioned list was out of print and virtually unobtainable. In place of the above it was recommended that abbreviations not be used except in the case of deceased authors whose names, by reason of the importance of their published work, will be easily recognized even if abbreviated.

Special problems arise when an author changes his name during the period when he is actively publishing (Mitzmain to Mayne) or assumes a title (Laporte to le Comte de Castelnau). More common, of course, are the changes in name of women scientists at marriage. In the latter case it would be well to retain the maiden name as part of the full name which is cited, *e.g.*, Dorothy McKey-Fender, or to continue publishing under the maiden name.

Unfortunately the vanity of certain authors has sometimes been the cause of descriptions and the incentive for the excessive naming of species by persons who "like to see their names in print" or by those who are suffering from so-called "mihi itch." It has therefore been repeatedly suggested that the system be abolished entirely (*e.g.*, Darwin, 1849; Jacot, 1930, 1938; Ball, 1946). Although the sentiments underlying this proposal are understandable, the suggestion is not practical, for the following plainly utilitarian reasons: (1) authority citation makes it possible to distinguish between two or more different species with the same scientific name; (2) it gives an immediate clue to the original description and an indirect clue to the quality of work and to the location of the type specimen; and (3) it reveals something of the history of the name. In other words, the author's name is a link between nomenclature and classification; it is a tag by which a scientific name may be identified.

Certain well-known works of the late eighteenth century, for example, the *Vienna Catalogue* (1775), were published anonymously, and yet the names proposed therein were recognizable and came into general use. The International Commission (Paris, 1948) decided that when, prior to Jan. 1, 1951, a new name was published anonymously, over a pseudonym, or over initials only, that name was to be accepted if it satisfies the requirements of the law of priority. It was further ruled that such a name is not available if published on or after the above date unless it is republished by a named author, and the name shall rank for purposes of priority as from the date of republication.

CHAPTER 12

THE TYPE METHOD AND ITS SIGNIFICANCE

It is very difficult to characterize or to define a taxonomic entity solely by means of words. As a result, many of the Linnaean and early post-Linnaean species, particularly among the invertebrates, are unidentifiable on the basis of the description alone. It is obvious that more secure "standards" are needed to tie scientific names unequivocally to objective taxonomic entities. These standards are the *types*, and the method of using types to eliminate ambiguity is called the *type* method.

The modern type concept has developed slowly. The original draft of the International Rules (1901) did not include any directives concerning types. Provisions for generic types were adopted (Art. 30) at the Boston Congress (1907). As far as the types of species are concerned, they were first provided for in the Rules as a recommendation in Appendix A by the Monaco Congress (1913). Formal rules and recommendations regarding type specimens were adopted at the Paris Congress (1948).

The type of a species is a definite specimen, and the type of a genus or other higher category is a lower category. No matter how many new taxonomic categories and characters are discovered, the verbal definitions may be continuously modified and improved by reference to the types. In a group of sibling species, the type specimen of the earliest described species can be reexamined as soon as the minute differences of the species of the sibling complex are understood. In many groups of insects and arachnoids the emphasis in the species diagnosis has been shifted recently from exposed characters to concealed ones (genital armatures). Whenever types are available, it is an easy matter to check them for newly discovered taxonomic characters.

Early taxonomy was dominated by the typological concept (Chap. 1). All those specimens that conformed to the type were considered members of a species. Furthermore, all the specimens on which the original description was based were considered "typical" and thus regarded as types. The function of the types at that time was to form the basis of the description of the species.

The modern concept does not consider any specimen as typical in the strictest sense of the word. Subspecies and species are based on populations, and what is typical are mean values and ranges of variation. As Simpson (1945) has pointed out,

It is a natural but mistaken assumption that types are somehow typical, that is, characteristic, of the groups in which they are placed.   It is, of course, desirable that they should be typical because then they are less likely to be shifted about from group to group, carrying their names with them and upsetting nomenclature, but there is no requirement that a type be typical, and it frequently happens that it is quite aberrant.   Types are almost never really average specimens within a species, or fully central species in a genus.   Types were formerly, and still are by many students, supposed to be not only name-bearers but also the bases on which group concepts are erected and the standards of comparison for those concepts.   They cannot possibly serve either function in modern taxonomy and the requirements of these functions are flatly incompatible with the requirement of name-bearing which types can and do serve.

In spite of this concept, taxonomists still recognize types.   Only the function of the type has shifted.   It has happened thousands of times in the history of taxonomy that the material on which the original description of a species was based actually included several species, as revealed by more discriminating subsequent analysis.   If a single type specimen is available, it can be determined by reexamination of this type to which of the several species the name given by the original author should be applied.

The function of the type specimen has therefore been described as that of a "name bearer."   Simpson (1940) has actually suggested that one might drop the misleading term *type* and call the name-bearing specimen the *onomatophore* (Greek for name bearer).   The term *type*, however, is too firmly fixed in the taxonomic tradition for such a change of terms to be practical.

Since the type is the name bearer, it is obvious that it has full authority only if it is unique.   Ideally for every name of a species or subspecies there should be only a single type.   If there are two type specimens, there is danger that the second specimen may at some subsequent date be found to belong to a second species.   It would then be questionable to which of the two the name should be applied.

However, since a single type specimen cannot reflect the total variability of the species population, the description must be supplemented by information derived from a study of all the available material of a species.   To minimize the danger of a composite species description, a statement should be added as to how the type specimen differs from other specimens.   To draw attention to the significance of the total *material* used for description, Simpson (1940) has introduced the term *hypodigm*.   A *hypodigm* is all the available material of a species.   This term is mentioned here because it is occasionally used in the paleontological literature.   It is unlikely that it will replace the well-known and generally used term *material*.

The original type specimen is the last court of appeal in cases of doubt as to the applicability of a name. If a description and a type specimen seem to apply to different entities, the name should be assigned to the species to which the type specimen belongs, provided that it is certain that it is the type selected by the original describer. Unfortunately this is not always evident. It was, for example, customary in one or two European museums in the first half of the nineteenth century to substitute "new" type specimens when the old ones became faded or were damaged by insect pests. In other instances there are known cases of inadvertent transfer of labels from one specimen to another which have caused an obscuring of the identity of type specimens. However, a specimen labeled as the type should be accepted as such unless clear proof to the contrary exists.

TYPES OF SUBSPECIES

Types of subspecies are subject to the same rules as types of species. The type of a species is always simultaneously the type of its nominate subspecies.

KINDS OF TYPE SPECIMEN

In the early days, when taxonomy was still dominated by the typological concept of taxonomic categories, and when any specimen that agreed with the description was considered "typical," many authors had in their collection large series of "types," or "cotypes," or "syntypes." This system contributed to many of the ambiguities and difficulties described above. A transition period followed, during which the proper function of the type as a name bearer was realized, but authors were still anxious to have several types. They were reluctant to abandon special names for specimens that were significant because they had been identified by the original author or collected simultaneously with the holotype or for similar reasons.

Recognizing the danger of loose type designation, Waterhouse (see Thomas, 1893) proposed the restriction of the term *type* to a single specimen which was before the original describer and the use of the term *co-type* for each of the specimens when two or more were used as the basis for the description. This suggestion for defining various kinds of types more precisely was followed by Thomas (1893) in an article entitled, "Suggestions for the More Definite Use of the Word Type and its Compounds, as Denoting Specimens of a Greater or Lesser Degree of Authenticity." Thomas proposed the terms *paratype* (or *side type*) for the remaining specimens of the original series when one particular example had been selected as the type; *topotype* (or *place type*) for a specimen from the original locality; and *metatype* for a specimen from the original locality subsequently identified by the original author. Walsingham and Durrant (1896) added *homotype* for a specimen identified by another than the original author after comparison with the type and altered the meaning of *metatype* slightly to include any specimen subsequently identified by the original author of the species.

From these humble beginnings, growing out of a need for more exact designation of specimens which had served as a basis for previous work, a large body of type nomenclature quickly grew.

Frizzell (1933) and Fernald (1939) list, define, and give the authority for more than one hundred type terms. These may be divided into three main groups as follows: (1) primary types: the original specimens of any described or figured new species (including *holotypes, allotypes, paratypes, syntypes, lectotypes,* etc.); (2) supplementary types: the described or figured specimens used by any authors to supplement or correct knowledge of a previously defined species (including *neotypes, plesiotypes,* etc.); and (3) typical specimens: specimens that have not been used in published descriptions or figures, but which consist of material which "authors" have worked on or such as have been collected at the original locality (including *homotypes, metatypes, topotypes,* etc.)

Some of these kinds of types are classified and defined below:

I. Primary types

    A. *Holotype* (or simply *type*). The single specimen designated or indicated as "the type" by the original author at the time of publication of the original description or the only specimen known at the time of the original description.

    B. *Allotype.* A paratype of the opposite sex to the holotype which is designated or indicated as such.

    C. *Paratype.* A specimen other than the holotype which is before the author at the time of original description and which is designated as such or is clearly indicated as being a specimen upon which the original description was based.

    D. *Syntype* (= *cotype*). One of several specimens on which an author bases an original description when no single specimen is designated as the holotype.

    E. *Lectotype.* One of a series of syntypes which is selected subsequent to the original description and thenceforth serves as the definitive type of the species. In order to be effective, such selection must be made known through publication.

II. Supplementary types

    A. *Neotype.* A specimen selected as type subsequent to the original description in cases where the primary types are definitely known to be destroyed. Here again selection must be made known through publication.

    B. *Plesiotype.* A specimen or specimens on which subsequent descriptions or figures are based.

III. Typical specimens

    A. *Topotype.* A specimen not of the original type series collected at the type locality.

    B. *Metatype.* A specimen compared by the author of the species with the type and determined by him as conspecific with it.

    C. *Homotype.* A specimen compared by another than the author of a species with the type and determined by him to be conspecific with it.

The International Commission at its Paris meeting (1948) officially sanctioned the use of three kinds of types—holotypes, syntypes, and lectotypes—as being "available to supplement the characters noted in the original description." No action was taken at Paris on the subject of neotypes, but the secretary was instructed to prepare a full report on this subject for formal consideration at the next meeting of the Commission.

Actually most of this elaborate nomenclature of types is superfluous. As Williams (1940) has stated correctly, "There can be no possible reason for having any other type except a single one for each name." Only holotypes, syntypes, lectotypes, and neotypes have nomenclatural significance. On the other hand, a few of the additional terms for types mentioned above have proved useful on zoological grounds.

FIXATION OF TYPE SPECIMENS

Since nomenclaturally the information concerning type specimens is the most important information given with a description, it has become customary in taxonomic literature to record the type immediately after the description or immediately following the new name. In the latter case the information concerning the type takes the same place in the sequence as the synonymy in a redescription (Chap. 6).

Since in its modern interpretation the type is no longer the "most typical" specimen of the species, but rather the specimen to which the name of the species is anchored, the study of types has become of greater concern to nomenclature than to taxonomy. The International Commission has realized this and has therefore (Paris, 1948) inserted in the Rules a recommendation strongly urging that every author who publishes a description and gives a new name to a species should clearly designate a single specimen to be the holotype and should indicate in the original description (1) the full locality and other data on the labels attached to the specimen, (2) the sex of the specimen, (3) the developmental stage or form (if significant) to which the specimen is referable, (4) in the case of parasites, the name of the host species, (5) the name of the collector, (6) the collection in which the holotype is deposited and the collection number assigned to the specimen, (7) in the case of living species, the elevation or depth in meters above or below sea level at which the holotype was taken, (8) in the case of fossil species, the estimated geological age of the species. It was further recommended that the same principles be observed in publishing the selection of a lectotype.

Banks and Caudell (1912) suggest the following rules for the fixation of type specimens, to be applied in the order given. The following of these suggestions will eliminate many potential difficulties for later workers:

In the case of Coccids or other insects where the description is based on specimens in the natural condition, and on ones mounted on slides, the specimens in the natural condition may be considered as type material, and the slide (or one of the slides if there are more than one) as the type slide, but in case of doubt, or a mixture of species, the type slide shall retain the name.

In case of minute insects or acari where more than one specimen is mounted on a slide one should label but one slide as the type slide, and if there is doubt or a mixture of species it shall be treated as a case where the author has labeled more than one specimen as type.

The following rules apply for the fixation of types of species in the order given.

A. Author's fixation in the original description

a. If a specific name is based on but one specimen, that specimen is the type.

b. If an author labels or, in the original description, designates a certain specimen as type, that specimen is the type.

c. If an author in the original description designates a series or collection of specimens as type, then the type is among such designated material.

B. Fixation by others than the author, or by the author subsequent to the original description

d. A specimen to be chosen as type must be found among material presumably examined by the author at the time of its description.

e. The type shall not be selected from among material indicated in the original description as variational or aberrational nor from material doubtfully included in the species.

f. If it is anywhere stated in a work that a new species described therein is based on material wholly from a source other than the author's own collection, the type is to be selected from among such material.

g. If there are distributed to two or more collections specimens of a species all labeled by the author as types, or none labeled as type, the type should be selected from the specimens retained, if any, in the collection of the author. In case of a joint work the first author has precedence.

h. If two or more species are included in the original series of specimens upon which a new species has been based and the author has not labeled, nor has he nor anyone else designated one as type, nor restricted the type material, and it results that one of the included species is a synonym of an older valid species or has been afterwards (knowingly or unknowingly) described as a new species, then the type is restricted to the remaining material. Example.—*Alpha alba* Latreille 1831, described without type fixation from two specimens, *a* and *b*, which prove to represent two species, *a* proving to be the *Alpha brunnea* of Linnaeus 1758. Thus the type of *Alpha alba* Latreille is the specimen *b* by restriction according to the above rule. The same would have resulted had the species *a* been described as new prior to the type designation of *alba*.

i. The first intentional definite type designation in accord with the above rules is final. The mere reference to a specimen as type is not considered as type fixation.

Where the type of a species is lost, or destroyed, the first interpretation shall obtain unless later acquired information clearly proves it should be otherwise, when a change is allowable.

In cases where specimens have been labeled as types by others than the author of the species such type labels shall be interpreted independently by each investigator since there is much variation in the credibility of such labels.

A species based wholly on a figure has the original of that figure as the type.

The type of a specific name proposed to replace a preoccupied specific name is the same as the type of the name replaced, irrespective of any attached description.

In the case of fossil material, if the type consists of many individual pieces (*e.g.*, bones) it is advisable to designate the most diagnostic of them as type, if there is any doubt as to whether the pieces actually belong to a single individual. Many "types" of formerly described fossil species have, on reexamination, turned out to be composites of several different species. Designating a single piece as the type and other pieces as paratypes prevents the confusion created by such composite types.

The selection of lectotypes should be undertaken with great care. It is unethical for a curator who obtains by exchange a single syntype from the museum that has the entire syntypical series to make this single specimen the lectotype (see *g*, above). If the series of syntypes is heterogeneous, the same considerations should govern the selection of the lectotype as govern the selection of the holotype from the original material (see below). A selection of lectotypes should be undertaken only when it leads to the clarification of a taxonomic problem, not merely in order to add a type specimen to the collection. If one of the syntypes was illustrated it should—other things being equal—be selected as lectotype. If the description of the species is clearly based on a particular specimen, that specimen should be made the lectotype.

The following additional suggestions may be offered with regard to types:

1. Type designation and fixation should always be completed before publication.

2. Type designation should be clear and unambiguous; location and museum number of types should always be recorded.

3. Types of undescribed species should not be generally distributed prior to publication.

4. Type labels should never be changed or replaced.

5. Types should be carefully preserved.

6. Type fixation for species of older authors should be attempted only by a specialist.

MARKING TYPES IN COLLECTIONS

Since type specimens have a special significance and value, they should be marked with special labels (in most museums red labels are used).

If possible the label should give reference to the original publication. If the name is a synonym, this information may also be placed on the label. With small specimens such as insects and with material in special preservatives (alcohol, formalin), it is better to have this special information in a separate card catalog. See Chap. 4 for additional remarks on type collections.

TYPE LOCALITIES

Species can be identified by single specimens, subspecies usually only by adequate samples representing populations. It is immaterial for the status of the type specimen of a species from what part of the range of the species it comes, as long as it represents the species. The type locality is relatively unimportant at the species level. The reverse is true for subspecies, for which the type locality is much more important zoologically than the type specimen.

The type locality is the locality where the type specimen was collected. It is the locality where the population lives from which the type specimen was taken. Specimens collected at the type locality are called *topotypes*, and the population that occurs at the type locality is called the *topotypical population*. The taxonomic importance of this population is obvious. In view of the fact that populations as little as 400 ft. apart are sometimes visibly distinct (Welch, 1938) and that genetic tests have shown that populations only a few miles apart (*Drosophila*) or only a few feet apart (some ecotypes in plants) may be different, it is important that the type locality be fixed with extreme accuracy. This is even more critical in paleontology, where a few inches may mark a change from one horizon to another.

The type locality can usually be fixed only as accurately as is permitted by the data given on the labels of the specimens. Hence the importance of accurate labeling (Chap. 3). If the collector is still alive, it is sometimes possible to obtain from him more precise data than are available on the locality labels. In other cases such information may be found in published or unpublished journals or field books.

The Selection of a Type Locality. Often a worker has before him material from many localities within the range of a new species or subspecies. It is his duty to make as prudent a choice of type locality as is possible. In this he should be guided by the following considerations, among others:

It is advisable to choose a type locality from which many topotypes are available which constitute a fair sample of the population and illustrate its variation.

In the case of a variable species or subspecies, the type locality should be placed in the area from which the populations come which the describer considers most typical for the new form.

If a new subspecies is composed of populations which, together with populations of another subspecies, form a cline, the type locality should be placed as near as possible to that end of this character gradient which is most distant from the other subspecies.

Type localities should not be selected from areas of intergradation or hybridization.

The Restriction of Designated Type Localities.   Earlier authors, not appreciating the need for exact type localities, often described new species from "California" or "Brazil" or "Africa." When later collections indicate that the species from "Brazil" is geographically variable and consists of two or more subspecies, it becomes necessary to determine the exact locality from which the type of the nominate subspecies came.

The International Rules do not contain any provisions governing the secondary restriction of a designated type locality.   However, many workers accept the principle that the "first reviser," the person who first realizes the geographical variability of such a species, has the right to designate arbitrarily a more restricted type locality, provided that evidence derived from a study of the type itself does not contradict his selection.   Such a fixation is usually followed, unless it can be shown that the action of the first reviser was erroneous.   Obviously, if the first reviser restricts to Rio de Janeiro the type locality of a species from "Brazil," his restriction should not be binding if the type is still in existence and belongs to a subspecies which is confined to the neighborhood of Cayenne.   To avoid such mistakes, the first reviser should make a careful investigation of the probable route of the collector.   Even in the absence of exact information, certain conclusions may be obvious.   Thus a type collected in China in 1775 most likely came from Canton or some part of Fukien, not from Szechuan, Kansu, or some other place far in the interior.

In the case of a "voyage" it is often possible to determine the exact locality by a study of the course of the voyage.   For example, a small owl, *Ninox ocellata*, collected by the Voyage au Pôle Sud was described by Hombron and Jacquinot as having come from Chile, South America. This is an obvious error, since the genus does not occur in America. Later on, Mathews, believing *ocellata* to be an earlier name of *N. roseo-axillaris* Hartert 1929 (San Cristobal, Solomon Islands), restricted the type locality of *ocellata* to San Cristobal.   However, it is stated in the report of the Voyage au Pôle Sud that the expedition landed in the Solomon Islands only on Ysabel Island (and adjacent St. George), where no owl resembling *ocellata* occurs.   Mathews's restriction of the type locality is therefore untenable.   Subsequently it was shown by Peters that the Coburg Peninsula, Northern Territory, Australia, is the only locality touched by the Voyage au Pôle Sud where an owl occurs that agrees with the description of *N. ocellata*. Peters therefore restricted the type locality to Coburg Peninsula, and this restriction has been universally accepted. The restricting of type localities should normally be reserved for a specialist.

Correction of Wrong Type Locality. There are two sets of circumstances under which an error in the originally stated selection of the type locality can be corrected:

1. Exact type locality given in the original description. If the author or some subsequent worker can prove beyond doubt that the type(s) did not come from the locality given in the original description (owing to some error or misinformation), he can shift the type locality to the place from which the type really came. Actually this is not a shift of the type locality but only of the "stated" type locality, since the type never came from the originally designated locality.

The type locality should not be altered because an author finds that the population at a different locality is "more typical" or because he has received "better material" from a new locality. Proposals for the shift of type localities for these and similar reasons should be rejected.

2. Exact type locality not given in the original description. If no type locality is given, or only a vague one ("India"), the first reviser may designate a restricted type locality. Such a restriction may later be set aside if it conflicts with the available evidence. Such an action is justifiable, however, only if the case is unequivocal. A fixation of type locality should not be set aside because that locality, at the time of the collection, was "less accessible" than some other locality, or because the species is "rather rare" at that locality. It should be changed, however, if it is clearly outside the range of the species.

TYPES OF HIGHER CATEGORIES

The types of higher categories are not definite specimens, as are types of species, nor are they the names of other categories. The type of a genus is a species. The type of a tribe or family is a genus. The procedures that govern the selection of these types are explained in Chaps. 14 and 15.

CHAPTER 13

SPECIFIC AND INFRASPECIFIC NAMES

Scientific names in zoology are of five kinds, each kind or group of names differing in form and method of treatment. The five groups of names are as follows:

1. Specific group: specific and subspecific trivial names
2. Infrasubspecific group: names for individual variants
3. Generic group: generic and subgeneric names
4. Family group: names for categories above the genus and below the suborder
5. Order, class, and phylum group: names for categories above the superfamily

In the following chapters it will be seen that each of these groups is distinct and is subject to a more or less independent set of rules or nomenclatural practices.

THE SPECIFIC GROUP OF NAMES

In order to understand the terminology of the specific group of names, a short historical survey may be helpful. Authors before Ray made no clear distinction between genus and species. When referring to an animal or a plant they used indiscriminately mononominals, binominals, or polynominals. Linnaeus not only accepted Ray's distinction of genus and species but also expressed it in his scientific names. The polynominal specific name was for Linnaeus a differential diagnosis, a word which does not occur in Linnaeus's writings. "The specific name was a series of descriptive words (*differentiae specificae*) selected according to rules laid down in *Philosophia botanica*, by which each species was to be differentiated at first glance from all others in the genus" (Svenson, 1945). These polynominal *differentiae* were not fixed but had to be elaborated and changed each time a new species was added to the genus. This procedure is equivalent to the modern practice of altering a diagnostic key when additional species are discovered. It is interesting to compare the changes in the *differentiae specificae* for the same species from the pre-Linnaean authors to Linnaeus and through the various editions of the works of Linnaeus.

246

As these names became more and more elaborate, they performed their function as diagnoses more and more efficiently.   However, the foremost function of a name, to serve as an identifying label, was sacrificed to this diagnostic perfection.   To satisfy the evident need for such a "label" for each species, Linnaeus introduced the *nomen triviale*.   At first (1749) these trivial names were one of the words of the *differentiae specificae*, singled out by means of either italics or parentheses.   In the *Species plantarum* (1753) trivial names were employed consistently but were placed in the margin of the page.   For animals this method was employed for the first time in the tenth edition of the *Systema naturae* (1758).

Having a different function, the trivial name was for Linnaeus merely an accessory to the *differentiae specificae*.   The Latin word *triviale* means "commonplace," and it is evident from his discussions in the *Philosophia botanica* and the *Incrementa botanices* that Linnaeus considered trivial names merely a convenient device and of no scientific significance.   So useful was the new device of a unique binominal combination for every species, however, that it soon became the best known element of nomenclature.   As a result, the specific name of Linnaeus, consisting of the generic name and the *differentiae specificae*, was speedily replaced by the combination of generic name and *nomen triviale*.   Furthermore, it soon became customary to call the trivial name the *specific name*.   In the transition period Murray (1784) stated that the binominal consisted of (1) a generic *cognomen gentilitium*, and (2) a specific *praenomen triviale*. The replacement of *trivial* by *specific* became so universal by 1800 that the original Linnaean usage of the terms was almost entirely forgotten by the taxonomists.   For instance, De Candolle stated in 1813: "Linné . . . proposes . . . that the name of an organism shall be composed of two words: the first he called the generic name . . . and the second, which he called specific, should be unique [*propre*] for each species of the genus."

The obsolescence of the term *trivial name* was in part due to the change of function of the scientific name from that of a diagnosis to that of a handle.   The change of terms thus signified an important evolution in the philosophy of nomenclature.   The portion of the binominal which *specifies* the species is *specific*, and a precise counterpart to the *grouping* component, the *generic* name.   The use of *trivial* was very unfortunate anyhow, since it means *trifling* in some languages.   Furthermore, in most European languages the term *trivial name* is synonymous with *vernacular name*.   It is therefore not surprising that the term *trivial* fell into virtual oblivion in zoology after 1800, being used only in a few nomenclatural and antiquarian works.

The standard usage of a "scientific name (or species binominal), consisting of a generic and specific name" was adopted by all major codes of nomenclature from the Strickland Code (1842) and the A.O.U. Code (1889) to the International Rules (1901).

This usage, which has been stabilized for one hundred and fifty years, was changed by the Commission in Paris (1948) where the term *trivial* was reintroduced and the term *specific name* was shifted from the specific epithet to the species binominal. There has been much criticism of this shift, particularly by those Europeans in whose language *trivial* name means *vernacular name*. In this text the authors have endeavored to choose wordings that will prevent a confusion of the two usages of *specific name*.

Specific trivial names are the fixed portion of the binominal designation (scientific name) of an organism and follow the species through all of the vagaries of its classification. A specific trivial name may be synonymized, may be referred to any one of a dozen or more genera, or may even be shifted from one order or class to another without change, provided that it was properly formed and has never been used previously in any of the genera to which it is referred. Subspecific trivial names have the the same status as specific trivial names (Art. 35).

Specific trivial names are formed either from Latin words or from other words or combinations of letters which are Latinized. Ideally they should be short, descriptive, euphonious, and easy to pronounce. Practically, however, it should be remembered that names are not definitions, nor are they descriptions. They are merely "handles by which the objects are known." Hence, in the last analysis, any name, once published, might as well be regarded simply as an arbitrary combination of letters, because the law of priority rules that it cannot be changed except in rare instances, regardless of how ill chosen or inappropriate it may be.

In order to be *available* under the Rules, the designation of the scientific name of a species of animals has to satisfy certain conditions:

1. It must be binominal (or, in case of subspecies, trinominal).

2. It must be accompanied by a description (or indication or definition) (see Chap. 11).

3. It must be properly published (see Chap. 11).

4. It must be based on a taxonomic entity.

5. It must be a name.

Even if it satisfies the above conditions, the name of a species may be *invalid*.

6. If the same specific trivial name has been used previously in the same genus (homonym).

7. If an earlier name for the taxonomic entity (species or subspecies) is available (synonym). For a discussion of (6) and (7) see Chap. 11.[1]

[1] For a classification of species names in zoological nomenclature see H. M. Smith (1945).

The following comments on the above listed conditions may be helpful:

1. **Binominal Nomenclature.** The expression *binomial nomenclature* is commonly used to describe the system established by Linnaeus in 1758. However, the term *binominal* was used in Art. 2 of the International Rules: "The scientific designation of animals is uninominal for subgenera and all higher groups, binominal for species and trinominal for subspecies." This statement seems perfectly clear, but the issue was confused by the provision in Art. 25 that an author must apply "the principles of binary nomenclature." Thus zoologists were confronted with three more or less equivalent terms, *binomial*, *binominal*, and *binary*, none of which was precisely defined. It has been stated that a "phraseology of a deliberately ambiguous character" (Hemming, *Bul. Zool. Nomencl.*, **5**:155, 1950) was used so that zoologists could either accept or reject generic names proposed by nonbinominal authors. This confusion was cleared up at Paris when the Commission ruled that the expression *nomenclature binaire* is exactly equivalent to the expression *nomenclature binominale*. It was further ruled that an author must consistently apply the principles of binominal nomenclature throughout a given work. This rules out many of the early post-Linnaean authors who used single-word names and multiple-word names intermixed with binominal combinations.

Subgeneric names are not considered as part of the binominal combination. The combination *Passerella* (*Melospiza*) *melodia* is still considered binominal, because the parenthetical treatment of *Melospiza* takes it out of the actual combination. Nor does the addition of the author's name change the binominal status of a scientific name, because the author's name is not part of the scientific name.

2. **Nomina nuda.** A published name which does not meet the requirements of Art. 25 of the Rules as amended at Paris (1948) is called a *nomen nudum*.

Opinion 78 states that the citing of another author's manuscript name in the synonymy of a valid name constitutes an "indication" as demanded by Art. 25. This decision has been severely criticized, and Hemming, in his reissue of Opinion 4 (1944), states that

. . . in some groups the number of manuscript names and *nomina nuda* made available nomenclatorially through being published as synonyms of described names is very large. In most cases such names constitute a heavy, expensive and unnecessary burden on the systematics of the group concerned.

A petition to the International Commission is now pending to reverse the decision expressed in Opinion 78.

3. **Pre-Linnaean Names.** Names published prior to Jan. 1, 1758, are *pre-Linnaean* names and have no status. They do not become eligible

simply by being cited or reprinted with the original diagnosis. Not even the citation in synonymy or in a bibliographical reference after Jan. 1, 1758, establishes a pre-Linnaean name (Opinion 5). The citation of pre-Linnaean names in synonymies in the tenth (and later) editions of Linnaeus's *Systema naturae* does not make such names valid substitute names. Linnaeus and post-Linnaean authors have sometimes adopted pre-Linnaean names (*e.g., Turdus pilaris* Linnaeus, 1758 ex *Turdus pilaris* Gesner, 1551). Such names date from the time of adoption and are attributed to the new author.

Setting the year 1758 (arbitrarily fixed as Jan. 1, 1758) as the starting point for the law of priority deprived many excellent pre-Linnaean zoologists of the authorship of the new species found and described by them. However, the fixing of a base line for nomenclature was essential, and the tenth edition of the *Systema naturae* (1758) was the first publication in which binominal nomenclature was consistenly employed. To admit occasional pre-Linnaean names because they are binominal would lead to endless disputes and great nomenclatural uncertainty. However, at Paris (1948), an exception was made in the case of Clerck's *Aranei svecici* (1757) (*Bul. Zool. Nomencl.,* **4**:274, 315).

4. **Nomina dubia.** It was decided at Paris (1948) (*Bul. Zool. Nomencl.,* **4**:76, 1950) that where specialists are agreed that the available evidence is insufficient to permit the identification of a species, the name is to be treated as a *nomen dubium* and therefore not available for taxonomic purposes. It was further stated that where specialists disagree, the question at issue is to be referred to the International Commission for decision.

5. **Hypothetical Names.** Names for hypothetical or mythical forms have no status in nomenclature. A name in the sense of the Rules refers to the designation by which the actual objects are known. The objects themselves are named, not our conception of these objects (Opinion 2).

For instance, the name *Pithecanthropus* Haeckel, 1866, was based on a hypothetical missing link between ape and man. It has therefore no status under the Rules and does not invalidate the name *Pithecanthropus* Dubois, 1894, based on actual specimens.

6. **Status of Symbols and Formulae.** The scientific names of animals must be words which are either Latin or Latinized or are considered and treated as such in case they are not of classic origin. Symbols, numbers, and formulae have no status in nomenclature (Opinions 64, 72, etc.).

The Rules of Nomenclature mention two further categories of names of species.

a. Species inquirendae. These are species the taxonomic position of which was in doubt at the time of the original publication of a generic name, either because the species concerned were unknown to the author or because of difficulties in identifying the species.

b. Nomina rejecta. The proceedings of the Ninth International Congress at Monaco (1913) contain a list of permanently rejected names. Unfortunately this list was not kept up to date during the years when the Official List was being augmented. However, in 1948 the Commission recognized the need for separate lists of names which had been rejected by the Commission under the plenary powers. Accordingly official indexes were prepared of rejected and invalid generic and specific trivial names in zoology. Eighty-six generic names and thirty-six specific trivial names were placed on the list at Paris (*Bul. Zool. Nomencl.,* **4**:694–698).

FORMATION OF SPECIFIC TRIVIAL NAMES

In order to assist in proposing new names, certain simple rules of Latin grammar are given below, together with examples of the formation of specific trivial names of each type. Words taken from a Latin dictionary will be adjectives, nouns, or verbs or their participles.

Adjectives. If an adjectival name has been selected as a specific trivial name, the International Rules state that it "must agree grammatically with the generic name" (Art. 14). Thus the descriptive adjective *albus,* meaning white, retains its *us* ending if referred to a masculine genus (*Turdus albus*) but changes to an *a* ending if the genus is feminine (*Muscicapa alba*) and to a *um* ending if the genus is neuter (*Dicaeum album*). This is the simplest case of an adjective of the first or second declension. Adjectives of the third declension end in *is,* masculine and feminine (*Cervus brevis, Rana brevis*), and in *e,* neuter (*Therium breve*).

It is sometimes difficult to determine the gender of the name of the genus to which the new species is to be referred. Particularly confusing to students without training in the classical languages are such names as *Venus,* a feminine name with a masculine ending (*Venus maculata* Linnaeus) and *Conosoma,* a Greek neuter with an ending which in Latin usually indicates the feminine gender. In this last case some authors have erroneously employed masculine endings, *e.g., Conosoma parvulus* Horn instead of *C. parvulum.* A Latin noun ending in *es* is usually feminine, a Greek noun ending in *es* is usually masculine.

Grensted (1944) discusses the gender of generic names, especially those derived from Greek roots, and points out that we have the alternatives of determining the gender by (1) the meaning of the word, (2) its general form, or (3) the gender of the Greek in one of its parts.

In an attempt to clarify the situation, the International Commission (Paris, 1948) ruled that

1. Where a generic name is a classical Latin word, the specific trivial name, if an adjective, should agree in gender with the generic name.

2. Where a generic name consists of a word which is unknown in classical Latin but is found in the later history of the Latin language, the specific trivial name, if an adjective, should agree in gender with the ascertained gender of the word selected as the generic name.

3. Where a generic name consists of a word unknown in any stage of the history of the Latin language except as used today for scientific nomenclature, the following rules should be observed:

a. If the word ends with any of the terminations used for nouns in classical or later Latin, the gender of the generic name shall be assumed to be the gender usually applicable to a noun having that termination.

b. If the generic name has a termination not found in Latin other than Latin as used in scientific nomenclature, the gender of that noun shall be deemed to be masculine.

Simple adjectives may be altered to indicate fullness by the endings *osus, -a, -um,* thus *Muscicapa fuliginosa.* Comparatives may be indicated by the ending *ior,* masculine and feminine (*Cervus brevior, Rana brevior*), or *ius,* neuter (*Dicaeum brevius*). Superlatives may be indicated by the endings *issimus, -a, -um,* thus *Muscicapa brevissima* or, in the case of adjectives ending in *er,* by *errimus, -a, -um,* thus *M. nigerrima.*

Nouns or Substantives. If a noun is selected as a specific trivial name, it may either be appositional (qualifying) nominative (as *Felis leo, Capra ibex,* or *Astrapia helios*) or in the possessive genitive (*Musca fagi,* of the or belonging to the beech). Dedicatory ("*smithi*") or geographical names ("*italiae*") are often nouns in the genitive. If several things are involved, the genitive plural is used (*X-us rosarum, X-us insularum*).

Participles. Present or past participles are often used as specific trivial names. They consist of verbs altered to an adjectival form and in general denote action. Present participles end in *ans* or *ens* (*fulminans,* light or brilliant; *virens,* green). The ending, *scens,* added to the stem denotes action (*virescens,* becoming green). These endings are the same in masculine, feminine, and neuter. Past participles are passive and have the usual adjectival endings, *us, a, um* (*productus, -a, -um,* produced).

Compound Words. Specific trivial names are often formed of two or more Latin words (*duodecimpunctata,* twelve-spotted) or modified by prefixes or suffixes (*subnitida,* slightly shining). Such compound words of classical origin should always be pure Latin (*rufipectus*) or pure Greek (*rhodothorax*), never a hybrid combination of the two (*rufithorax*). Some purists such as Horvath (1913) felt so strongly about this that they renamed hybrid generic names which came to their notice (*Macrocranella* Horvath, 1913, for *Leptocimex* Roubaud, 1913). Unfortunately for scholarly scientists, this is not permissible because of the disastrous effect such a practice would have on the stability of our nomenclature.

Compound nouns, if used as specific trivial names, cannot be changed to take the gender of the generic name. It is *Papilio rhodogaster,* not *P. rhodogastris:* and *Therium rhodogaster,* not *Th. rhodogastre* or *Th. rhodogastrum.* It is *Dicaeum albipectus* (with *pectus,* breast, a noun) not *D. albipectum.*

Prefixes frequently used to indicate degree of relationship or resemblance should be employed only with words derived from the same language, *e.g., sub* with Latin (*subalbidus*) and *pseudo* with Greek words (*pseudodelta, pseudognatha*). The same applies to prefixes denoting number (*diops,* Greek, *binoculus,* Latin, *monacantha,* Greek, *unispina,* Latin). Neither should be used with proper names (*parasmithi, pseudojonesi*). The terminations *oides* and *ides,* (similar to), should likewise never be used in combination with proper names (*smithoides*).

In addition to the above grammatical categories, most specific names will fall into one of the following classes.

Descriptive Names. The earliest (1758) trivial names of Linnaeus were often one-word condensations of the descriptive *differentiae specificae.* However, since the function of the single trivial name was that of a call word and not a description, it was not necessarily descriptive. With the tremendous increase in number of species since 1758, it has frequently happened that the very characteristic to which attention was called by a descriptive name was the least typical or the most variable in the species. Moreover, a Linnaean species named *minuta* (small) may have been followed by a smaller Fabrician species, *minutissima* (smallest), but what of the many still smaller species discovered since that time? Nevertheless a descriptive name, when selected judiciously, is a useful aid to the memory, particularly if it is a well-known Latin word with a standard spelling and pronunciation. Such names are easily memorized and are considered more desirable than mere heterogeneous combinations of letters.

The Rules suggest that it is well to avoid the introduction of the names *typicus* and *typus,* since these words are used with special nomenclatural significance in taxonomic papers, and their use as scientific names is liable to result in later confusion.

Geographical Names. These are frequently used to indicate type localities or the general distribution of a species, especially when such distribution is unusual or significant. According to the International Rules of Zoological Nomenclature (Art. 16), geographical names "are to be given as substantives in the genitive [*arizonae, sanctaehelenae*] or are to be placed in adjectival form [*arizonicus, arizonensis*]." Here, again, an originally appropriate name such as *mexicanus* may lose its significance if a dozen additional species of the same genus are subsequently discovered in Mexico. Likewise, geographic names frequently become trite through repeated use in various groups of organisms for a single geographic region; for example, the hundreds of animals and plants bearing the specific trivial name *hawaiiensis*. Geographical names are often particularly appropriate for subspecies, especially for those with well-defined ranges, such as island or mountain races. If there is a Latin equivalent for a barbaric geographical name, its use is preferred (*e.g.*, Lutetia = Paris, Batavi = Holland, Lugdunum = Lyon, etc.).

Ecologic Names. Many specific trivial names refer to the particular habitat of the species (*subterraneus*, subterranean; *conicola*, cone-inhabiting; *xerophila*, desert-loving). If the habitat is unique within the genus or group, such names are excellent; otherwise they are subject to the same disadvantages as inappropriate geographic names.

Patronymic Names. Specific names based upon the surnames of persons, such as the original collector or a person who has made an outstanding contribution to the particular field, have some utilitarian value, because they may indicate indirectly the approximate time or place of collection. They are primarily considered as memorials to, or as recognition for, the efforts of individual scientists. Whether justifiable or not, the practice of naming species after persons is apparently here to stay. However, the scientific world frowns upon abuse of the practice. Patronymics should always be used with restraint. A publication filled with such dedicatory names is an indication of poor taste.

The rules of nomenclature that were considered by the first two international congresses of zoology (1889, 1892) stated that patronymic names should *always* be written with the first letter capitalized. Previously (1885) the American Ornithologists' Union had ruled that all specific trivial names, regardless of derivation or reference to persons or places, be written with lower-case letters. For nearly half a century the International Rules left the matter optional, but during that time the lower-case initial letter came into general use by nearly all zoologists except in a few western European countries. Accordingly the International Commission at Paris (1948) prescribed the uniform use of a small initial letter for such names.

In the formation of patronymic names, the person's surname is considered as the stem of a Latin noun, even though the name may have a true Latin form. To this stem, with the exact and complete original spelling, is added the genitive ending denoting possession. As shown for Latin nouns above, these endings are *i* (singular) or *orum* (plural) in the masculine and *ae* (singular) or *arum* (plural) in the feminine.

The following exceptions to the above rule were agreed upon (Paris, 1948): (1) The names of Linnaeus, Fabricius, and Poda should be treated as Latin nouns in the genitive—*linnaei, fabricii, podae*. (2) If a surname ends with the letter *q*, the letter *u* is to be inserted immediately after the letter *q* and before the appropriate genitive termination. (3) When the surname is preceded by a nobiliary particle (*e.g., de, di, von,* etc.), that particle is to be omitted (de Lessert becoming *lesserti*) except where the particle is actually attached to the surname (Dujardin) or where, by long custom, it forms an integral part of the surname (DeGeer); thus *dujardini* and *degeeri.* The particle is also retained in names based upon such surnames as MacCook and O'Connor (*maccooki, o'connori*). (4) Names formed from a modern French surname preceded by the definite article *le, la,* or *les* should include the definite article, *e.g., lesueuri.*

Nonclassical Names. Barbaric names have long been frowned upon by purists. This view has come down from the period when all scientists wrote in Latin. More recently, perhaps owing as much to ignorance or carelessness as to the multiplicity of names now in use, barbaric words have come into general use (*ziczac*). However, it is obviously undesirable to use without change words in common use for other purposes (*box*).

Barbaric names can either be treated as nouns in apposition or declined as if Latin words: *Zosterops malaitae* (from Malaita Island, Solomon Islands). Very often they are Latinized as adjectives: *mexicanus, luzonica, congensis,* etc. This is particularly true for geographical names of barbaric origin.

Names without Definite Meaning. These have been strongly urged by some zoologists in order to avoid possible undesirable or erroneous implications of meaningful names. It has been pointed out that most new species are described from relatively few individuals from a limited area, and that hence authors are not in a position to generalize on their characteristics. Some authors meet the criticism by using such names as *validus, novus, cognatus,* or names denoting similarity such as *similis, assimilis, confinis, soror, congener;* others by using meaningless combinations of letters. However, an appropriate descriptive or geographical name is always superior if relevant information is available.

Undesirable Names. The proposal of a new scientific name should not be taken lightly. Under the Rules, all names, whether good or bad, are permanently preserved and hence are handed down as a legacy to future generations. Each name will stand through the centuries as a monument to the intelligence, taste, judgment, and ethics of its author. Long, awkward names are impractical and show lack of judgment on the part of their author (*anteromediobasalimagnofasciatipennis*).[1] The same is true of facetious names such as Thomson's *Amphionycha knownothing* or irreverent names such as *Eudaemonia jehovah.*[2] Such meaningless and

---

[1] The International Commission (Paris, 1948) recommended that unnecessarily long names be avoided and that the words selected should be euphonious.

[2] A ruling of the International Commission (Paris, 1948) prohibits the use for a scientific name of a word which can reasonably be regarded, in any language, as calculated to cause political, religious, or personal offense.

repetitious names as those of Kearfott (1907) have become the laughing-stock of the scientific world (see *Ent. Soc. London, Proc.*, 1912).   In the genus *Eucosma* many names were proposed simply by altering the first letter, thus: *bandana, landana,* etc.   One of the worst features of Kear-fott's system is the fact that some of the resulting names are pronounced alike (*xandana* and *zandana, cocana* and *kokana*) while others are distin-guishable with difficulty (*vandana, wandana*).

Since the rank of genus is arbitrary, and since many taxonomic groups are decidedly oversplit at the present time, it is safe to predict that future revisers will do a considerable amount of generic lumping.   For this rea-son it is wise never to propose a specific trivial name that is also used in related genera.   The danger is too great that such a name will eventually become a homonym.   It is wise when proposing a new name in a large genus not to utilize a very common name, such as *major, punctatus, littoralis,* or *niger.*

It is particularly bad taste for an author to give a name to a taxonomic entity which an earlier author described but deliberately left unnamed. A name should be given to such an entity only after additional *new* mate-rial has become available.

INFRASPECIFIC NAMES

The species of Linnaeus and of his immediate successors was monotyp-ical and typological.   The category *variety* was used only sparingly and in many cases in the same sense as the modern *subspecies.*   During the nineteenth century the polytypic species became firmly established and with it the definite recognition of the subspecies.

The International Rules originally provided for subspecific names as follows:

Article 2.   The scientific designation of animals is uninominal for subgenera and all higher groups, binominal for species, and trinominal for subspecies.

Article 11.   Specific and subspecific names are subject to the same rules and recommendations, and from a nomenclatural standpoint they are coordinate, that is, they are of the same value.   [See also Art. 35.]

Article 12.   A specific name becomes a subspecific name when the species so named becomes a subspecies, and *vice versa.*

Article 17.   If it is desired to cite the subspecific name, such name is written immediately following the specific name, without the interposition of any mark of punctuation.   Example: *Rana esculenta marmorata* Hallowell.

Article 35.   A specific (or subspecific) name is to be rejected as a homonym when it has previously been used for some other species or subspecies of the same genus.

The subspecies is the only taxonomic category within the species that is nomenclaturally recognized.   Since the days of Linnaeus, however, names have also been given to infrasubspecific variants, to "individual variants." The various possible kinds of such individual variants have been listed in Chap. 4. They are not taxonomic categories but nonrandom samples from populations. The females, for instance, within a population are *not* a taxonomic category distinct from the males and do not deserve a different scientific name, nor do the immature stages or the individuals in winter plumage.

The fact is, however, that this distinction between categories (= populations) and individual variants (= nonrandom samples within populations), which is now generally accepted by biologists, was not fully understood by the earlier taxonomists and still is not completely understood by some dilettante collectors. Some collectors are interested merely in having in their collections specimens with as many names as possible and therefore do not hesitate to name every individual which differs from the type. The status of names given to these variants and aberrations is often in doubt, particularly since some of these authors made no distinction either in form or in principle between subspecies and individual variants. It is therefore not possible to ignore these names completely. Since the original Rules dealt with the status of subspecies names only, there was much doubt concerning the validity of the thousands or tens of thousands of names that were *not* clearly proposed as new subspecies. Realizing this deficiency, the International Commission at its Lisbon meeting directed the secretary to confer with specialists in representative branches of the animal kingdom in order to determine what status should be accorded to names given to forms of less than subspecific rank, with a view to the formulation of an Opinion on the subject.

The secretary's report was submitted to the International Commission at Paris (1948) and, after considerable discussion was adopted in much the following form:

Definitions: *"Subspecies"*: A geographical or ecological population within a species which differs from any other such population within the same species. *"Infrasubspecific form"*: Any form of a species other than a subspecies as defined above. This term therefore includes seasonal forms and minority elements of all kinds within a species, such as sexual forms, transition forms, aberrations, etc.

Provisions: (*a*) Any trivial name published prior to January 1, 1951 as the name of a taxonomic unit of less than specific rank shall be classified for the purposes of the Rules as follows:—(i) as the trivial name of a subspecies, when at the time of the original publication of the name the author concerned either (1) clearly indicated that he regarded the unit named as of subspecific rank or (2) did not clearly indicate the status attributed by him to the form so named, that is to say, whether he regarded it as being a subspecies or as being a form of infra-subspecific rank; (ii) as the trivial name of an infrasubspecific form, only when at the time of the original publication of the name the author concerned expressly indicated that he regarded the form so named as being a form of infrasubspecific rank.

(*b*) Any trivial name published after the point of time specified above as the name of a taxonomic unit of less than specific rank shall be classified for the purposes of the Rules as follows:—(i) as the trivial name of a sub-species, only when, at the time of the original publication of the name, the author concerned clearly indicated that he regarded the form so named as being a subspecies; (ii) as the trivial name of a form of infrasubspecific rank, in all cases where, at the time of the original publication of the name, the author concerned either expressly indicated that he regarded the form so named as being a form of infra-subspecific rank or if he did not so indicate the status of the form, where he failed to indicate clearly that he regarded that form as being a subspecies.

(*c*) It is strongly recommended that an author when proposing a trivial name for a previously unnamed subspecies, or when re-naming a subspecies, the only published name for which is invalid under Article 35, should cite that name in a trinominal combination consisting of (1) the generic name, (2) the specific trivial name and (3) the subspecific trivial name and further that, by using the expression "ssp. n." or otherwise, he should clearly indicate both that the name is a new name and that it is intended to apply to a subspecies.

(*d*) The trivial names of subspecies shall be co-ordinate with the trivial name of species.

(*e*) A name given to any infra-subspecific form shall be co-ordinate with the name given to any other infra-subspecific form of the same species but not with names of subspecies and species.

(*f*) A name originally published as the name of an infra-subspecific form, if elevated to subspecific or specific rank by a subsequent reviser, shall rank in its new status for purposes of priority as from the date on which it was so elevated and shall be attributed to the author by whom it was so elevated.

(*g*) For the purposes of (*f*) above, an author need not expressly state that he is elevating the status of a name originally published as the name of an infra-subspecific form but he must so treat the name as to make it clear that he is in fact treating that name as the name of a subspecies.

(*h*) It is recommended that every author, when elevating to subspecific rank a name originally published as the name of an infra-subspecific form, should expressly state that he is so doing.

(*i*) Where a name, originally published as the name of an infra-subspecific form, is elevated to subspecific rank under (*f*) above but some other author does not recognize the taxonomic validity of the action taken by the previous reviser and in consequence continues to regard the organism in question as referable not to a subspecies but to an infra-subspecific form, the name for any such author shall retain its original priority and shall be attributed to its original author.

(*j*) Where a name originally published as the name of a species or sub-species is treated by a subsequent reviser as applying to an infra-subspecific form, the name shall retain its original priority and shall be attributed to its original author.

(*k*) When an author desires to cite by name an infra-subspecific form, he should cite that name immediately after the trivial name of the species, if no subspecific name is to be cited, and immediately after the subspecific trivial name, if a subspecific name is to be cited, provided: (i) that a comma be inserted immediately after the trivial name of the species or the subspecies, as the case may be; and (ii) that an expression indicating the status of the infra-subspecific form in question (*e.g.*, an expression such as "form vern.", " ♀ -form," or "ab.") be inserted immediately before the name of the infra-subspecific form.

(*l*) When different names are applied to parallel infra-subspecific forms occurring in two or more allied species (*i*) the International Commission may, on application of specialists in the groups concerned, use their plenary powers to establish technical designations to be applied to such parallel forms, such designations: (1) to consist of Latin or Latinized words or words treated as such; and (2) to comply with the provisions in the *Rules* relating to the formation of specific and subspecific trivial names, and (*ii*) where a given term has been prescribed under the fore-going procedure to be the technical designation of a parallel form occurring in two or more allied species, the term so prescribed shall have absolute priority over: (1) any name which may already have been, or may thereafter be given to that form in any of the species concerned, and over (2) any other use of the same word as the name of any other infra-subspecific form of any species in the same genus or genera.

Procedure. The legal status of infraspecific names is defined in the above rules. It remains for the working taxonomists to decide in each group which, if any, of the infrasubspecific forms should appropriately be named and to which of the two "realms" a particular form pertains. This requires a clear understanding of infraspecific categories and concepts (see Chaps. 2 and 5) and in some cases unfortunately more information than is available in the usual museum collections.

The essential points of this ruling are (1) that only those trinominals proposed after Jan. 1, 1951, have status under the Rules which are clearly indicated as new subspecies by the author; (2) that the name of an infrasubspecific form that is elevated to subspecies rank dates from the date of such elevation and has as author the person who proposes the change of rank; (3) that the names of infrasubspecific forms do not affect the nomenclature of specific or subspecific names.

The long ruling of the International Commission does not clearly bring out that the infrasubspecific forms are not taxonomic categories in the sense of all the other taxonomic categories: *They are not populations.* Infrasubspecific forms are based on arbitrarily selected individuals within populations or on arbitrarily selected generations within populations.

The specialists of butterflies and other variable groups of insects, as well as of mollusks, seem to feel that the extraordinary variability of their material calls for a special nomenclatorial treatment. They therefore segregate (arbitrarily) the conspicuous variants within an investigated population into definite groups and give a special variety (=infrasubspecific) name to each of these groups. One might illustrate this procedure by applying it to human systematics. It would correspond to the procedure of an anthropologist who gave names not only to the conventionally recognized human races, such as to Mongolians, Australian aboriginals, Pygmies, Negroes, and so forth, but also to red-haired, black-haired, brown-haired, blond-haired individuals, also to those with blue eyes or brown eyes, with straight, wavy, curled hair, of small or large stature, and so forth. In addition he would give special names to aberrations, that is, to individuals which showed rarer deviations from the normal, such as harelip, clubfoot, birthmarks, and so forth. By applying this procedure to the species *Homo sapiens*, it becomes obvious how absurd it is, and this is equally true for other animals. The nomenclature of some genera of beetles, Lepidoptera, and snails has become so top-heavy with names given to "varieties" and "aberrations" (individual variants), that the picture of the significant intraspecific variation and population structure has become completely obscured (Mayr, 1942, p. 104).

In consequence, the naming of individual variants ("infrasubspecific forms") is on the whole frowned on by the biologically trained taxonomist.

Linsley (1944) has suggested a method for treating infraspecific variation which is presented in modified form below:

I. Subspecific realm (populations)

    A. Namable when recognized

        1. Subspecies (= populations which are more or less isolated as distinct geographical or ecological races)

II. Infrasubspecific realm (individual variants)

    A. Naming optional (but not ordinarily recommended)

        1. Varieties (recurrent discontinuous variations in a single interbreeding population, *e.g.*, Mendelian variations)

    B. Naming not advisable (may be designated by standard terminology or symbols rather than by scientific names)

        1. Sexual dimorphs (*X-us albus*, ♂; ♀)

        2. Castes (*X-us albus*, soldier; ergate; ♀ dealate; ♀, etc.)

        3. Alternate generations (*X-us albus*, agamic form; bisexual form; etc.)

        4. Polymorphic forms (*X-us albus*, minor ♂; brachypterous ♀, fundatrix, migrant; etc.)

        5. Seasonal forms (*X-us albus*, vernal form; Brood I; etc.)

        6. Pathological forms (*X-us albus*, phthisogyne; mermithogyne, etc.)

        7. Freaks, teratological specimens, and other aberrations.

CHAPTER 14

GENERIC NAMES

Perhaps the most important group of names in systematic nomenclature is the generic group. The generic name is not only the mainstay to which specific trivial names are attached, but it is also the foundation for the names of possible higher categories. Hence it must be unique, that is to say, different from every other generic name ever proposed for an animal.[1] That about 220,000 generic and subgeneric names have now been proposed in zoology further emphasizes the need for great caution and judgment in adding to this enormous list and in applying rules for the interpretation of the names already proposed.

In order to be available nomenclaturally, a generic or subgeneric name must satisfy two important conditions: (1) it must have been published (see p. 221); (2) publication must have been accompanied by an indication (see p. 222), or by a definition, or by a description. If originally published before 1758, it becomes valid only if expressly adopted by an author after Jan. 1, 1758; and if published after Dec. 31, 1930, it must be accompanied by (1) a statement indicating the characters of the genus concerned or, (2) in the case of a name proposed as a substitute for a name which is invalid by reason of being a homonym, with a reference to the name which is thereby replaced, and further, (3) it must include a type species designated in accordance with one or other of the Rules prescribed for determining the type species of a genus or subgenus solely on the basis of the original publication.[2] Also, it must not have been used as an intermediate term of the kind rejected by Opinion 124; it must have been published in the nominative singular (Opinion 183).

An author proposing a new generic name should make certain that his proposal does not omit any of the following five essential points:

1. A clear statement that it is a new genus: *X-us*, new genus
2. Coining of a generic name which does not violate the rules and recommendations

[1] However, "a generic name . . . is not invalidated by the earlier publication of the identical or a similar name of higher rank" (Opinion 102) or by the use of the same name in the plant kingdom (Art. 1).

[2] Paraphrased from Art. 25 of the International Rules of Zoological Nomenclature, Opinion 184 of the International Commission on Zoological Nomenclature, and minutes of the Paris meetings of the International Commission.

3. Ascertaining that the newly proposed name is not a homonym (pre-occupied by earlier usage in some other group of animals) or a synonym (of a previously proposed name for the same group of species)

4. Presentation of a diagnosis which contains a clear statement of the characters in which the new genus differs from previously described genera

5. Unambiguous citation of the type species

The generic name denotes the general kind of animal. It is essentially a group designation, much like our surname, and serves as a category to which are assigned various specific trivial names (see also Chap. 3 for the concept of the genus). Because of the flexibility of generic limits as interpreted by different authors, it is necessary to settle upon a type species for each genus. This type becomes the focal point of the genus. Each subsequent student may have his own ideas concerning the limits of the genus and may add or remove one or one hundred species, but unless the generic name falls into synonymy or homonymy, it must always be used for the type species (see Chap. 12).

Formation of Generic Names. Generic names are single words in the nominative singular written with a capital initial letter. They are usually of classical origin, customarily Latinized names of Greek origin. Here, even more than in the case of species, good taste and judgment should be exercised in the formation of names, because a generic name is of concern to a larger group of people. Such absurdly long names as *Dolichocephalocyrtus* in the Coleoptera and *Electroheliocopsyche* in the Trichoptera inconvenience all who have occasion to use them.[1] Pronunciation of such beetle names as *Aaages* and *Zyzzyva* is difficult. Ridiculous names involving a play on words, such as Kirkaldy's (1904) *Peggichisme* (pronounced Peggy kiss me), *Polychisme*, *Nanichisme*, *Marichisme*, *Dolichisme*, and *Florichisme*, were condemned by the Zoological Society of London (1912).

The following types of word employed as nouns in the nominative singular may be taken as generic names:

1. Latinized Greek nouns selected from lists of Greek roots or combining forms or obtained by transliteration from a Greek lexicon. Examples: *Ancylus, Amphibola, Aolysia, Pompholyx, Physa, Cylichna.* The letters of the Greek alphabet are as follows:

A α α	alpha	a		Δ δ ∂	delta	d
B β б	beta	b		E ε	epsilon	e
Γ γ	gamma	g		Z ζ	zeta	z

[1] The International Commission has formally rejected (Opinion 105) a series of long, awkward generic, subgeneric and specific trivial names in the Crustacea proposed by Dybowski. This Opinion quotes the following as one example of his names: *Cancelloidokytodermogammarus* (*Loveninuskytodermogammarus*) *loveni* Dybowski, 1926.

H η	eta	e		Π π	pi	p
Θ θ ϑ	theta	th		P ρ	rho	r, rh
I ι	iota	i		Σ σ ς	sigma	s
K κ ϰ	kappa	k		T τ	tau	t
Λ λ	lambda	l		Υ υ	upsilon	y, u
M μ	mu	m		Φ φ φ	phi	ph
N ν	nu	n		X χ	chi	ch
Ξ ξ	xi	x		Ψ ψ	psi	ps
O o	omicron	o		Ω ω	omega	o

2. Compound Greek words, in which the attributive should precede the principal word.[1] Examples: *Stenogyra, Pleurobranchus, Tylodina, Cyclostomum, Sarcocystis, Pelodytes, Hydrophilus, Rhizobius.* This does not, however, exclude words, formed on the model of *Hippopotamus*, in which the attributive follows the principal word. Examples: *Philydrus, Biorhiza.*

3. Latin substantives. Examples: *Ancilla, Auricula, Dolium, Harpa, Oliva.*

4. Compound Latin words. Examples: *Stiliger, Dolabrifer, Semifusus.*

5. Greek or Latin derivatives expressing diminution, comparison, resemblance or possession. Examples: *Dolium, Doliolum; Strongylus, Eustrongylus; Limax, Limacella; Limacia, Limacina, Limacites, Limacula; Lingula, Lingulella, Lingulepis, Lingulina, Lingulops, Lingulopsis; Neomenia, Proneomenia; Buteo, Archibuteo; Gordius, Paragordius, Polygordius.* Such words should always be pure, *i.e.*, both elements of Latin or both of Greek, never hybrids combining elements of both languages.

6. Mythological or heroic names. Examples: *Osiris, Venus, Brisinga, Velleda, Crimora.* If these are not Latin, they should be given a Latin termination. Examples: *Aegirus, Göndulia.*

7. Proper names used by the ancients. Examples: *Cleopatra, Belisarius, Melania.*

8. Modern patronymics, to which is added an ending denoting dedication. Rules for the formation of patronymic generic names are as follows: (*a*) Names terminating with a consonant take the ending *ius, ia,* or *ium* (*Selysius, Lamarckia, Köllikeria, Mülleria, Stålia, Krøyeria, Ibañezia.* (*b*) Names terminating with the vowels *e, i, o, u,* or *y* take the ending *us, a,* or *um* (*Blainvillea, Wyvillea, Cavolinia, Fatioa, Bernaya, Quaya, Schulzea*). (*c*) Names terminating with *a* take the ending *ia* (*Danaia*). (*d*) Particles are omitted if not coalesced with the name (*Blainvillea, Benedenia*), while articles are retained (*Lacepedea, Dumerilia*). (*e*) With patronymics consisting of two words, only one should be used (*Selysius,*

---

[1] Grensted (1944) states that "when, in a compound, an attributive expresses action or activity, or even a state, it may either precede or follow the noun with which it is conjoined. When it expresses a quality it must precede it."

Targionia, Edwardsia, Duthiersia, Buenoa). (*f*) **Proper** names should not be combined with Greek or Latin attributive or principal words to form compound names. Names such as *Eugrimmia, Buchiceras,* or *Lichtensteinipicus* are monstrosities.

9. Names of ships. These should be treated in the same manner as mythological names or as modern patronymics. Examples: *Blakea, Hirondellea, Challengeria.*

10. Barbarous names (words of nonclassical origin). Examples: *Vanikoro, Chilosa.* Such words may be given a Latin termination. Examples: *Yetus, Fossarus.*

11. Words formed by an arbitrary combination of letters. Examples: *Neda, Clanculus, Salifa, Torix, Syndyas, Anaxo, Edeta, Amytis, Daria.*

12. Names formed by anagram. Examples: *Acledra, Claerda, Clardea, Clerada, Dacerla, Daclera, Daerlac, Dalcera, Eldarca, Erlacda, Lecadra, Racelda.*

In actual practice most zoologists decide on one or more distinctive features, either morphological or biological, of a new genus and then select several Greek words or combining forms which represent or describe these characteristics. Appropriate Greek words may be found by reference to an English-Greek lexicon or to dictionaries of Greek and Latin combining forms (Jaeger, 1944). Names are formulated by various combinations of Greek or Latin combining forms as detailed above. The names are then checked in Neave's *Nomenclator zoölogicus* and, for the period since the last volume of Neave, in the *Zoological Record.* If care is taken to avoid the commonest combining forms, *e.g., acantho* (spiny), *stoma* (mouth), it is surprisingly easy to coin a word which has never been used before. A convenient method, in the absence of other appropriate words or combining forms, is to modify the generic name of a near relative, *e.g., Paratriatoma* Barber, *Neotriatoma* Pinto, and *Eutriatoma* Pinto, all inspired by Laporte's genus *Triatoma.* Another procedure which is useful both to the coiner of the new name and to subsequent users of the name is to follow a traditional series, *e.g., Chionaspis, Diaspis,* etc., in the scale insects; *Leptocoris, Gelastocoris, Geocoris,* etc. in the true bugs; *Chirothrips, Taeniothrips,* etc., in the Thysanoptera.

The gender of generic names has been discussed in a previous chapter in connection with the agreement in endings of adjectival trivial names. It is well in forming new generic names to select words with classical endings, so that the gender of the name will not have to be established arbitrarily.

Homonymy. A generic name that has previously been used for some other genus of animals is to be rejected as a homonym. Example: *Trichina* Owen, 1835, nematode is rejected as a homonym of *Trichina* Meigen, 1830, insect (Art. 34). **The** extent to which names are to be considered homonyms if they differ only in minor details of spelling is stated in Art. 35 (see Chap. 11). Generic names that differ only slightly in their endings are not considered homonyms. Both names are valid in the following pairs of names: *Picus, Pica; Lorius, Loria; Chlorurus, Chlorura,* etc. (Art. 36, recommendations).

Designation of Type Species of Genera. There has been more controversy over the rules and practices of selecting generic types[1] than perhaps over any other single nomenclatural question. As seen above, stability is to a great extent dependent on a uniform system of designating the types and thus fixing generic names.

The genera of the Linnaean period were very wide, in fact, many Linnaean genera correspond to several modern families combined. The result is that in the post-Linnaean period one species after another was removed from the Linnaean genera and included in new genera. At this period there was no clear understanding of the type method, and all the species left in the genus after each elimination of species not belonging to it were considered as typical. This method was called *type fixation by elimination* and was the prevailing method of handling the delimitation of genera during the eighteenth and a good part of the nineteenth century. This is unfortunate, because the method and its application involved many uncertainties and ambiguities. Let us, for instance, consider genus A with the species $a, b, c, d, e, f, g,$ and h. Subsequent author 1 proposed that species b and c ought to be eliminated by removal to the new genus B, and that species $f, g,$ and h should be transferred to the previously known genus C. This left a, d and e in genus A. Author 2 disagreed with author 1; he considered $a, b,$ and c as typical for genus A, made a new genus for d and e, and transferred $f, g,$ and h to C. Finally, author 3 made a new genus for species a. By that time all the species of genus A had been eliminated, and the genus had become an empty shell. It was therefore realized by some authors that the only way to have certainty was to apply the type method (Chap. 12) to genera as well as to species. This method did not become universal until the latter half of the nineteenth century and was in fact not even included in the first versions of International Rules (1901). Article 30, which governs the fixation of generic types, was not included in the Rules until 1907.

The conflict between the elimination and the type-fixation principles has had an exceedingly adverse effect on the stability of generic nomenclature. There are literally thousands of cases where an original genus A with species $a–h$ had been split by elimination into, let us say, genera A with species $a–c$, B with species $d–f$, and C with species g and h, but where the original revisers had neglected to fix a type species for genus A

---

[1] The International Commission (Paris, 1948) recommends that the term *genotype* not be used because of possible confusion with the same word as used in genetics.

(because it was not customary at that time).   If now a subsequent reviser chose *d* as the type species of genus *A*, the name *A* had to be transferred to species *d–f*, the name *B* became a synonym of *A*, and the species *a–c* required a new generic name *D*.   One of the main objects of the Monaco Resolution (for suspension of the Rules) was to mitigate the effects of the application of the type-fixation principle.   This difficulty does not affect recently proposed genera, since the type-fixation principle has been in fairly universal use since 1850 and was made obligatory in 1930.   If at the time of the drafting of the International Rules a compromise had been made between the two principles with respect to the names without orig-inally fixed types, many upsetting changes of nomenclature could have been avoided.   However, the proposal to go back at this late stage to the elimination principle, as advocated by Poche (1937) would lead to new nomenclatural turmoil and is to be rejected categorically.

The International Rules list detailed rules for the designation[1] of type species of genera proposed before Jan. 1, 1930, to be applied in the follow-ing order of precedence (Art. 30):

I. Cases in which the generic type is accepted solely upon the basis of the original publication:

(*a*) When in the original publication of a genus, one of the species is definitely designated as type, this species shall be accepted as type, regardless of any other consideration.   (Type by original designation.)   It was ruled (Opinion 7) that the formula "n.g., n.sp.," when used for only one of the new species under a new genus, is to be considered as type by original designation.

(*b*) If in the original publication of a genus, *typicus* or *typus* is used as a *new* specific trivial name for one of the species, such use shall be construed as "type by original designation."

(*c*) A genus proposed with a single original species takes that species as its type.   (Monotypical genera.)   According to Opinion 47 the foregoing statement is applicable irrespective of whether or not the author concerned regarded the genus as monotypical.

(*d*) If a genus, without originally designated (see *a*) or indicated (see *b*) type, contains among its original species one possessing the generic name as its specific or subspecific trivial name, either as valid name or synonym, that species or sub-species becomes *ipso facto* type of the genus.   (Type by absolute tautonymy.)

II. Cases in which the generic type is accepted not solely upon basis of the original publication:

(*e*) The following species are excluded from consideration in determining the types of genera.   (1) Species which were not included under the generic name at the time of its original publication.*   (2) Species which were *species inquir-*

---

[1] The International Commission decided (Paris, 1948) that the word *designation* should apply to Rule (*a*); *indication* to Rules (*b*), (*c*), and (*d*); and *selection* to Rule (*g*).

* According to Opinion 35, to be eligible for consideration in determining the types of genera, it is not necessary that a species should have been cited under a binomial name when cited in the original publication.   Furthermore (Opinion 46), if no species

endae from the standpoint of the author of the generic name at the time of its publication. (3) Species which the author of the genus doubtfully referred to it.

(*f*) In case a generic name without originally designated type is proposed as a substitute for another generic name, with or without type, the type of either, when established, becomes *ipso facto* type of the other. It was further ruled (*Bul. Zool. Nomencl.* **4**:155,1950) that any of the species cited under the original as well as under the substitute name, where some or all of these are different, is eligible for selection as the type species of the genus.

(*g*) If an author, in publishing a genus with more than one valid species, fails to designate (see *a*) or to indicate (see *b*, *d*) its type, any subsequent author may select the type, and such designation is not subject to change. (Type by subsequent designation.) Furthermore (Opinion 64), a type may be selected irrespective of whether the nominal species is already the type of another nominal genus.

For the special case where there are only two originally included nominal species, the commission has ruled that type selection by elimination applies, *e.g.*, when one of the two originally included species is designated as the type of a new monotypical genus, that action automatically constitutes the selection of the remaining species as the type of the original genus.

Occasionally an author cites a nominal species as the type of a genus under the erroneous belief that it was correctly designated or selected by a previous author, or under the erroneous belief that the species was the type under some provision (such as the "Law of Elimination") not recognized in the Rules. It was ruled at Paris that in such cases the author is to be treated as having selected the type provided that he makes it clear that he accepts, for whatever reason, the species in question as the type species of the genus concerned.

The meaning of the expression "select the type" is to be rigidly construed. Mention of a species as an illustration or example of a genus does not constitute a selection of a type.

III. Recommendations. In selecting types by subsequent designation authors will do well to govern themselves by the following recommendations:

(*h*) In case of Linnean genera, select as type the most common or the medicinal species. (Linnean rule, 1751.)

(*i*) If a genus, without designated type, contains among its original species one possessing as a specific or subspecific trivial name, either as valid name or synonym, a name which is virtually the same as the generic name, or of the same origin or same meaning, preference should be shown to that species in designating the type, unless such precedence is strongly contraindicated by other factors. (Type by virtual tautonymy.)

(*j*) If the genus contains both exotic and nonexotic species from the standpoint of the original author, the type should be selected from the nonexotic species.

---

was originally referred to the genus by name, then the first nominal species to be subsequently referred to it by the same or another author and agreeing with the generic description is considered as an originally included species and becomes the type species of the genus. When the first subsequent author to refer such species to such a genus referred to it two or more species and did not designate or indicate one as the type, all the species so referred become the sole originally included species from which the type may be selected by a subsequent author.

(*k*) If some of the original species have later been classified in other genera, preference should be shown to the species still remaining in the original genus. (Type by elimination.)

(*l*) Species based upon sexually mature specimens should take precedence over species based upon larval or immature forms.

(*m*) Show preference to species bearing the name *communis, vulgaris, medicinalis,* or *officinalis.*

(*n*) Show preference to the best-described, best-figured, best-known, or most easily obtainable species, or to one of which a type specimen can be obtained.

(*o*) Show preference to a species which belongs to a group containing as large a number of species as possible. (De Candolle's Rule.)

(*p*) In parasitic genera, select, if possible, a species which occurs in man or some food animal, or in some very common and widespread host species.

(*q*) All other things being equal, show preference to a species which the author of the genus actually studied at or before the time he proposed the genus.

(*r*) In case of writers who habitually placed a certain leading or typical species first as "chief de file," the others being described by comparative reference to this, this fact should be considered in the choice of the type species.

(*s*) In case of those authors who have adopted the "first species rule" in fixing generic type, the first species named by them should be taken as the types of their genera.

(*t*) All other things being equal, page precedence should obtain in selecting a type.

These rules seem simple enough, but numerous complexities arise, and indeed, it might be said that each case is a problem in itself. Special problems are raised by the cases in which no type was designated and no species included at the time when a new generic name was first proposed. Under these circumstances it is assumed that all the species in the world which agree with the description are potential candidates for inclusion in the genus and thus for selection as the type of the genus. The first subsequent reviser to include such species and the first to select one of these as the type fixes the genus. Thus the law of priority also applies to the actions of the first revisers.

The proper form for proposing a new generic name has been the subject of several rulings of the International Commission. The minimal requirements are stated in Art. 25 (see above), but at the Budapest Congress (1927) it was decided that as of Jan. 1, 1931, more rigorous requirements would be set up. According to the amended rules, a generic name had to be published either (1) with a summary of characters which differentiate or distinguish it from other genera or (2) with a definite bibliographical reference to such characters and (3) with the definite unambiguous designation of the type species.

This apparently desirable amendment created certain difficulties in actual practice, as follows: the words *definite bibliographic reference* were interpreted rigidly by the International Commission (Lisbon, 1935) (Opinion 138), so that a new name published as a substitute name had to be accompanied by a bibliographical reference consisting of the name to be replaced, its author, the date of its publication, the work in which it was published, the number of the volume, and the number of the page on which the name appeared.

This so-called "ritualism" had the effect of invalidating many otherwise perfectly clear taxonomic works merely because of the failure of an author to comply with the particular form prescribed by the Commission. The question was considered at Paris (1948), and it was decided that such ideal procedures in regard to a bibliographic reference, while desirable, should be promulgated not as inflexible rules but rather as recommendations.

MISIDENTIFIED GENERIC TYPES

It is a *species*, not a name, that is the type of a given genus. A species is a natural object, a zoological unit. It is this object which is the type of the genus, just as a definite object, namely, a type specimen, is the type of a species. If the name of the object, namely, of the type species of the genus, changes, such a change does not affect its status as generic type. It is evident from the whole theory of taxonomy (Chap. 12) that it is not the name of the species which is the type of the genus, but the natural object which carries the name. In order to avoid confusion, it is well to select as generic types species the type specimens of which have been carefully studied and positively identified. Otherwise there is always the danger of misidentification and subsequent nomenclatural upheaval.

It is obviously impossible for subsequent authors to check in each case whether the species that was made the type of a genus was correctly identified and carried the correct name. Normally, "if an author designates a certain species as generic type, it is to be assumed that this determination of the species is correct" (Opinions 65 and 168). However, if there is evidence that the author based his genus on certain specimens which he misidentified, "it would be well to submit the case, with full details, to the Commission." Such cases are by no means rare.

For example, the genus *Gastrodes* was proposed by Westwood in 1840 with *Cimex abietis* Linnaeus as the type. A brief description was given, together with a bibliographical reference to a good figure of the species, *i.e.*, Panzer, (1805). *Gastrodes* was used in the above sense for half a century. Then Horvath, in 1898, examined the type of *C. abietis* Linnaeus in the collection of the Linnaean Society of London and found that it was an entirely different insect, known at the time as *Eremocoris erraticus* Fabricius.

If it is assumed that Westwood's determination of *C. abietis* Linnaeus was correct, then the name *Gastrodes* must be used for the large and well-known genus *Eremocoris*, and the species formerly belonging to *Gastrodes* must take the name of an old and very obscure junior synonym, *Oimoctes* Gistel. But in the above case we know that Westwood's determination was incorrect, because Panzer's colored illustration shows clearly the distinctive characters of *C. abietis* of authors, not Linnaeus. Accordingly, the case was submitted to the International Commission (China, 1943) and it was decided at Paris that the insect described by Westwood and illustrated by Panzer, and later named *Gastrodes abietum* by Bergroth, is to be taken as the type of *Gastrodes*, not the name *C. abietis* Linnaeus, which is now applicable to the species which stood formerly under the name *Eremocoris erraticus* Fabricius.

THE DIVIDING OR COMBINING OF GENERA

Special problems are raised when genera are divided or combined. In the former case, the valid name of the genus must be retained for the restricted genus which contains the type of the genus. If, on the other hand, two or more genera are combined, *e.g.*, synonymized, the oldest of the available generic names becomes the valid name, and this name retains as its type the nominal species previously designated, indicated, or selected.

Subgeneric Names. Subgeneric names "are subject to the same rules and recommendations" as generic names "and from a nomenclatural standpoint . . . are co-ordinate, that is, . . . of the same value" (Art. 6). A subgeneric name becomes a generic name if the subgenus is raised to full generic standing, and vice versa. If a genus is divided into two or more subgenera, the subgenus containing the original type of the genus is the typical or nominate subgenus and retains the name of the genus. This is not true in the botanical code but is universally accepted in zoology. The subgeneric name is cited in parentheses between the generic and specific trivial names thus: *Lygus (Lygus) pabulinus* Linnaeus, for a typical or nominate subgenus; and *L. (Neolygus) invitus* Say for a subgenus other than the nominate one.

To eliminate ambiguity in Art. 2, "The scientific designation of animals is uninominal for subgenera and all higher groups, binominal for species, . . . " the International Commission agreed (Paris, 1948) that, as the subgenus is an optional category, the name of a subgenus is not to be taken into account when determining the number of words comprised in the designation of species or subspecies.

CHAPTER 15

FAMILY NAMES

The names of the categories above the genus are always uninominal. It is their function to serve as name labels for the higher categories in which the species are classified.

The names of the higher categories are always in the plural, and many have a uniform termination that reveals their rank at a glance. Names for all categories from just above the (super)genus to and including the rank of superfamily (subtribe, tribe, subfamily, family, and superfamily) are based upon type genera. Names of still higher categories are of independent classical origin. The names of all the categories above the (super)genus are single words that are to be considered Latin plurals (whatever the actual etymological derivation). This must be kept in mind to avoid grammatical mistakes. One can say, "The family Fringillidae *is* the largest family of songbirds," but must say, "The Fringillidae *are* the largest . . . ." The same is true for orders, classes, and all other higher categories.

THE FAMILY GROUP OF NAMES

Family names, although not utilized by Linnaeus, were employed soon after his time (de Jussieu, 1789) and are now an essential part of our system of nomenclature. Actually most of the Linnaean genera were raised to families when the number of known species began to increase. At the present time family names are widely used in textbooks and in elementary courses in biology. This is particularly true for insects because of the large numbers of species. Even a professional entomologist relies on family names for insects outside his special field of investigation, and it is a rare taxonomist who knows *all* the families of insects that occur even in his immediate vicinity.

Family names are important to the economic entomologist and the general biologist, who use such names as *tachinid* and *noctuid* in the absence of any other group name for these well-known insects. Consequently, as Sabrosky (1947) has stated,

The changing of familiar and long-recognizable [family] names and the continued use of conflicting names by different specialists contribute not only to confusion but to a low regard in some quarters for both taxonomy and nomenclature. For example, the pictured-winged flies of the family long known as the

271

Trypetidae are commonly called the trypetids, and they are widely known and recognized because of such common species as the cherry fruitflies, the apple maggot, or "railroad worm," the Mediterranean fruitfly, the goldenrod gall maker, and many others. Yet the appearance of such names for this family as Trupaneidae, Trypaneidae, Euribiidae and Tephritidae leaves the average reader only bewildered.

THE FORMATION OF FAMILY NAMES

The first somewhat vague and inconsistent attempts to introduce the category *family* in zoology were made in the seventies and eighties of the eighteenth century. Latreille (1796) was the first to apply the family concept to insects. He divided all insects into *families*, which he characterized but did not name. Duméril (1800) arranged the insects by orders and families (*familles naturelles*) but used family names in the French vernacular that were not based on the names of included genera (for instance, Lamellicornes and Brachelytres in the Coleoptera). Other authors in the following decade used vernacular family names that were based on included genera (*e.g.*, Latreille, 1802). Kirby (1813) first suggested the uniform ending *idae* as "a patronymic appellation . . . for instance, Coleoptera *Scarabaeidae*, Coleoptera *Staphylinidae*, Coleoptera *Sphaeridiadae*, Orthoptera *Gryllidae* . . . ." This termination is a Greek plural meaning *like*.

Article 4 of the International Rules formalizes this practice as follows: "The name of a family is formed by adding the ending -*idae*, the name of a subfamily by adding -*inae*, to the stem of the name of the type genus." This has been extended by Van Duzee (1916) and others to include the endings *oidea* for superfamilies, *ini* for tribes, *i* or *ae* for subtribes, and *aria* for divisions.

Article 4 seems clear enough but has proved confusing in actual practice. The chief difficulty lies in determining just what is the stem of a generic name. The Strickland Code (1842) furnishes more help in this regard, stating that "these words are formed by changing the last syllable of the genitive case into *idae* or *inae*, as *Strix, Strigis, Strigidae, Buceros, Bucerotis, Bucerotidae*, not *Strixidae, Buceridae*." Formation of family names from generic names which differ only in Latin termination in the nominative and genitive is more obvious. Thus, *Carabus, Carabi, Carabidae*. If the stem ends in *i*, the resulting double *ii* is preserved, thus *Acridium, Acridii, Acridiidae*.

Some names are of unknown or nonclassical origin, and in such cases one cannot be sure of the stem. Thus it is not clear whether *Aphis* has as its stem *Aphi* or *Aphidid*. Furthermore certain genera like *Anthomyia* have an *ā* in their stem, which would result, according to Art. 4, in *Anthomyiaidae*. To avoid such difficulties Grensted (1947) proposed, and the International Commission (Paris, 1948) accepted, the following:

We can retain the general use of -idae, and -inae and also retain Article 4 in its present form, if we re-define the word "stem," using it not in the grammatical sense, with reference to classical Latin, but in a practical sense, applicable to scientific Latin. . . . This could be secured by a note attached to the Article in the following terms:

"For the purposes of Article 4 the term 'stem' is to be taken to mean either the grammatical and classical stem or such part of it as will make wholly clear the relation between the generic name and the name of the family or subfamily, and will at the same time give the family or sub-family name the simplest and most euphonious form compatible with that relationship. The stem, in this sense, will normally be found by putting the generic name into the genitive case and then cutting off the termination, -ae, -i, -is, or -ius, according to the ordinary rules of Latin declension."

THE SELECTION OF THE TYPE GENUS

No mention was made in the original Rules of the method of selecting the type genus of a family. The Strickland Code (1842) suggested "the earliest known, or most typically characterized genus." This suggestion grew out of Latreille's method of selecting a Linnaean genus which represented a general type of animal. Doubtful or annectent types were not utilized, because an effort was made to set aside a more or less uniform group centered around the single, presumably most typical, example upon which the name was based. This principle was not definitely formulated but was simply followed in a rather loose way, subsequent workers selecting typical, or sometimes (as it may now appear) atypical, genera.

During the early twentieth century, the "oldest genus type principle" found strong advocates in Kirkaldy, McAtee, Karny, and others. In actual practice these workers created such confusion that systematics was seriously impeded for a number of years. Kirkaldy at various times called the bed bug family Cimicidae, Cacodmidae, and Clinocoridae, and the chinch bug family Lygaeidae, Myodochidae, Geocoridae, and Pyrrhocoridae. Oberholser (1920) summarized the objections to the "oldest genus" method of selecting the type genera of families as follows:

(a). The family name would be changed when any genus with an older name is added to the group.

(b). The transfer of an older genus to another family would cause confusion by the corresponding transfer of the family name.

(c). Its universal application would produce wholesale changes in nomenclature.

(d). There would be no permanent concept of a family type.

The International Commission (Paris, 1948) agreed that, without prejudice to the thorough study of the problem of nomenclature of families which the secretary was invited to prepare for consideration by the Commission at the Fourteenth Congress, words should be inserted in Art. 4 to make it clear (1) that the genus bearing the oldest available generic name in a family need not be taken as the type genus of a family; (2) that an author, when establishing a new family, is free to select as the type whatever genus he considers the most appropriate; (3) that the name of a family is to be based on the name of its type genus, and that the selection of a generic name to be the basis of a family name constitutes *ipso facto* a definite designation of the genus bearing that name to be the type genus of the family. Thus the principles expressed in Opinions 133 and 141 were formally incorporated in the Rules.

THE CHANGING OF FAMILY NAMES

In view of the tremendous importance of family names, particularly for nonspecialists, every effort should be made to preserve those that are well established. Article 5 of the International Rules states that "the name of a family or subfamily is to be changed when the name of its type genus is changed." Here, as at other levels in the taxonomic hierarchy, certain changes are inevitable as a result of new discoveries. Thus when two families are found to be synonymous, perhaps through the discovery of intermediate forms, one of the names must be suppressed. Most taxonomists also agree that it is undesirable to have two identical family names, at least in the same phylum or class of the animal kingdom. Hence the name of a family is changed if the type genus is found to be a homonym of the type genus of another family. The special problem of identical family names, such as Cyprinidae based upon *Cyprina* Lamarck, 1818, a mollusk, and *Cyprinus* Linnaeus, 1758, a fish, is to be dealt with by *ad hoc* decisions of the International Commission during the present period when the whole subject of the nomenclature of family names is *sub judice*.

Article 5 does not distinguish between the various types of name change to which the type genus of a family may be subjected. One of the commonest reasons for changing any name is, of course, synonymy. Such synonymy is usually subjective and therefore open to different opinions. The Committee on Generic Nomenclature of the Royal Entomological Society of London decided that there is no need to change a family name in such cases, if its type genus is an available synonym in the family (E. E. Green and W. E. China, *The Generic Names of British Insects*, Part 8, **235**, 1943). Although unofficial, this decision has been welcomed because it permits the use of many well-known names, some of which have even become the base for vernacular names (chironomid based upon *Chironomus* Meigen, 1803, a synonym of *Tendipes* Meigen, 1800).

It should be carefully considered by the Commission whether Art. 5 could not be revised in such a manner as to conform with the modern type concept. Since it is the zoological genus which is the type of the family, not the name of the genus, there seems to be no reason for changing the name of the family when the name of the type genus is changed, even though the name of the family is originally formed from the name of the type genus.

GENERAL RECOMMENDATIONS

Although the entire subject of family names is *sub judice*, certain practices have come into general use and will undoubtedly form the basis for the formal treatment of the subject which the International Commission proposes to undertake. In lieu of a formal ruling, the following statements modified from Horvath (1912), Van Duzee (1916), Oberholser (1920), and Sabrosky (1939) may serve as a guide in the selection of family names:

1. The type of a family is a genus.

2. The first family name proposed and formed from a valid generic name shall stand, whether the genus be the oldest or youngest included in the group. The family concept will henceforth center about this type and may be enlarged or reduced by the addition or withdrawal of allied genera by subsequent revisers.

3. Such a family name is valid whether originally accompanied by a description or specific designation of a type genus or not, provided that it is clearly formed from an available generic name.

4. If the original name was written in colloquial form or with tribal, divisional, subfamily, or other ending but with the root of the type genus still indubitably recognizable, the name is valid, but the termination should be changed to *idae*, for family, etc.

5. The family always retains its original type genus.

6. The same rules apply to all categories above generic rank and below ordinal rank (superfamily, family, tribe, division, etc.), and transference of a name from one category to another simply involves a change to the appropriate termination, the type genus remaining the same.

7. If two or more families are united, the family name first proposed takes precedence, not the family name based on the older generic name.

8. The author of the family name is the one who first proposed the name, regardless of its termination. If the termination has been changed, the name may be placed in parentheses with the name of the reviser following, as in the case of authority citation for specific names.

CHAPTER 16

NAMES OF ORDERS, CLASSES, AND PHYLA

Names above the superfamily differ from all the lower group names in that they are not tied to a type. Higher group names are single words, usually of classical origin, and usually descriptive in a general way (Coleoptera = sheath-winged; Vertebrata = backboned, etc.). They are in the form of Greek or Latin plurals, so that in the case of insect orders we speak of one Coleopteron but of several Coleoptera.

Although names for higher groups are still not officially recognized in the International Rules,[1] they were used by Linnaeus in 1758. Under Regnum Animale, for example, he recognized six classes, Mammalia, Aves, Amphibia, Pisces, Insecta, and Vermes. Within each class he recognized orders, some of which remain today essentially as he proposed them. In the Insecta, for example, six of the seven orders of Linnaeus, i.e., Coleoptera, Hemiptera, Lepidoptera, Neuroptera, Hymenoptera, and Diptera are recognized today in the same sense and, with certain exceptions, with the same limits as at the time of their original proposal. The seventh order, Aptera, was composite and has been broken up into several distinct groups.

Names have been changed as taxonomic knowledge increased, the Primates being the only Linnaean order of mammals which retains its original status (Simpson, 1945), whereas Glires Linnaeus, 1758, is now a "cohort," Ferae Linnaeus, 1758, is a "superorder," etc.

Despite the lack of rules governing the formation and use of higher group names, a surprising degree of stability has been achieved. Thus most general textbooks agree in the names of phyla and classes and even in the more numerous ordinal names. A notable exception, in the case of orders, is the confusion which exists in the Insecta. This situation dates back to the last half of the eighteenth century.

The system of classification employed by Linnaeus for the separation of insect orders was based on the structure of the wings. Hence Linnaeus's seven original ordinal names refer to wing characteristics and are formed by adding a descriptive prefix to the Greek *ptera* (wings): *e.g.*, Coleoptera (sheath wings), Lepidoptera (scale wings), Hemiptera (half

---

[1] The subject of names for higher categories is *sub judice*, the secretary having been asked (Paris, 1948) to prepare a full report on this subject for the next meeting of the Commission, scheduled for Copenhagen, 1953.

wings), etc. Fabricius (1798) on the other hand, based his ordinal classification on the structure of the mouth-parts. Although he made a great contribution to the fundamental classification of insects by calling attention to the importance of these structures, he created several synonyms. For example, under the Fabrician system the Coleoptera were known as Eleutherata (free), referring to the free or distinctly separated mouth-parts; the Lepidoptera became Glossata (tongue); and the Hemiptera, the Rhyngota, later emended to Rhynchota (snout). The earlier ordinal names of Linnaeus are now accepted for all the Fabrician orders except one, the Odonata (a tooth), a name proposed for the dragonflies and damselflies which Linnaeus had included among the Neuroptera (nerve wings). Thus the eighth name for an insect order did not contain the ending *ptera*. This departure was followed by Latreille, who added the ordinal names Thysanura (tassel tail), Parasita (parasites), etc. Kirby (1813), foreseeing possible confusion, made a plea for the adoption of a uniform *ptera* ending for all ordinal names of insects, and a majority of the names since proposed have conformed to this rule. Some workers, including Shipley (1904), have gone so far as to emend those names without the *ptera* ending, with ludicrous results etymologically. For example, the *Embiidina* (lively), referring to the rapid running of the insects in their silken tunnels, became *Embioptera* (lively winged), a descriptive term which is highly inappropriate in a group where the females are mostly wingless and the males are slow, feeble fliers.

Even the principle of priority has not been universally applied for insect orders, with the result that modern textbooks refer to the earwigs as Dermaptera *or* Euplexoptera, the thrips as Thysanoptera *or* Physopoda, the fleas as Siphonaptera *or* Aphaniptera, etc.

Another source of confusion is the matter of uniform endings for names of a particular category. As shown in a previous section, uniform endings have been adopted for the various categories of names in the family group. This scheme is very useful, because the position of the name and the status of the group which it represents can be determined at a glance. As shown above, an attempt has been made to secure uniformity of the *ptera* ending for insect orders. This attempt has not been successful because of the absurdity of the resulting words (cf. Embioptera, above), and because such a ruling would threaten many old familiar names, such as Odonata (as against Paraneuroptera).

Some nomenclaturists want to go even further and propose a uniform ending for all ordinal names from the Protozoa up to the mammals. The ending that has been suggested most frequently is *formes*, to be attached to a type genus. Instead of Primates we might have Hominiformes, and Papilioniformes instead of Lepidoptera. The only group in which the ending *formes* for orders has been used with any degree of consistency is the birds, and even there it threatens many familiar names, as, for instance, Tubinares (for shearwaters and petrels). Consequently several recent bird taxonomists (*e.g.*, Stresemann) continue with the time-honored ordinal names in the plural (*e.g.*, Alcae, Psittaci, Passeres, etc.). In the mammals, likewise, the ordinal names Primates, Rodentia, Insectivora, Edentata, Lagomorpha, Carnivora, Perissodactyla, etc., are much too well established to be upset "for the sake of uniformity."

Until the International Commission settles on detailed rules for names of higher categories, zoologists would do well to avoid drastic changes in well-known names. In cases of doubt or choice of several names, a few common-sense rules may be applied as follows:

1. The first higher group name proposed in an unambiguous manner should be accepted, regardless of the ending employed.

2. The author and date of higher group names should be cited, just as in the case of a name of a lower category.

3. When a composite group is divided, the original name should be retained for the "typical" group and a new name should be applied to the newly recognized group. Unfortunately, it is not always possible to determine the "typical" group because, unlike the situation with families, the name is not a positive indication of the type group but is only a clue. Thus if the insects with uniform wing texture (Homoptera) are removed from the Hemiptera, those insects with *half wings* and half leathery coverings logically should retain the original designation, Hemiptera. On the other hand, the loose assemblage of unrelated forms included by Linnaeus under the term Aptera pertains to several different arthropod classes, and the term gives no clue as to the "typical" group. In this and a few other cases the loosely applied term has been generally ignored, and the first clear definition of the separate groups involved has been accepted. On the other hand, an equally valid argument might be advanced for the arbitrary assignment of the name to a particular group by the first reviser.

CHAPTER 17

ETHICS IN TAXONOMY

A so-called "Code of Ethics" to be observed in the renaming of homonyms was adopted by the International Commission on Zoological Nomenclature at its Monaco meeting in 1913. In the report of that meeting the Commission pointed out "that there exists in the zoological profession no recognized and generally adopted code of ethics that is comparable to the code of ethics existing in the medical profession of certain countries. Without presuming to be the arbiter of points of general ethics . . . " the Commission has from time to time issued Declarations or Opinions, which together constitute at least a start toward a code of ethics in the field of nomenclature.

The original point which prompted the Monaco Resolution was the procedure to be followed upon discovery of a preoccupied name. Three distinct problems are involved in this case: (1) procedure when the author of the preoccupied name is living; (2) procedure when the author is dead; and (3) procedure involving names outside the particular group with which the worker is concerned. The first of these problems is covered by Declaration 1 of the International Commission as follows:

Resolved, That when it is noticed by any zoologist that the generic or specific name published by any living author as new is in reality a homonym, and therefore unavailable under Articles 34 and 36 of the Rules of Nomenclature, the proper action, from a standpoint of professional etiquette, is for said person to notify said author of the facts of the case, and give said author ample opportunity to propose a substitute name.

When the author of a newly discovered generic or specific homonym is dead, the discoverer is free to rename the genus or species as he likes. It is common practice in such circumstance to rename the category after the author of the homonym. However, this practice is by no means universal, nor is it always possible or desirable, and it is not a matter of ethics.

An ethical problem does arise, however, when a taxonomist discovers a homonym outside the group in which he is working. Under such circumstances it is the ethical procedure to permit the change to be made by someone who is familiar with the group and in a position to judge whether or not the change is required on zoological, as well as nomenclatural, grounds. Neave (1939) has recently set such an example in his invaluable *Nomenclator zoologicus*. In the preface to the work he makes the following statement: " . . . many apparent homonyms have been, or require to be, sunk as synonyms on systematic grounds. I would therefore urge very strongly on my zoological colleagues that in their revisionary work they should confine themselves in [proposing new names for apparent homonyms] to the groups in which they are specialists . . . "

The question of what action should be taken in cases of breach of ethics was considered by the Commission at its Lisbon meeting (1935). At that time the Commission reaffirmed the Code of Ethics but at the same time "recorded their considered opinion that the question whether the Code of Ethics had been complied with in any given case was not a matter on which they were authorized to enter."

At Paris (1948) the Commission added a recommendation to the Rules

. . . condemning the selection as a generic name of a word which purported to be an arbitrary combination of letters but which, when pronounced, appeared to be a word or words in some language other than Latin, especially where those words had a bizarre, comic or otherwise objectionable meaning.

In contrast to the above recommendations, it was *ruled* that names "which can reasonably be regarded, in any language, as calculated to give offense on political, religious or personal grounds" are prohibited and, upon submission to the International Commission, are to be suppressed.

Still another point in ethics was dealt with in Declaration 4 by the Commission at Monaco (1913). This was "the need for avoiding intemperate language in discussions on zoological nomenclature." Obviously this point is just as pertinent to general scientific writing as to the special field of nomenclature.

In the general field of systematic zoology a certain body of ethics has been built up, most of which is rather obvious to anyone who has a sense of moral responsibility, courtesy, and sensitivity to his fellow workers. However, it may be worth while to call attention to some of the points which, although obvious, are sources of offense, mistrust, and misunderstanding among taxonomists. It should be added that ethics in taxonomy is, of course, only a part of the larger subject of ethics for science as a whole (Pigman and Carmichael, 1950).

Credit. The giving of proper credit is one of the most important ethical responsibilities of the scientist. Acknowledgment should be made of all unpublished observations, determinations, and data derived from others. This not only involves ethics but should be practiced for self-protection if for no other reason. This credit should be given in a dignified manner. It is particularly bad practice to give credit by means of unauthorized quotations from letters. If an unpublished statement is to be quoted, the author of the statement should be allowed to prepare it especially for that purpose.

Previously published data should never be utilized in such a way as to appear original.

Acknowledgment should be made of borrowed and donated specimens studied. The means by which this may best be accomplished vary with the amount of material received from any one source and the general plan of presentation of the paper. Usually ways may be found for such acknowledgment even in complex cases.

Photographs, drawings, and other illustrative material lent or donated by others should be credited. Credit should also be given to artists and photographers for their work, whether or not they received pay for their efforts. Good drawings or good photographs are scientific contributions on a par with descriptive work and are frequently far more accurate and useful.

Credit should be given to the collector, who, after all, is the real discoverer of the material and *not* the describer.

Assistance in outlining a research program (including the help of a major professor or senior colleague) should be acknowledged, as well as aid in the preparation of a manuscript by critical reading. Such acknowledgment should not be presented in such a manner, however, that the reader receives the impression that the persons involved necessarily approve of the conclusions or vouch for the results.

Finally, acknowledgment should be made of financial grants or of institutional aid, such as the use of laboratory facilities, libraries, etc. Frequently such help is a primary factor in making a particular taxonomic research project possible.

Collections. Obviously anyone who wishes may make a collection of animals. He may do so for any one of many reasons other than purely scientific ones. However, if his collection, or any part thereof, becomes the basis of a published scientific study, its status has immediately been changed and it has lost its wholly private nature. This is especially true if it contains type material. Types, in essence, belong to science as a whole, and the owner may be regarded as holding them in trust for science. This means that he is ethically bound to care for them and to make them available for any qualified scientist who wishes to come and examine them. No one who is unwilling to accept this responsibility and the obligations which it implies has any right to dabble in science, much less to pose as a scientist or patron of science. What is true at the individual level is equally true of institutions. Those responsible for institutional policy have a moral and ethical obligation to maintain and protect the collections in their care, to provide facilities for those who may wish to study them, to respond to requests for information on types, etc. If the authorities involved are unable or unwilling to accept this responsibility, they should turn their collections over to an institution that will.

Type specimens assume such an important role in the taxonomy of lesser known groups that some workers have taken the stand that ethically, no one has the right to retain them in a private collection after their study has been completed. There is much to recommend this viewpoint, although there are some who insist on the right to retain types throughout their own lifetime, compensating for their monopoly by distributing paratypes, when available, as widely as possible.

Borrowed Material. No one is under obligation to lend material which he has collected, although most collectors, at either the amateur or the professional levels, are happy to do so. However, when a loan has been made, certain matters of custom and ethics affect both the borrower and the lender. The borrower is under ethical obligation to study the material as quickly as possible and return it in good condition within a reasonable length of time. This obligation obtains regardless of whether the loan was initiated by the borrower or the lender. In certain groups (*e.g.*, many invertebrates) where long series are usual, the borrower is entitled, by custom, to retain a certain proportion of the material in payment for his determinations. The lender should expect this, but unless arrangements to the contrary were made in advance, he also expects that all unique specimens and types will be returned. Some specialists expect the privilege of keeping the second specimen of each species if they so desire and every third specimen thereafter up to a short series. A few may expect to retain as much as half the series. Most, however, will keep but a small percentage of the material studied, and few abuse this privilege. In any event, the specialist should return a list of the material retained and the localities represented, especially for specimens borrowed from an institutional collection. It is advisable that an agreement on the division of the material be made at the time when the loan of the collection is arranged.

Exchange of Material. The exchange of specimens with other workers provides one of the simplest and least expensive methods of building up a representative collection in any group. In general, it is poor taste to insist upon exchanging specimen for specimen, except where institutional requirements or some other unusual factor demand it. Relationships with other workers can be maintained far more satisfactorily if the exchanger follows the general policy of always attempting to give more than value received. No specimen is important enough to the individual to justify quibbling or a quarrel with fellow taxonomists. Exchanges are particularly important on the species and genus level to permit the building up of complete synoptic series. The exchanging of specimens of subspecies is often undesirable, since it breaks up samples of variable local populations. This is particularly true when there is an overlap of characters between two or more variable populations.

Relations with Coworkers. A taxonomist's relations with his coworkers run the gamut of problems in human relationships. Two points only are singled out for special mention. He has an obligation to his science to maintain relationships on a level which permits the free exchange of ideas and to resist any outside influence which may be brought to bear to restrict the free exchange of ideas and scientific information. Further, for the welfare of systematics in general, he should keep his fellow workers informed as to what he is doing. This frequently forestalls needless duplication of effort or permits workers to supplement each other's efforts, or even to collaborate to the over-all benefit of the field. However, this procedure is subject to abuse, and no taxonomist should use this method to preempt a field or to restrict the research activities of others.

Suppression of Data. Obviously no scientist who is worthy of the appellation would deliberately suppress data. This is sometimes done by taxonomists inadvertently, however, or through carelessness, or through lack of understanding of the significance of their acts. This most frequently occurs through failure to mention specimens which do not "fit" the description or will not "run out" properly in the key. The author may be tempted to dismiss such specimens as atypical, or as freaks, aberrations, etc., or he may simply honestly not know just what to do with them. In any event, it is his responsibility in most cases to mention these specimens, since they may later provide a most valuable clue in the clarification of a taxonomic problem.

Undesirable Features of Taxonomic Papers. It hardly seems necessary to call attention to certain undesirable features of some taxonomic papers, especially since these involve bad taste rather than bad ethics; yet a perusal of contemporary publications reveals how frequently the reader is offended by them. The author should make a definite attempt to avoid (1) emotional phraseology, (2) controversy, (3) personal attacks, (4) too much use of the first person, and (5) evaluation of his own work. These five features probably offend the reader more than any other incidental aspects of a published article. Criticism is an important and all too infrequently exercised part of the scientific method, but it should be conducted in a dignified and constructive manner. In general, the author who indulges in personal attacks and pure controversy does more harm to his own reputation than to that of the worker with whom he disagrees.

Letter Writing. Letter writing involves certain elements of ethics, custom, and taste which are important to the taxonomist. Only a few such points are here emphasized.

The taxonomist frequently finds it necessary to write letters requesting information, especially with regard to types.   Such requests should ask for definite and specific information and should not be in general terms. The request that is too general not only offends the person who receives it but nearly always results in the receipt of an unsatisfactory reply. Letters requesting reprints should also be specific.   Most authors resent a request for "a set of reprints of your papers," except under unusual circumstances.   Few authors have an inexhaustible supply of their papers, and the majority prefer to distribute their limited stock to those who will obtain the greatest use from them.   It is only rarely that all the reprints of any one author are of scientific interest to any other single author.   For this reason the ethical thing to do is to request desired reprints by title.   If the author wishes to send all his reprints, he is still free to do so.   The receipt of reprints should be acknowledged, and in some cases, especially where the expense of shipment amounts to a significant item, the recipient should offer to refund the postage involved.

Requests for the loan of specimens should also be specific, in so far as possible, and should be accompanied by a statement of the reason for the request and some indication as to the length of time for which the material is needed.   The qualified beginner may be unable to borrow certain material except through a loan to his institution, or a well-known colleague, or his major professor.   In such cases any laxity in carrying out the conditions of the loan reflects not only on himself but also on the sponsoring individual or institution.   In any case, if it should develop that the borrower is unable to complete his studies in the time designated, he should inform the party or institution which made the loan, without waiting and placing them in the embarrassing position of having to write and ask about the status of the study.

Finally, it should be remembered that most scientists save their correspondence, and that most institutional letter files are semipublic.   For this reason, nothing should be included in a letter that the writer is not willing for any person to read.   Personalities should not be discussed in a derogatory manner, and all letters should be carefully and tactfully prepared.   Carbon copies of scientific correspondence should be retained by the writer both as a matter of scientific record and future reference and for reasons of self-protection.

Although ethics and good taste are not technically a part of the science of taxonomy, they are an important part of the relationship of the taxonomist with his fellow workers, and they may seriously influence his ability to contribute his share to the advancement of science.

BIBLIOGRAPHY

Chapter 1. Taxonomy, Its History and Functions

Baird, Spencer F. 1852. Directions for collecting, preserving, and transporting specimens of natural history. Smithsonian Institution, Washington, 23 pp.

Bartlett, H. H. 1940. History of the generic concept in botany. *Bul. Torrey Bot. Club*, **67**:349–362.

Bates, M. 1940. The nomenclature and taxonomic status of the mosquitoes of the *Anopheles maculipennis* complex. *Ann. Ent. Soc. Amer.*, **33**:343–356.

Bauhin, Caspar. 1623. Pinax theatri botanici, Basel, 24 + 522 + 23 pp.

Brunfels, Otto. 1530. Herbarum vivae eicones, Argent. Vol. 1. 8 + 266 + 28 pp.

Burtt, B. L., *et al.* 1951. Lectures on the practice of botanical and zoological classification. Linnaean Society, London, 64 pp.

Candolle, Aug. P. de. 1813. Théorie élémentaire de la Botanique. Paris, viii + 500 + 27 pp.

Clausen, C. P. 1942. The relation of taxonomy to biological control. *Jour. Econ. Ent.*, **35**:744–748.

Crampton, H. E. 1916. Studies in the variation, distribution, and evolution of the genus *Partula*. The species inhabiting Tahiti. *Carnegie Inst. Wash. Pub.* 228, 311 pp.

———. 1932. Studies on the variation, distribution, and evolution of the genus *Partula*. The species inhabiting Moorea. *Carnegie Inst. Wash. Pub.* 410, 335 pp.

Darwin, Charles. 1859. On the origin of species by means of natural selection, or the preservation of favoured races in the struggle for life. John Murray, London, ix + 502 pp.

Dobzhansky, Th. 1951. Genetics and the origin of species, 3d. ed. Columbia University Press, New York, 364 pp.

Elton, C. 1947. Animal ecology. Sidgwick & Jackson, Ltd., London, xx + 209 pp., 13 figs.

Ferris, G. F. 1942. The needs of systematic entomology. *Jour. Econ. Ent.*, **35**:732–738.

Fisher, R. A. 1930. The genetical theory of natural selection. Clarendon Press, Oxford, xiv + 272 pp.

Gulick, J. T. 1905. Evolution, racial and habitudinal. *Carnegie Inst. Wash. Pub.* 25, 269 pp.

Hackett, L. W. 1937. Malaria in Europe. Oxford University Press, London, xvi + 336 pp., 60 figs.

Haeckel, E. 1866. Generelle Morphologie der Organismen. II. Georg Reimer, Berlin, vii-clx, 462 pp.

Huxley, J. S., *et al.* 1940. The new systematics. Clarendon Press, Oxford, viii + 583 pp.

Keifer, H. H. 1944. Applied entomological taxonomy. *Pan-Pacific Ent.*, **20**:1–6.

Kobelt, W. 1881. Exkursionen in Süditalien. *Jahrb. Deut. Malak. Gesell.*, **8**:50–67.

Linnaeus, C. 1735. Systema naturae, sive regna tria naturae systematice proposita per classes, ordines, genera & species. Lugduni Batavorum, 12 pp.

————. 1746. Fauna svecica sistens animalia sveciae regni: quadrupedia, aves, amphibia, pisces, insecta, vermes, distributa per classes, ordines, genera & species, cum differentiis specierum, synonymis autorum, nominibus incolarum, locis habitationum, discriptionibus insectorum. Laurentii Salvii, Stockholmiae, xxvii + 411 pp., 2 pls.

————. 1758. Systema naturae per regna tria naturae, secundum classes, ordines, genera, species cum characteribus, differentiis, synonymis, locis, Editio decima, reformata, Tomus I. Laurentii Salvii, Holmiae, 824 pp.

Mason, H. L. 1950. Taxonomy, systematic botany and biosystematics. *Madroño*, **10**:193–208.

Mayr, E. 1942. Systematics and the origin of species. Columbia University Press, New York, 334 pp.

————. 1946. The number of species of birds. *Auk*, **63**:64–69.

Merrill, E. D. 1943. Some economic aspects of taxonomy. *Torreya*, **43**:50–64.

Metcalf, Z. P. 1940. How many insects are there in the world? *Ent. News*, **51**:219–222.

Nordenskiöld, E. 1928. The history of biology. Alfred A. Knopf, Inc., New York, x + 629 pp.

Pearl, R. 1922. Trends of modern biology. *Science* (n.s.), **56**:583.

Ramsbottom, J. 1938. Linnaeus and the species concept. *Proc. Linn. Soc. London, 150th Sess.*, pp. 192–219.

Raven, Charles E. 1942. John Ray, naturalist. His life and works. Cambridge University Press, London, 502 pp.

Remane, A. 1933. Verteilung und Organisation der benthonischen Mikrofauna der Kiel Bucht. *Wiss. Meeresuntersuch. Abt. Kiel* (n.s.), **21**:163.

Sabrosky, Curtis W. 1950. Taxonomy and ecology. *Ecology*, **31**:151–152.

Sarasin, P. u. F. 1899. Die Landmollusken von Celebes. C. W. Kreidel, Wiesbaden, 8 + 248 pp., 31 pls. (cf. pp. 229–240).

Silvestri, F. 1929. The relation of taxonomy to other branches of entomology. *Fourth Internatl. Cong. Ent.*, **2**:52–54.

Simpson, G. G. 1945. The principles of classification and a classification of mammals. *Bul. Amer. Mus. Nat. Hist.*, **85**:1–350.

Sprague, T. A., *et al.* 1950. Lectures on the development of taxonomy delivered during the session 1948–1949. Linnaean Society of London in conjunction with the Systematics Association, London, 83 pp.

Chapter 2. The Species and the Infraspecific Categories

Anderson, E. 1949. Introgressive hybridization. John Wiley & Sons, Inc., New York, 109 pp.

Arkell, W. J., and J. A. Moy-Thomas. 1940. Palaeontology and the taxonomic problem. *In* The new systematics, ed. by J. Huxley, pp. 395–410.

Blair, A. P. 1941. Variation, isolating mechanisms, and hybridization in certain toads. *Genetics*, **26**:398–417.

Burma, Benjamin H. 1949. The species concept: a semantic review. *Evolution*, **3**:369–370.

Cazier, M. A. (in ms.) Monograph of the genus *Cicindela* of North America north of Mexico.

Dice, Lee R. 1941. Ecologic and genetic variability within species of *Peromyscus*. *Biol. Symposia*, **2**:21–30.

Dobzhansky, Th. 1951. Genetics and the origin of species, 3d. ed. Columbia University Press, New York, 364 pp.

Dunbar, Carl O. 1950. The species concept: further discussion. *Evolution*, **4**:175–176.

Huxley, J. S. 1939. Clines: an auxiliary method in taxonomy. *Bijdr. Dierk*, **27**:491–520.

———. 1940. Towards the new systematics. *In* The new systematics, pp. 1–46.

———. 1942. Evolution, the modern synthesis. George Allen & Unwin, Ltd., London, 645 pp.

Kleinschmidt, O. 1900. Arten oder Formenkreise? *Jour. f. Ornith.*, **48**:134–139.

Mayr, E. 1931. Notes on *Halcyon chloris* and some of its subspecies. *Amer. Mus. Novitates*, no. 469, pp. 1–10.

———. 1942. Systematics and the origin of species. Columbia University Press, New York, 334 pp.

———. 1946. The number of species of birds. *Auk*, **63**:64–69.

———. 1949. The species concept: semantics versus semantics. *Evolution*, **3**:371–372.

Newell, Norman D. 1947. Infraspecific categories in invertebrate paleontology. *Evolution*, **1**:163–171.

Petersen, Björn. 1947. Die geographische Variation einiger Fennoskandischer Lepidopteren. *Zool. Bidr. Uppsala*, **26**:330–531.

Ray, John. 1686–1704. Historia plantarum. London, 3 vols.

Rensch, B. 1929. Das Prinzip geographischer Rassenkreise und das Problem der Artbildung. Verlagsbuchhandlung Gebrüder Bornträger, Berlin, 206 pp.

Semenov-Tian-Shansky, A. 1910. Die taxonomischen Grenzen der Art und ihrer Unterabteilungen. Friedländer & Sohn, Berlin, 24 pp.

Setzer, H. W. 1949. Subspeciation in the kangaroo rat, *Dipodomys ordii*. *Univ. Kansas Pub., Mus. Nat. Hist.*, **1**:415–573.

Simpson, G. G. 1943. Criteria for genera, species, and subspecies in zoology and paleozoology. *Ann. N.Y. Acad. Sci.*, **44**:145–178.

———. 1945. The principles of classification and a classification of mammals. *Bul. Amer. Mus. Nat. Hist.*, **85**:1–350.

Stresemann, Erwin. 1936. The Formenkreis-theory. *Auk*, **53**:150–158.

Sylvester-Bradley, P. C. 1951. The subspecies in paleontology. *Geol. Mag.*, **88**:88–102.

Turesson, G. 1922. The genotypical response of the plant species to the habitat. *Hereditas*, **3**:211–350.

Vaurie, Charles. 1949. A revision of the bird family Dicruridae. *Bul. Amer. Mus. Nat. Hist.*, **93**:205–342.

White, M. J. D. 1945. Animal cytology and evolution. Cambridge University Press, London, viii + 375 pp.

Chapter 3. Classification and the Higher Categories

Arkell, W. J., and J. A. Moy-Thomas. 1940. Paleontology and the taxonomic problem. *In* The new systematics, ed. by J. Huxley, pp. 395–410.

Bather, F. A. 1927. Biological classification: past and future. *Geol. Soc. London, Quart. Jour.*, **83**:LXII.

Brues, C. T., and A. L. Melander. 1932. Classification of insects. *Bul. Mus. Compar. Zoöl.*, **73**:1–672.

Delacour, J., and E. Mayr. 1945. The family Anatidae. *Wilson Bul.*, **57**:3–55.

Dobzhansky, Th. 1951. Genetics and the origin of species, 3d. ed. Columbia University Press, New York, 364 pp.

Friese, H. 1926. Die Insekten Mitteleuropas. Bd. 1. Hymenopteren. Franckh, Stuttgart, Teil 1, vi + 192 pp.

Handlirsch, A. 1929. Gegen die übermässige Zersplitterung der systematischen Gruppen. *Zool. Anz.*, **84**:85–90.

———. 1926–1930. In W. Kükenthal, Handbuch der Zoologie, 4 Bd., 1:403–892. De Gruyter, Berlin and Leipzig (Orthoptera, pp. 687–796).

Lack, David. 1947. Darwin's finches. Cambridge University Press, London, 208 pp.

Linnaeus, C. 1737. Critica botanica. Lugduni Batavorum, xiv + 270 pp.

Mayr, E. 1942. Systematics and the origin of species. Columbia University Press, New York, 334 pp.

——— and Dean Amadon. 1951. A classification of recent birds. *Amer. Mus. Novitates*, no. 1496, pp. 1–42.

McAtee, W. L. 1926. Insect taxonomy: preserving a sense of proportion. *Wash. Ent. Soc. Proc.*, **28**:68–70.

Michener, C. D. 1944. Comparative external morphology, phylogeny, and a classification of the bees (Hymenoptera). *Bul. Amer. Mus. Nat. Hist.*, **82**:157–326.

Parker, T. J., and W. A. Haswell. 1940. A textbook of zoology, 6th ed. The Macmillan Company, London, 2 vols.

Perrier, Edmond. 1893–1932. Traité de Zoologie. Masson et Cie, Paris, vols. 1–10.

Rensch, B. 1934. Kurze Anweisung für zoologisch-systematische Studien. Akademische Verlagsgesellschaft m.b.H., Leipzig, 116 pp.

Richards, O. W. 1938. The formation of species. *In* Evolution, ed. by G. R. de Beer. Clarendon Press, Oxford, pp. 95–110.

———. 1940. Phylogeny and taxonomy. *Proc. Linn. Soc. London*, **152**:241.

Simpson, G. G. 1945. The principles of classification and a classification of mammals. *Bul. Amer. Mus. Nat. Hist.*, **85**:1–350.

Smith, W. R. 1947. The content of genera. *Yearbook Roy. Soc. Edinb.*, pp. 5–11 (reprint).

Stresemann, E. 1927–1934. Aves. *In* W. Kükenthal, Handbuch der Zoologie, **7B**:729–853. De Gruyter, Berlin and Leipzig.

———. 1950. The development of theories which affected the taxonomy of birds. *Ibis*, **92**:123–131.

Wetmore, Alexander. 1940. A systematic classification for the birds of the world. *Smiths. Inst. Misc. Collect.*, **99** (7):1–11.

Chapter 4. Collecting and Collections

Anderson, R. M. 1948. Methods of collecting and preserving vertebrate animals, 2d. ed. *Bul. Natl. Mus. Canada, Dept. Mines*, no. 69, *Biol. Ser.* 18 (Ottawa), 162 pp.

Anthony, H. E. 1945. The capture and preservation of small mammals for study. *Amer. Mus. Nat. Hist. Sci. Guide* 61, 54 pp.

Camp, C. L., and G. D. Hanna. 1937. Methods in paleontology. University of California Press, Berkeley, 23 + 153 pp.

Guyer, M. F. 1936. Animal micrology, 4th ed. University of Chicago Press, Chicago, xvi + 331 pp.

Kinsey, A. C. 1936. The origin of higher categories in *Cynips*. *Ind. Univ. Pub. Sci. Ser.* 4, 334 pp.

Lee, A. B. 1937. The microtomist's vademecum. A handbook of the methods of microscopic anatomy, 10th ed. The Blakiston Company, Philadelphia, 784 pp.

Lynes, H. 1930. Review of the genus *Cisticola*. *Ibis*, sup., 673 pp.

Oman, P. W., and A. D. Cushman. 1946. Collection and preservation of insects. *U.S. Dept. Agr. Misc. Pub.* 601, 42 pp.

Peterson, A. 1934, 1937. A manual of entomological equipment and methods. Pt. 1, Ann Arbor, Mich., 1934, 21 pp., 138 Pls. Pt. 2, St. Louis, Mo., 1937, 334 pp.

Van Tyne, Josselyn. 1952. Principles and practices in collecting and taxonomic work. *Auk*, **69**:27–33.

Chapter 5. Identification and Taxonomic Discrimination

Agassiz, L., and H. E. Strickland. 1848. Bibliographia Zoologiae et Geologiae. London, Ray Society, vols. 1–4.

Balazuc, J. 1948. La tératologie des Coléoptères et expériences de transplantation sur *Tenebrio molitor* L. *Mém. Mus. Natl. d'Hist. Nat.* (n.s.), **25**:1–293.

Biological Abstracts. Published with the cooperation of educational and research institutions, biological industries, and biological journals generally. Sponsored by the Union of American Biological Societies. 1950—21 volumes completed. Published monthly: January to May; bimonthly: June to September; monthly: October and November; semimonthly in December.

Brooks, John L. 1946. Cyclomorphosis in *Daphnia*. I. An analysis of *D. retrocurrata* and *D. galeata*. *Ecol. Monog.*, **16**:409–447.

Brücke, E. 1852. Untersuchungen über den Farbenwechsel des afrikanischen Chamäleons. *Denkschr. Akad. der Wiss. Wien, Math.-Nat. Kl.*, **4**:179–210.

Brues, C. T., and A. L. Melander. 1932. Classification of insects. *Bul. Mus. Compar. Zool.*, **73**:1–672.

Cappe de Baillon, P. 1927. Recherches sur la tératologie des insectes. Encyclopédie Entomologie (A) **8**:5–291.

Carpenter, G. D. Hale. 1949. *Pseudacraea eurytus* (L.) (Lep. Nymphalidae): A study of a polymorphic mimic in various degrees of speciation. *Trans. Roy. Ent. Soc., London*, **100** (3):71–133.

Catalogue of scientific papers. 1800–1863. Compiled by Royal Society of London, vols. 1–6, London, 1867–1872. (Continued for ten-year periods up to 1900.)

Coker, R. E. 1939. The problem of cyclomorphosis in *Daphnia*. *Quart. Rev. Biol.*, **14**:137–148.

Cuénot, L. 1936. L'Espèce. G. Doin et Cie., Paris, 310 pp.

Dahl, F. 1925 *et seq.* Die Tierwelt Deutschlands. Gustav Fischer, Jena, 37 pts. *et seq.*

Dall, W. H. 1898. Contributions to the tertiary fauna of Florida. *Trans. Wagner Free. Inst. Sci. Phila.*, **3**:675–676.

Dobzhansky, Th. 1943. Genetics of natural populations. IX. Temporal changes in the composition of populations of *Drosophila pseudoobscura*. *Genetics*, **28**:162–186.

Driver, Ernest C. 1950. Name that animal. A guide to the identification of the common land and fresh-water animals of the United States, with special reference to the area east of the Rockies. Kraushar Press, Northampton, Mass., 558 pp.

Ebeling, W. 1938. Host-determined morphological variation in *Lecanium corni*. *Hilgardia*, **11**:613–631.

Engelmann, W. 1846. Bibliotheca Historico-Naturalis. Verzeichnis der Bücher über Naturgeschichte 1700–1846. W. Englemann, Leipzig, 786 pp.

Faune de France. 1921 *et seq.* P. Lechevalier, Paris, 55 pts. *et seq.*

Faure, J. C. 1943*a*. The phases of the lesser army worm, *Laphygma exigua* (Hübn.). *Farming in So. Africa*, **18**:69–78.

————. 1943b. Phase variation in the army worm, *Laphygma exempta* (Walk.). *Union So. Africa Dept. Agr. For. Bul.*, **234**:1–17.

Ford, E. B. 1940. Polymorphism and taxonomy. *In* The new systematics, ed. by J. Huxley, pp. 493–513.

————. 1945. Polymorphism. *Biol. Rev.*, **20**:73–88.

Gerould, J. J. 1921. Blue-green caterpillars; the origin and ecology of a mutation in hemolymph color in *Colias* (*Eurymus*) *philodice*. *Jour. Expt. Zool.*, **34**: 385–415.

Goldschmidt, R. 1933. Lymantria. *Bibliog. Genetica*, **11**:1–185.

————. 1945. Mimetic polymorphism, a controversial chapter of Darwinism. *Quart. Rev. Biol.*, **20**:147–164, 205–230.

Grimpe, G., and E. Wagler. 1925 *et seq*. Die Tierwelt der Nord-und Ostsee. Bd. 1 *et seq*.

Holmgren, N. 1913. Termitenstudien IV. *Svenska Vetensk. Akad. Handl.*, **50**:1–276.

Imms, A. D. 1937. Recent advances in entomology, 2d ed. J. and A. Churchill, Ltd., x + 431 pp.

Kemner, N. A. 1925. Larva termitovorax. *Arkiv för Zool.*, **17A**:1–15.

Kerr, W. E. 1950. Genetic determination of castes in the genus Melipona. *Genetics*, **35**:143–152.

Kinsey, A. C. 1930. The gallwasp genus *Cynips*. *Indiana Univ. Studies*, **16**:1–577.

Lang, E. M. 1946. Ueber die Brutgewohnheiten des Schneefinken. *Ornith. Beob.*, **43**:33–43.

Linsley, E. G. 1937. The effect of stylopization on *Andrena porterae*. *Pan-Pacific Ent.*, **13**:157.

Mayr, E. 1940. *Pericrocotus brevirostris* and its double. *Ibis*, **82**:712–722.

————. 1942. Systematics and the origin of species. Columbia University Press, New York, 334 pp.

————. 1948. The bearing of the new systematics on genetical problems. The nature of species. *Advances in Genetics*, **2**:205–237.

————. 1951. Speciation in birds. Progress report on the years 1939–1950. *XI Internatl. Ornith. Cong. Proc.* (Uppsala), pp. 1–30.

———— and E. Stresemann 1950. Polymorphism in the chat genus *Oenanthe* (Aves). *Evolution*, **4**:291–300.

Park, O., W. C. Allee, and V. E. Shelford. 1939. A laboratory introduction to animal ecology and taxonomy with keys, etc. University of Chicago Press, Chicago, x + 272 pp., 1–17 pls.

Parker, G. H. 1948. Animal colour changes and their neurohumours. Cambridge University Press, London, vii + 377 pp.

Ramme, W. 1930. Revisionen und Neubeschreibungen in der Gattung Pholidoptera Wesm. (Orth., Tettigon.). *Berlin Zool. Mus. Mitt.*, **16**:798–821 (esp. p. 800).

Riech, E. 1937. Systematische, anatomische, ökologische und tiergeographische Untersuchungen über die Süsswassermollusken Papuasiens und Melanesiens. *Arch. f. Naturgesch.* (n.s.), **6**:37–153.

Salt, G. 1927. The effects of stylopization on Aculeate Hymenoptera. *Jour. Expt. Zool.*, **48**:223–331.

————. 1941. The effects of hosts upon their insect parasites. *Biol. Rev.*, **16**:239–264.

Schnitter, H. 1922. Die Najaden der Schweiz. *Rev. Hydrol.*, Sup., **2**:1–200.

Sherborn, C. D. 1902. Index animalium, 1758–1800. Cambridge University Press, London, 1195 pp.

————. 1922–1933. Index animalium, Section 2, Parts 1–33. British Museum.

Smart, J. 1942. Bibliography of key works for the identification of the British fauna and flora. Association for the Study of Systematics in Relation to General Biology, Publ. 1, John Smart, editor, London, 105 pp.

Smith, H. S. 1942. A race of *Comperiella bifasciata* successfully parasitizes California red scale. *Jour. Econ. Ent.*, **35**:809–812.

Smith, R. C. 1942. Guide to the literature of the zoological sciences. Burgess Publishing Company, Minneapolis, 128 pp.

Uvarov, B. P. 1921. A revision of the genus *Locusta*, L. (*Pachytylus* Fieb.), with a new theory as to the periodicity and migrations of locusts. *Bul. Ent. Res.*, **12**:135–163.

————. 1928. Locusts and grasshoppers. Imperial Bureau of Entomology, London, xiii + 352 pp.

[Wiegmann's] *Archiv für Naturgeschichte*. 1835 *et seq.* Bericht über die Leistungen im Gebiete der Naturgeschichte während des Jahres 1834 [. . . 1922].

Wood, Casey A. 1931. An introduction to the literature of vertebrate zoology. Oxford University Press, London, xiii–xix + 643 pp.

Zoological Record. 1862–1950 *et seq.* Printed for the Zoological Society of London in cooperation with the British Museum (Natural History) and the Commonwealth Institute of Entomology.

Chapter 6.   Taxonomic Characters

Bates, M. 1940. The nomenclature and taxonomic status of the mosquitoes of the *Anopheles maculipennis* complex. *Ann. Ent. Soc. Amer.*, **33**:343–356.

de Beer, G. R. 1940. Embryology and taxonomy. *In* The new systematics, ed. by J. Huxley, pp. 365–393.

————. 1951. Embryos and ancestors, rev. ed. Clarendon Press, Oxford, v–ix, 1–159 pp.

Boyden, A. 1943. Serology and animal systematics. *Amer. Nat.*, **77**:234–255.

————. 1951. A half-century of systematic serology. *Serological Mus. Bul.*, 6, pp. 1–3.

Brooke, M. M., and H. O. Proske. 1946. Precipitin test for determining natural insect predators of immature mosquitoes. *Jour. Natl. Malaria Soc.*, **5**:45–56.

Buchner, P. 1940. Symbiose und Anpassung. *Nova Acta Leopoldina*, **8**:257–374.

Cantrall, I. J. 1943. The ecology of the Orthoptera and Dermaptera of the George Reserve, Michigan. *Misc. Pub. Mus. Zool., Univ. Michigan*, **54**:3–182.

Clausen, Jens. 1951. Stages in the evolution of plant species. Cornell University Press, Ithaca, N.Y., v–viii, 1–206 pp.

————, D. D. Keck, and W. M. Hiesey. 1948. Experimental Studies on the nature of species. III. Environmental responses of climatic races of *Achillea. Carnegie Inst. Wash., Pub.*, **581**:1–129.

Clay, Theresa. 1949. Some problems in the evolution of a group of ectoparasites. *Evolution*, **3**(4):279–299.

Craighead, F. C. 1921. Hopkins host-selection principle as related to certain cerambycid beetles. *Jour. Agr. Res.*, **22**:189–220.

Dobzhansky, Th. 1951. Genetics and the origin of species, 3d ed. Columbia University Press, New York, 364 pp.

Emerson, A. E. 1935. Termitophile distribution and quantitative characters of physiological speciation in British Guiana termites (Isoptera). *Ann. Ent. Soc. Am.*, **28**:369–395.

Hackett, L. W., and A. Missiroli. 1935. The varieties of *Anopheles maculipennis* and their relation to the distribution of malaria in Europe. *Riv. di Malariol.*, 14:45–109.

Hopkins, G. H. E. 1949. The host-association of the lice on mammals. [*London*] *Zool. Soc. Proc.*, 119:387–604.

Jacobs, W. 1950. Vergleichende Verhaltungsstudien an Feldheuschrecken. *Ztschr. Tierpsychol.*, 7:169–216.

Jordan, K. 1905. Der Gegensatz zwischen geographischer und nichtgeographischer Variation. *Ztschr. f. Wiss. Zool.*, 83:151–210.

Kellogg, V. L. 1896. New Mallophaga. I. *Proc. Calif. Acad. Sci.*, 6:31–168.

———. 1913. Distribution and species-forming of Ectoparasites. *Amer. Nat.*, 47:129–158.

Kraus, R. 1897. Ueber specifische Reaktionen in keimfreien Filtraten aus Cholera —Typhus—Pestbacillenkulturen, erzeugt durch homologes Serum. *Wien. Klin. Wchnschr.*, 32:736.

Lack, David. 1947. Darwin's finches. Cambridge University Press, London, i–x, 1–208 pp.

———. 1949. The significance of ecological isolation. *In* G. L. Jepsen, E. Mayr, and G. G. Simpson, Genetics, paleontology and evolution, pp. 299–308.

Landsteiner, K. 1945. The specificity of serological reactions, rev. ed., Harvard University Press, Cambridge, Mass., i–xiv, 1–310 pp.

Lorenz, Konrad. 1941. Vergleichende Bewegungsstudien an Anatinen. *Jour. f. Ornith.*, sup., 3:194–294.

Matthey, Robert. 1949. Les chromosomes des vertébrés. F. Rouge, Lausanne, Switzerland, 356 pp.

Mayr, E. 1942. Systematics and the origin of species. Columbia University Press, New York, 334 pp.

———. 1948. The bearing of the new systematics on genetical problems. The nature of species. *Adv. Genetics*, 2:205–237.

———. 1951. Speciation in birds. Progress report on the years 1938–1950. *XI Internatl. Ornith. Cong. Proc.* (Uppsala), pp. 1–30.

Metcalf, M. M. 1929. Parasites and the aid they give in problems of taxonomy, geographical distribution, and paleogeography. *Smithsn. Inst. Misc. Collect.*, 81 (8):1–36.

Nuttall, G. H. F. 1901. On the formation of specific antibodies in the blood following upon treatment with the sera of different animals, together with their use in legal medicine. *Jour. Hyg.* [*London*], 1:357–387.

Rensch, B. 1934. Kurze Anweisung für zoologisch-systematische Studien. Akademische Verlagsgesellschaft m.b.H., Leipzig, 116 pp.

Simpson, G. G. 1944. Tempo and mode in evolution. Columbia University Press, New York, 237 pp.

Smith, H. S. 1941. Racial segregation in insect populations and its significance in applied entomology. *Jour. Econ. Ent.*, 34:1–13.

Spieth, Herman T. 1947. Sexual behavior and isolation in *Drosophila*. I. The mating behavior of species of the *willistoni* group. *Evolution*, 1:17–31.

Steinhaus, E. A. 1949. Principles of insect pathology. McGraw-Hill Book Co., Inc., New York, 757 pp.

Thorpe, W. H. 1930. Biological races in insects and allied groups. *Cambridge Phil. Soc. Biol. Rev.*, 5:177–212.

———. 1940. Ecology and the future of systematics. *In* The new systematics, ed. by J. Huxley, pp. 341–364.

Turesson, G. 1922. The genotypical response of the plant species to the habitat. *Hereditas*, **3**:211–350.

White, M. J. D. 1945. Cytology and evolution. Cambridge University Press, London, 375 pp.

———. 1949. Cytological evidence on the phylogeny and classification of Diptera. *Evolution*, **3**:252–261.

Wood, Albert E. 1950. Porcupines, paleogeography and parallelism. *Evolution*, **4**:87–98.

Zarapkin, S. R. 1934. Zur Phänoanalyse von geographischen Rassen und Arten. *Arch. f. Naturgesch.* (n.s.), **3**:161–186.

Chapter 7. Quantitative Methods of Analysis

Amadon, Dean. 1943. Bird weights as an aid in taxonomy. *Wilson Bul.*, **55**: 164–177.

———. 1949. The seventy-five per cent rule for subspecies. *Condor*, **51**:250–258.

Anderson, E. 1949. Introgressive hybridization. John Wiley & Sons, Inc., New York, 109 pp.

Blair, W. F. 1947. An analysis of certain genetic variations in pelage color of the Chihuahua deer-mouse (*Peromyscus maniculatus blandus*). *Contr. Lab. Vert. Biol. Michigan*, **35**:1–18.

Burma, B. H. 1948. Studies in quantitative paleontology. 1. Some aspects of the theory and practice of quantitative invertebrate paleontology. *Jour. Paleontol.*, **22**(6):725–761.

———. 1949. Studies in quantitative paleontology. 2. Multivariate analysis—a new analytical tool for paleontology and geology. *Jour. Paleontol.*, **23**:(1): 95–103.

Carson, H. L., and H. D. Stalker. 1947. Gene arrangements in natural populations of *Drosophila robusta* Sturtevant. *Evolution*, **1**(3):113–133.

Cazier, M. A., and A. Bacon. 1949. Introduction to quantitative systematics. *Bul. Amer. Mus. Nat. Hist.*, **93**:347–388.

Dobzhansky, Th. 1951. Genetics and the origin of species, 3d. ed. Columbia University Press, New York, 364 pp.

Fisher, R. A. 1938. The statistical use of multiple measurements. *Ann. Eugenics*, **8**:376–386.

Fitch, Henry S. 1940. A biogeographical study of the ordinoides artenkreis of garter snakes. *Calif. Univ Pubs., Zool.*, **44**(1):1–150.

Hubbs, C. L., and A. Perlmutter. 1942. Biometric comparison of several samples, with particular reference to racial investigations. *Amer. Nat.*, **76**:582–592.

Johnson, C. G. 1939. Taxonomic characters, variability, and relative growth in *Cimex lectularius* L. and *C. columbarius* Jenyns (Heteropt. Cimicidae). *Roy. Ent. Soc., London, Trans.*, **89**(11):543–577.

Klauber, L. M. 1936–1940. A statistical study of the rattlesnakes. *Occas. Papers San Diego Soc. Nat. Hist.*, I, no. 1, pp. 1–24 (1936); V, no. 4, pp. 1–53 (1938); VI, no. 5, pp. 1–61 (1939); VII, no. 6, pp. 1–62 (1940).

———. 1941. Four papers on the applications of statistical methods to herpetological problems. I. The frequency distributions of certain herpetological variables. II. Illustrations of the relationship between populations and samples. III. The correlation between scalation and life zones in San Diego County snakes, etc. *Bul. Zool. Soc. San Diego*, no. 17, pp. 5–95.

———. 1943a. The correlation of variability within and between rattlesnake populations. *Copeia*, pp. 115–118.

————. 1943*b*. 1. Tail-length differences in snakes with notes on sexual dimorphism and the coefficient of divergence. 2. A graphic method of showing relationships. *Bul. Zool. Soc. San Diego*, no. 18, pp. 5–76.

————. 1945. Herpetological correlations. 1. Correlations in homogeneous populations. *Bul. Zool. Soc. San Diego*, no. 21, pp. 5–101.

Mather, K. 1947. Statistical analysis in biology. Interscience Publishers, New York, 267 pp. (2d. ed., Am. Photo Offset Reprint).

Mayr, E. 1932. Birds collected during the Whitney South Sea Expedition. XVIII. Notes on Meliphagidae from Polynesia and the Solomon Islands. *Amer. Mus. Novitates*, no. 516, pp. 1–30.

————. 1944. The birds of Timor and Sumba. *Bul. Amer. Mus. Nat. Hist.*, **83**:157.

Oliver, J. A. 1943. The status of *Uta ornata lateralis* Boulanger. *Copeia*, pp. 97–107.

Parr, A. E. 1949. An approximate formula for stating taxonomically significant proportions of fishes with reference to growth changes. *Copeia*, pp. 47–55.

Rand, A. L., and M. A. Traylor. 1950. The amount of overlap allowable for subspecies. *Auk*, **67**:169–183.

Simpson, G. G. 1941. Range as a zoological character. *Amer. Jour. Sci.*, **239**: 785–804.

———— and A. Roe. 1939. Quantitative zoology. McGraw-Hill Book Co., Inc., New York, 414 pp.

Snedecor, George W. 1946. Statistical methods, 4th ed. Iowa State College Press, Ames, Iowa, 485 pp.

Stone, F. L. 1947. Notes on two darters of the genus *Boleosoma*. *Copeia*, pp. 92–96.

Storer, R. W. 1950. Geographical variation in the pigeon Guillemots of North America. *Condor*, **52**:28–31.

Chapter 8. Presentation of Findings. Descriptions, Keys, Phylogenies

China, W. E. 1933. A new family of Hemiptera-Heteroptera with notes on the phylogeny of the suborder. *Ann. and Mag. Nat. Hist.*, **12**(10):180–196.

Darwin, C. 1859. On the origin of species by means of natural selection, or the preservation of favoured races in the struggle for life. John Murray, London, ix + 502 pp.

Ferris, G. F. 1928. The principles of systematic entomology. *Stanford Univ. Pubs., Biol. Sci.*, **5**:103–269.

Haeckel, E. 1866. Generelle Morphologie der Organismen. II. G. Reimer, Berlin, 462 pp., 8 pls.

Jepsen, G. L. 1944. Phylogenetic trees. *Trans. N. Y. Acad. Sci.*, Ser. 2, pp. 81–92.

Lam, H. J. 1936. Phylogenetic symbols, past and present. *Acta Biotheoretica*, **2**:153–193.

Maerz, A., and M. R. Paul. 1950. A dictionary of color, 2d ed. McGraw-Hill Book Co., Inc., New York, 206 pp. (over 7,000 sample colors).

Mayr, E., and C. Vaurie. 1948. Evolution in the family Dicruridae. *Evolution*, **2**:238–265.

Michener, C. D. 1949. Parallelisms in the evolution of the saturniid moths. *Evolution*, **3**:129–141.

Milne, M. J., and L. J. Milne. 1939. Evolutionary trends in caddis worm case construction. *Ann. Ent. Soc. America*, **32**:533–542.

Newell, N. D. 1947. Infraspecific categories in invertebrate paleontology. *Evolution*, **1**(3):163–171.

Osborn, Herbert. 1895. The phylogeny of Hemiptera. *Wash. Ent. Soc. Proc.*, **3**(3):185–189.

Rensch, B. 1934. Kurze Anweisung für zoologisch-systematische Studien. Akademische Verlagsgessellschaft, Leipzig, 116 pp.

Ridgway, R. 1912. Color standards and color nomenclature. A. Hoen Co., Washington, 44 pp., 53 plates (with 1,115 named colors).

Simpson, G. G. 1944. Tempo and mode in evolution. Columbia University Press, New York, i–xviii, 1–237 pp.

———. 1945. The principles of classification and a classification of mammals. *Bul. Amer. Mus. Nat. Hist.*, **85**:1–350.

Svenson, H. K. 1945. On the descriptive method of Linnaeus. *Rhodora*, **47**(562): 273–302 and (563):363–388.

Villalobos-Domínguez, C., and Julio Villalobos. 1947. Atlas de los colores. El Ateneo, Buenos Aires, xv + 74 pp., 38 col. charts, 2 plates (showing 7,279 sample colors).

Chapter 9. Preparation of Taxonomic Papers

Cannon, H. Graham. 1936. A method of illustration for zoological papers. Association of British Zoologists, London, x + 36 pp.

Ferris, G. F. 1928. The principles of systematic entomology. *Stanford Univ. Pubs., Univ. Ser., Biol. Sci.*, **5**:103–269.

Hurt, Peyton. 1949. Bibliography and footnotes. A style manual for college and university students, rev. ed. University of California Press, Berkeley, xii + 167 pp.

Kuhl, Willi. 1949. Das wissenschaftliche Zeichnen in der Biologie und Medizin. Waldemar Kramer, Frankfurt am Main, 179 pp.

Peters, J. L. 1931–1951. Check-list of birds of the world. Harvard University Press, Cambridge, 7 vols.

Ridgway, John L. 1938. Scientific illustration. Stanford University Press, Stanford, Calif., 173 pp.

Trelease, Sam F. 1951. The scientific paper. How to prepare it. How to write it. The Williams & Wilkins Company, Baltimore, 163 pp.

U.S. Government Printing Office. 1945. Style manual, rev. ed. Washington, D.C., v + 435 pp.

Vaurie, C. 1949. A revision of the bird family Dicruridae. *Bul. Amer. Mus. Nat. Hist.*, **93**:203–342.

Chapter 10. Historical and Philosophical Basis of Nomenclature

Bartlett, H. H., *et al.* 1940. Concept of the genus. *Bul. Torrey Bot. Club*, **67**(5): 349–389.

Buchanan, R. E., and R. St. John-Brooks. 1948. Proposed bacteriological code of nomenclature. Iowa State College Press, Ames, Iowa, 59 pp.

Dall, W. H. 1877. Nomenclature in zoology and botany. *Proc. Amer. Assoc. Adv. Sci.*, **1877**:7–56.

Douvillé, H. 1881. Règles proposées par le Comité de la Nomenclature paleontologique. *Cong. Géol. Internatl.* (1881), *Compt. Rend. 2me Sess., Boulogne*, **1881**:594–595.

Fabricius, J. C. 1778. Philosophia entomologica, sistens scientiae fundamenta, adjectis definitionibus, exemplis, observationibus. Impensis C. E. Bohnii, Hamburgi et Kilonii, 178 pp.

Felt, E. P. 1934. Classifying symbols for insects. *N.Y. Ent. Soc. Jour.*, **42**: 373–392.

———— and S. C. Bishop. 1926. Science and scientific names. *Amer. Nat.*, **60**: 275–281.

Heikertinger, F. 1916. Nomenklatorische Reformen. I. Das Systemzeichen in Gattungsnamen. *Zool. Anz.*, **47**:198–208, 209–221.

————. 1918. Die Nichteignung des Prioritätsprincips zur Stabilisierung der Nomenklatur. Das Kontinuitäts prinzip in der Tier- und das Utilitätsprinzip in der Autornennung. *Wien. Ent. Ztg.*, **37**:129–147.

Herrera, A. L. 1899. (See Opinion 72, International Commission on Zoological Nomenclature. *Smithsn. Inst. Misc. Collect.*, **73**(1):19, 1922).

Linnaeus, C. 1751. Philosophia botanica, in qua explicantur fundamenta botanica, cum definitionibus partium, exemplis terminorum, observationibus rariorum, adjectis figuris aeneis. Stockholmiae, i–ix, 1–362 pp.

————. 1758. Systema naturae per regna tria naturae, secundum classes, ordines, genera, species cum characteribus, differentiis, synonymis, locis, Editio decima, reformata, Tomus I. Laurentii Salvii, Holmiae, 824 pp.

Moufet, T. 1634. Insectorum sive minimorum animalium theatrum. Londini ex Officina typographica Thom. Cotes, 326 pp.

Needham, J. G. 1910. Practical nomenclature. *Science*, **32**:295–300.

————. 1911. The law that inheres in nomenclature. *Science*, **33**:795–796.

Règles internationales de la nomenclature zoologique adoptées par les congrès internationaux de zoologie. 1905. F. R. de Rudeval, Paris, 57 pp.

Rhumbler, L. 1910. Ueber eine zweckmässige Weiterbildung der Linné'schen binären Nomenklatur. Ein vorläufiger Vorschlag. *Zool. Anz.*, **36**:453–471.

Richter, Rudolf. 1948. Einführung in die Zoologische Nomenklatur durch Erläuterung der Internationalen Regeln. W. Kramer, Frankfurt am Main. 252 pp.

Rudolphi, C. A. 1801. Beobachtungen über die Eingeweidewürmer. *Archiv f. Zool. u. Zootomie*, **2**(1):1–65.

Stiles, C. W. 1905. The International Code of Zoological Nomenclature as applied to medicine. *U.S. Pub. Health and Mar. Hosp. Serv. Hyg. Lab. Bul.* **24**:5–50.

✓ Strickland, Hugh E. 1842. Rules for zoological nomenclature. Report of 12th meeting of British Association held at Manchester in 1842. *Brit. Assoc. Adv. Sci. Rpt.*, **1842**:105–121.

Svenson, H. K. 1945. On the descriptive method of Linnaeus. *Rhodora*, **47**(562): 273–302 and (563):363–388.

Tornier, G. 1898. Grundlagen einer wissenschaftlichen Thier- und Pflanzennomenclatur. *Zool. Anz.*, **21**:575–580.

Van Cleave, H. J. 1943. An index to the opinions rendered by the International Commission on Zoological Nomenclature. *Amer. Midland Nat.*, **30**:223–240.

Chapter 11. The Principle of Priority

Ball, Carleton R. 1946. Why is taxonomy ill supported? *Science*, **103**:713.

Blackwelder, Richard E. 1948. The principle of priority in biological nomenclature. *Washington Acad. Sci. Jour.*, **38**:306–309.

————. 1949. Synonyms and genotypes. *Coleopterists' Bul.*, **3**:73–75.

————, J. B. Knight, and C. W. Sabrosky. 1948. A revised proposal for errors and emendations in the rules of zoological nomenclature. *Science*, **108**:37–38.

Darwin, C., letter to H. Strickland, 1849. *In* Life and letters of Charles Darwin, ed. by F. Darwin, 1904,**1**:333–335.

Heikertinger, F. 1943. Kann Kontinuität der Tiernamen mit der Prioritätsregel erreicht werden? *Zool. Anz.*, **141**:35–52.

Jacot, A. P. 1930. Nomenclature and me. *Science*, **72**:272–273.

————. 1937. Principles of scientific publication. *N.Y. Ent. Soc. Jour.*, **45**: 127–129.

Journal of the Society for the Bibliography of Natural History, 1936 *et seq.* British Museum (Natural History), London, vols. 1 and 2.

Kirby, H. 1944. Une faute de transcription, d'orthographe, ou d'impression. *Science*, **100**:425–427.

Lindroth, C. H. 1949. Die Fennoskandischen Carabidae. *Göteborgs K. Vet. Samh. Handl.* B4(3), 911 pp.

Mayr, E. 1933. Notes on Polynesian flycatchers and a revision of the genus *Clytorhynchus* Elliot. *Amer. Mus. Novitates*, no. 628, pp. 1–21.

Osgood, W. H. 1939. An outworn nomenclatural practice. *Science*, **89**:9–11.

Schaum, A. 1858. Bericht der entomologischen Versammlung Dresden. *Ent. Ztschr.* (Berlin), vol. 2, App., p. viii.

Thienemann, A. 1938. Rassenbildung bei *Planaria alpina. Jub.-Festschr. Grig., Antipa*, pp. 1–21 [from *Zool. Ber.*, **49**(1940):84–85].

Chapter 12. The Type Method and Its Significance

Banks, N., and A. N. Caudell. 1912. The entomological code. Judd and Detweiler Press, Washington, D.C., 31 pp.

Fernald, H. T. 1939. On type nomenclature. *Ann. Ent. Soc. Amer.*, **32**:689–702.

Frizzell, D. L. 1933. Terminology of types. *Amer. Midland Nat.*, **14**:637–668.

Simpson, G. G. 1940. Types in modern taxonomy. *Amer. Jour. Sci.*, **238**:413–431.

————. 1945. The principles of classification and a classification of mammals. *Bul. Amer. Mus. Nat. Hist.*, **85**:1–350.

Thomas, O. 1893. Suggestions for the more definite use of the word "type." [*London*] *Zool. Soc. Proc.*, **1893**:241–242.

Walsingham, Lord, and J. H. Durrant. 1896. Rules for regulating nomenclature with a view to secure a strict application of the law of priority in entomological work. London, 18 pp.

Welch, D. A. 1938. Distribution and variation of *Achatinella mustelina* Mighels in the Waianae Mountains, Oahu. *Bernice P. Bishop Mus. Bul.*, **152**:1–64.

Williams, C. B. 1940. On "type" specimens. *Ann. Ent. Soc. Amer.*, **33**:621–624.

Chapter 13. Specific and Infraspecific Names

Grensted, L. W. 1944. The formation and gender of generic names. *Ent. Monthly Mag.*, **80**:229–233.

Hemming, F. 1944. Opinion 4. *Opinions and Declarations Rendered, Internatl. Comm. Zool. Nomencl.*, **1**(13):103–114.

Horvath, G. 1913. A propos de deux Cimicides du Soudan francais. *Bul. Soc. Ent. de France*, **1913**:370–372.

Kearfott, W. D. 1907. New North American Tortricidae. *Trans. Amer. Ent. Soc.*, **33**:1–94.

Mayr, E. 1942. Systematics and the origin of species. Columbia University Press, New York, 334 pp. (p. 104).

Murray, J. A. 1784. Caroli Linné. Systema Vegetabilium . . . Editio decima quarta praecedente longe auctior et correctior curante. pp. xx + 987 [17]. Gottingae, J. A. Murray.

Linsley, E. G. 1944. The naming of infra-specific categories *Ent. News*, **55**(9): 225–232.

Smith, H. M. 1945. Categories of species names in zoology. *Science*, **102**:185–189.

Svenson, H. K. 1945. On the descriptive method of Linnaeus. *Rhodora*, **47**:273–302 and 363–388.

Chapter 14. Generic Names

China, W. E. 1943. The generic names of British Hemiptera-Heteroptera, with a check list of the British species. *Roy. Ent. Soc. London*, pp. 211–342.

Blackwelder, R. E. 1946. Fabrician genotype designation. *Brooklyn Ent. Soc. Bul.*, **41**:72–78.

Grensted, L. W. 1944. The formation and gender of generic names. *Ent. Monthly Mag.*, (4)**80** (965):229–233.

Jaeger, E. C. 1944. A source-book of biological names and terms. Charles C Thomas, Publisher, Springfield, Ill., 256 pp.

Kirkaldy, G. W. 1904. Bibliographical and Nomenclatorial Notes on the Hemiptera, No. 3. *Entomologist*, **37**:279–283.

Malaise, R. 1937. Fabricius as the first designator and original inventor of genotypes. *Ent. News*, **48**:130–134.

Neave, S. A. 1939–1940. Nomenclator zoologicus. A list of the names of genera and subgenera in zoology from the tenth edition of Linnaeus 1758 to the end of 1935. 4 vols. Vol. 5 (1936–1945). Zoological Society of London.

Poche, F. 1937. Ueber eine Neubearbeitung der Internationalen Nomenklaturregeln zwecks Erzielung einer eindeutigen, möglichst rationellen, einheitlichen und stabilen Benennung der Tiere. *12th Internat. Cong. Zool.*, *Lisbon*, **1933**:2405–2416.

Chapter 15. Family Names

Duméril, A. M. C. 1800. Leçons d'anatomie comparée de M. G. Cuvier, recueillies et publiées par Duméril et Duvernoy. Baudoin, Paris.

Grensted, L. W. 1947. On the formation of family names. A note on the implications of Opinion 143 of the International Commission on Zoological Nomenclature. *Ent. Monthly Mag.*, (4)**83**(997):137–141.

Horvath, G. 1912. Sur les noms des familles et des sousfamilles du Règne animal. *Verh. VIII Internat. Zool. Kong. Graz*, **1912**:851–855.

de Jussieu, A. L. 1789. Genera plantarum. Paris, 72 + 498 pp.

Kirby, W. 1813. Strepsiptera, a new order of insects proposed; and the characters of the order, with those of its genera laid down. *Linn. Soc. London, Trans.*, **11**:86–123.

Latreille, P. A. 1796. Précis des caractères génériques des Insectes, disposés dans un Ordre naturel. Paris, Boudeaux. pp. xiii + 198.

———. 1802. Histoire naturelle, générale et particulière des Crustacés et des Insectes. Dufart, Paris, Vols. 1–4.

———. 1806. Genera crustaceorum et insectorum, secundum ordinem naturalem in disposita, iconibus exemplisque plurimus explicata. Parisiis et Argentorat, vol. I, i–xviii, 1–302 pp.

Oberholser, H. C. 1920. The nomenclature of families and subfamilies in zoology. *Science*, **53**:142–147.

Sabrosky, C. W. 1939. A summary of family nomenclature in the order Diptera. *Verhandl. 7 Internatl. Kong. Ent., Weimar*, **1**:599–612.

———. 1947. Stability of family names, some principles and problems. *Amer. Nat.*, **81**:153–160.

Strickland, Hugh E. 1842. Rules for Zoological Nomenclature. Report of 12th Meeting of British Association held at Manchester in 1842. *Brit. Assoc. Adv. Sci. Rpt.*, **1842**: 105–121.

Van Duzee, E. P. 1916. Priority in family names and related matters. *Ann. Ent. Soc. America*, **9**:89–93.

Chapter 16.   Names of Orders, Classes, and Phyla

Fabricius, J. C.   1798.   Supplementum entomologiae systematicae.   Hafniae, Proft et Storch, 572 pp.

Kirby, W.   1813.   Strepsiptera, a new order of insects proposed; and the characters of the order, with those of its genera laid down.   *Linn. Soc. London, Trans.*, **11**:86–123.

Shipley, A. E.   1904.   The orders of insects.   *Zool. Anz.*, **27**:259–262.

Simpson, G. G.   1945.   The principles of classification and a classification of mammals.   *Bul. Amer. Mus. Nat. Hist.*, **85**:1–350.

Chapter 17.   Ethics in Taxonomy

Neave, S. A.   1939.   Nomenclator zoologicus.   A list of the names of genera and subgenera in zoology from the tenth edition of Linnaeus 1758 to the end of 1935.   4 vols. and vol. 5 (1936–1945).   Zoological Society of London.

Pigman, W., and E. B. Carmichael.   1950.   An ethical code for scientists.   *Science*, **111**:643–647.

GLOSSARY

Accessory sexual characters. The structures and organs (except the gonads) of which the genital tract is composed, including accessory glands and external genitalia (cf. Primary, Secondary sexual characters).

Acquired character. A character which arises during the life of an individual, either in response to the environment or from a functional cause (cf. Lamarckism).

Adaptation. The condition of showing fitness for a particular environment, as applied to characteristics of a structure, function, or entire organism; also the process by which such fitness is acquired (cf. Preadaptation, Environment).

Adaptive. Fitted for a particular environment (cf. Environment).

Adaptive convergence. The evolution, or presence within a series of comparable ecological niches, of only distantly related forms which superficially resemble one another in morphological and other characters, correlated with very similar or identical environmental conditions (cf. Adaptation, Adaptive radiation).

Adaptive radiation. Evolution and spread of a single phyletic line of organisms into several distinctive ecological niches resulting in a series of sometimes strikingly different forms, each adapted to a particular niche.

"Age and Area." The hypothesis (by Willis) that the older a species is, the wider will be its geographical distribution.

Albinism. In zoology, the absence of pigmentation, and particularly of melanins, in an animal (cf. Melanism).

Allele. An alternative expression of a gene having the same locus in homologous chromosomes (cf. Gene).

Allochronic species. Species which do not occur at the same time level (cf. Synchronic species).

Allometric development. Differential growth rate of one part of an individual in relation to another part or to the individual as a whole.

Allopatric. A term applied to two or more populations which occupy mutually exclusive (but usually adjacent) geographical areas (cf. Sympatric).

Allopatric hybridization. Hybridization between two allopatric populations (species or subspecies) along a well-defined contact zone (cf. Sympatric hybridization).

Allopatric speciation. Species formation during geographical isolation (cf. Sympatric speciation).

Allotype. A paratype of the opposite sex to the holotype (cf. Paratype).

Alpha taxonomy. The level of taxonomy concerned with the characterization and naming of species (cf. Beta taxonomy, Gamma taxonomy).

Alternation of generations. The alternation of a bisexual with a unisexual generation.

Amphiploid. A polyploid produced by the chromosome doubling of a species hybrid, that is, of an individual with two rather different chromosome sets.

Analogous. Similar in external features or function but not in essential structural pattern or origin (cf. homologous).

Anatomy. The science of internal morphology, as revealed by dissection.

Antibody. A serum globulin which is produced in the blood of an immunized animal in response to the introduction of a foreign antigen (cf. Antigen, Antiserum, Serum globulin, Serology).

301

Antigen. A substance capable of inducing the formation of antibodies when introduced into the blood stream of animals (cf. Antibody, Precipitin reaction, Serology).

Antiserum. Blood serum containing specific antibodies (cf. Antibody, Precipitin reaction).

A.O.U. Code. A code of nomenclature published in 1885 (revised 1908) by the American Ornithologists' Union for the standardization of bird nomenclature.

Archetype. A hypothetical ancestral type arrived at by the elimination of specialized characters (cf. Phylogeny).

Artenkreis (Rensch). Superspecies (q.v.).

Artificial classification. Classification based upon characters of convenience without relation to phylogenetic significance; classification based upon characters erroneously presumed to indicate phylogenetic relationship; also classification based on a single arbitrarily chosen criterion, instead of an evaluation of the totality of characters (cf. Classification, Phylogeny, Natural classification).

Asexual reproduction. Not involving the fusion of the nuclei of different gametes.

Atlas. In taxonomy, a method of presenting taxonomic materials primarily by means of comparative illustrations rather than by comparative descriptions (cf. Monograph).

Authority citation. The custom of citing the name of the author of a scientific name or name combination [*e.g.,* *X-us* Jones, *X-us albus* Jones, *Y-us albus* (Jones)]; **Double authority citation** includes the name of the author of the specific trivial name and the author of the currently accepted combination if different from the original combination [*e.g.,* *Y-us albus* (Jones) Smith].

Autosome. One of the chromosomes other than a sex chromosome; autosomes usually occur in identical numbers in the two chromosome sets of the same species (cf. Chromosome, Sex chromosome).

Available name. A name proposed in compliance with Art. 25 of the International Rules of Zoological Nomenclature (cf. Valid name).

Backcross. A cross between a hybrid and one of its parents; a cross between a heterozygote and a homozygote (cf. Hybridization, Heterozygous, Homozygous).

Beta taxonomy. The level of taxonomy concerned with the arranging of species into a natural system of lesser and higher categories (cf. Alpha taxonomy, Gamma taxonomy).

Bibliographical reference. For nomenclatural purposes, the citation of the name of the author and date of publication for a scientific name; a **Full bibliographical reference** includes, in addition, the citation of the exact place of publication of a scientific name (*i.e.,* title of book or journal, volume, page, etc.).

Binary nomenclature. Synonymous with, and to be replaced by, the term *binominal nomenclature,* by decision of the International Commission on Zoological Nomenclature (cf. Binominal nomenclature, Binomial nomenclature).

Binomial nomenclature. The system of nomenclature first standardized by Linnaeus and now generally referred to as binominal nomenclature (cf. Binominal nomenclature, Binary nomenclature).

Binominal nomenclature. The system of nomenclature adopted by the International Congress of Zoology, by which the scientific name of an animal is designated by both a generic and specific trivial name (cf. Binary nomenclature, Binomial nomenclature).

Biological character. A taxonomic attribute of a living organism (in contrast to the museum specimen), hence usually a character which is not strictly morphological (cf. Taxonomic character).

Biological race. Noninterbreeding sympatric populations, which differ in biology but not, or scarcely, in morphology; supposedly prevented from interbreeding by preference for different food plants or other hosts (cf. Sibling species).

Biota. The flora and fauna of a region (cf. Fauna, Flora).

Biotype. A population or group of individuals composed of a single genotype (cf. Population, Genotype).

Bisexual. A population composed of functional males and females; applied also to an individual possessing functional male and female reproductive organs (= hermaphrodite).

Blending characters. Characters which merge and do not show clear-cut Mendelian segregation (cf. Blending inheritance).

Blending inheritance. Inheritance (generally due to multiple factors) in which clear segregation is not evident in the F_2 generation (cf. Multiple factors).

Catalogue. An index to taxonomic literature arranged by taxonomic categories so as to provide ready reference to at least the most important taxonomic and nomenclatural references to the category involved (cf. Check list).

Category. *See* Taxonomic category.

Character. *See* Taxonomic character.

Character gradient. *See* Cline.

Check list. Usually a skeleton classification of a group listed by taxonomic categories for quick reference and as an aid in the arrangement of collections (cf. Catalogue).

Cheironym. A manuscript name (q. v.).

Chorology. The study of the geographical distribution of organisms.

Chromosome. One of the deeply staining chromatin bodies, formed in the nucleus of a cell during mitosis, which carries the genetic factors (cf. Gene).

Classification. The definition, ranking, and arrangement of taxonomic categories and taxonomic entities (cf. Taxonomy, Systematics, Horizontal classification, Vertical classification, Artificial classification, Natural classification).

Cline. A gradual and nearly continuous change of a character in a series of continuous populations; a character gradient (cf. Subspecies).

Clone. All the offspring derived by asexual reproduction from a single sexually produced individual.

Coefficient of difference. Difference of means divided by sum of standard deviations

$$\text{C.D.} = \frac{M_B - M_A}{\text{S.D.}_A + \text{S.D.}_B}$$

Coefficient of variability. The standard deviation as percentage of the mean:

$$\frac{\text{S.D.} \times 100}{M}$$

Coenospecies. All the ecospecies so related that they may exchange genes among themselves to a limited extent through hybridization (cf. Ecospecies, Introgressive hybridization).

Colloquial name. Common name = vernacular name (q.v.).

Common name. Colloquial name = vernacular name (q.v.).

Complex. A neutral term for a number of related taxonomic units, most commonly involving units in which the taxonomy is difficult or confusing (cf. Group, Neutral term).

Congeneric. A term applied to species of the same genus (cf. Genus).

Conspecific. A term applied to individuals or populations of the same species (cf. Species).

Contemporary species. Synchronic species (q.v.).

Continuity. In nomenclature, the principle that continuity of usage should supersede priority of publication in determining which of two or more competing scientific names should be adopted for a particular taxonomic category (cf. Law of priority).

Continuous variation. Variation in which individuals differ from each other by infinitely small steps, as variation in quality of expression of a character or group of characters (cf. Discontinuous variation).

Convergence. Morphological similarity in distantly related forms (cf. Adaptive convergence).

Cotype. Syntype (q.v.).

Cryptic species. Sibling species (q.v.).

Cyclomorphosis. A seasonal (and thus cyclic) nongenetic change of phenotype in species of planktonic fresh-water organisms, particularly cladocerans and rotifers.

Cytogenetics. The study of cell structures in relation to the phenomena of heredity.

Cytology. The study of the structure and physiology of the cell and its parts.

Dall Code. A code of nomenclature prepared by W. H. Dall at the direction of the American Association for the Advancement of Science (1877).

Definition. In taxonomy, a formal statement of characters which sets limits to a taxonomic category (cf. Description, Diagnosis, Differential diagnosis, Taxonomic category).

Deme. A population within a species [see *Nature*, **144**:333(1939)].

Dendrogram. A diagrammatic drawing in the form of a tree designed to indicate degrees of relationship as suggested by degrees of similarity (cf. Phylogenetic tree).

Description. In taxonomy, a more or less complete formal statement of the characters of a taxonomic category without special emphasis on those which set limits to the category or distinguish it from coordinate taxonomic units (cf. Definition, Diagnosis, Differential diagnosis Taxonomic category).

Diagnosis. In taxonomy, a formal statement of the characters (or most important characters) which distinguish a taxonomic category from other similar or closely related coordinate categories (cf. Differential diagnosis, Definition, Description, Taxonomic category).

Differentiae specificae. The descriptive method developed by Linnaeus whereby a series of descriptive words was used to distinguish each species from all others.

Differential diagnosis. A formal statement of the characters which distinguish a given taxonomic unit from other specifically mentioned equivalent units (cf. Diagnosis, Definition, Description, Taxonomic category).

Dimorphism. Occurrence of two distinct morphological types (forms) in a single population (cf. Sexually dimorphic, Polymorphism).

Diploid. Having a double set of chromosomes (2n), the normal chromosome number of the cells (except for mature germ cells) of a particular organism derived from a fertilized egg (cf. Haploid, Polyploidy, Chromosome).

Discontinuous variation. Variation in which the individuals of a sample fall into definite classes which do not grade into each other, as variation in qualitative characters (cf. Continuous variation).

Division. *See* Section.

Dollo's rule. That structures or functions once gained may be lost, but once lost they can never be regained.

Dominant. In ecology, genetics, and psychology, superior in frequency or rank; a gene that is expressed in the phenotype in like manner regardless of whether the individual is homozygous or heterozygous for this gene (cf. Recessive, Homozygous, Heterozygous).

Double authority citation. *See* Authority citation.

Douvillé Code. A code of nomenclature prepared by H. Douvillé (1881) for the International Congress of Geology and designed to set the procedures for the naming of fossils.

Drift. *See* Genetic drift.

Ecological isolation. A condition in which interbreeding between two or more otherwise sympatric populations is prevented by mating in different ecologic niches (cf. Reproductive isolation, Geographic isolation, Genetic isolation).

Ecological race. Subspecies (q.v.).

Ecology. The study of the relationship between organisms and their environment.

Ecophenotypic variation (habitat variation). A nongenetic modification of the phenotype by specific ecological conditions, particularly those of a habitat.

Ecospecies. "A group of populations so related that they are able to exchange genes freely without loss of fertility or vigor in the offspring" (Turesson).

Ecotype. A descriptive term applied to plant races of varying degrees of distinctness which owe their most conspicuous characters to the selective effects of local environments (cf. Subspecies).

Edaphic factor. The influence of soil properties on organisms (especially plants).

Emendation. In nomenclature, an intentional modification of the spelling of a previously published scientific name (Cf. Error, *Lapsus calami*).

Environment. The total of physical, chemical, and biotic conditions surrounding an organism.

Error. In nomenclature, an unintentional misspelling of a scientific name, as a typographical error or an error of transcription (cf. Emendation, *Lapsus calami*).

Eyepiece micrometer. A linear scale in the field of vision of the eyepiece (or one of a pair of eyepieces) of a microscope for use as a measuring device.

F_1 generation. The first-generation offspring of a particular mating.

F_2 generation. Progeny derived from a mating within the F_1 generation.

Facies. In taxonomy, the general aspect, appearance, or habitus of a species or group.

Family. A taxonomic category including one genus or a group of genera or tribes of common phylogenetic origin, which is separated from related similar units (families) by a decided gap, the size of the gap being in inverse ratio to the size of the unit (family).

Family name. The scientific designation of a family, recognized by the termination *idae*, which termination, by action of the International Commission on Zoological Nomenclature, may not be used in names of other taxonomic categories [for minor exceptions in specific trivial names, *see Bul. Zool. Nomencl.*, **4**:262 (1950)] (cf. Subfamily name).

Fauna. The animal life of a region (cf. Flora, Biota).

Faunal work. A method of presenting taxonomic materials defined primarily by geographic area rather than by phylogenetic units (cf. Local list, Monograph).

First Reviser. The first author to publish a definite choice of one among two or more conflicting nomenclatural or zoological interpretations which are equally available under the Rules; in order to qualify as first reviser an author must give evidence of a choice between available alternatives.

Flora. The plant life of a region (cf. Fauna, Biota).

Form. A neutral term for a single individual or taxonomic unit (cf. Group, Neutral term).

Formenkreis. A collective category of allopatric subspecies or species (Kleinschmidt); in paleontology, a group of related species or variants.

Full bibliographical reference. *See* Bibliographical reference.

Full bibliographical synonymy. A reasonably complete list of references to a given taxonomic category arranged so as simultaneously to serve the needs of nomenclature (chronology of names) and zoology (pertinent taxonomic and biological sources) (cf. Synonymy).

Gamma taxonomy. The level of taxonomy dealing with various biological aspects of taxa, ranging from the study of intraspecific populations to studies of speciation and of evolutionary rates and trends (cf. Alpha taxonomy, Beta taxonomy).

Gause's rule. The theory that no two species with identical ecological requirements can coexist in the same place.

Gene. A hereditary determiner; the unit of inheritance, carried in a chromosome, transmitted from generation to generation by the gametes, and controlling the development of the individual (cf. Chromosome).

Gene flow. The exchange of genetic factors between populations owing to dispersal of zygotes or gametes, *e.g.*, pollen.

Gene frequency. The percentage of a given gene in a population (cf. Gene, Population).

Generitype. Genotype in the nomenclatural sense (cf. Genotype).

Generotype. Genotype in the nomenclatural sense (cf. Genotype).

Genetic drift. Genetic changes in populations due to random fixation rather than to selection; the so-called "Sewall Wright effect" (cf. Local population).

Genetic isolation. A condition in which interbreeding between two or more populations is prevented by sterility barriers (cf. Reproductive isolation, Geographic isolation, Ecological isolation).

Genotype. In nomenclature (not recommended, International Commission, 1948), the type species of a genus (cf. Type species); in genetics, the class in which an individual falls on the basis of its genetic constitution, without regard to visible characters (cf. Phenotype).

Genus. A taxonomic category including one species or a group of species, presumably of common phylogenetic origin, which is separated from related similar units (genera) by a decided gap, the size of the gap being in inverse ratio to the size of the unit (genus).

Geographic isolation. A condition in which interbreeding between two or more allopatric populations is prevented by extrinsic barriers or geographic discontinuity (cf. Reproductive isolation, Ecological isolation, Genetic isolation).

Geographical race. Subspecies (q.v.).

Group. A neutral term for a number of related taxonomic units, especially an assemblage of closely related species within a genus (cf. Complex, Neutral term, Section).

Gynandromorph. An individual in which one part of the body is masculine, the other feminine; most frequent are bilateral gynandromorphs, in which the left and right halves are of different sex.

Handbook. In taxonomy, a publication designed primarily as an aid to field and laboratory identification rather than for the presentation of new taxonomic conclusions (cf. Manual, Monograph).

Haploid. The single or basic number (n) of chromosomes for the species as found in mature germ cells (cf. Diploid, Polyploidy, Chromosome).

Hermaphrodite. An individual having both male and female reproductive organs (cf. Intersex).

Heterozygous. Having different alleles at one locus (cf. Allele, Locus, Homozygous).

Hierarchy. In classification, the system of ranks which indicates the taxonomic level of various taxonomic categories (*i.e.*, kingdom to species) (cf. Taxonomic category).

Higher category. A taxonomic category of rank higher than the species (*i.e.*, from subgenus to kingdom) (cf. Supraspecific).

Holotype. "The single specimen designated or indicated as 'the type' by the original author at the time of the publication of the original description" [*see Bull. Zool. Nomencl.*, **4**:186 (1950)].

Homologous. Similarity of organs, parts, or functions with comparable features in another species or group as a result of a structural pattern derived from a common ancestor (cf. Analogous).

Homonym. In nomenclature, one of two or more identical but independently proposed names for the same or different taxa (cf. Senior homonym, Junior homonym, Primary homonym, Secondary homonym).

Homozygous. Having identical alleles at one locus (cf. Allele, Locus, Heterozygous).

Horizontal classification. Classification based upon organisms which coexist in time; classification which, according to Simpson, separates ancestral from descendent groups and unites contemporaneous groups, or those in a similar stage of evolution, if they are derived from a common ancestry (cf. Classification, Vertical classification).

Hybridization. The production of individuals from genetically unlike parents (cf. Heterozygous); in taxonomy, crossing between individuals from different populations, especially different species (cf. Sympatric hybridization, Allopatric hybridization).

Hypodigm. The entire known material of a species which is available to the taxonomist.

Industrial melanism. The evolutionary development of a darker population favored by selection in the darkened surroundings of an industrial area (cf. Melanism).

Infraspecific. Within the species; usually applied to categories (subspecies) and individual forms (varieties) (cf. Subspecies, Variety, Infrasubspecific form).

Infrasubspecific form. Individual and seasonal variants in a single interbreeding population (cf. Variety, Infrasubspecific name).

Infrasubspecific name. The trivial name of an infrasubspecific form (cf. Subspecific name, Infrasubspecific form) [for nomenclatural status *see Bul. Zool. Nomencl.* **4**:89–96 (1950)].

Intergradation. Merging gradually through a continuous series of intermediate forms or populations.

International Code. A term sometimes applied to the *Régles Internationales de la Nomenclature Zoologique* (International Rules of Zoological Nomenclature).

International Rules of Zoological Nomenclature. Règles Internationales de la Nomenclature Zoologique (q.v.).

Intersex. An individual more or less intermediate in phenotype between male and female (cf. Hermaphrodite).

Introgressive hybridization. The spread of one or more genes of one species into the germ plasm of another species as a result of hybridization (cf. Hybridization, Coenospecies).

Irreversibility. *See* Dollo's rule.

Isolating mechanism. Any intrinsic agent which hinders the interbreeding of groups of individuals.

Isophenes. Lines connecting points of equal expression of a character; lines at right angles to a cline on a map (cf. Cline).

Junior homonym. The more recently published of two or more identical names for the same or different taxonomic categories (cf. Homonym, Senior homonym).

Junior synonym. The more recently published of two or more available synonyms for the same taxonomic category (cf. Synonym, Senior synonym).

Karyological character.   A character involving chromosome structure or number (cf. Taxonomic character).

Key.   A tabulation of diagnostic characters of species (or genera, etc.) in dichotomous couplets facilitating rapid identification.

Lamarckism.   The theory advocated by Lamarck, that evolution is brought about by the inheritance of acquired characters.

Lapsus calami.   In nomenclature, a slip of the pen, especially an error in spelling (cf. Error, Emendation).

Law of priority.   The provision in the International Rules of Zoological Nomenclature that the correct name for a genus or species can be only that name under which it was *first* designated in conformance with the requirements laid down in those rules.

Lectotype.   One of a series of syntypes which, subsequent to the publication of the original description, is selected and designated through publication to serve as "the type" [*see Bul. Zool. Nomencl.* **4**:186(1950)] (cf. Syntype).

Line.   As a unit of measure, $\frac{1}{12}$ in. or 2.12 mm. (cf. Millimeter).

Local list.   A publication giving a listing of the animals or plants recorded from a locality or district.

Local population.   The individuals of a given locality which potentially form a single interbreeding community (cf. Natio, Subspecies).

Locus.   The hypothetical position of a gene in a chromosome (cf. Gene, Chromosome).

Lumper.   In taxonomy, one who tends to unite related units into a single taxon; one whose criteria for determining the level to be assigned to a given taxonomic category are such that the effect of his work is to lower the rank of existing categories (as families to subfamilies, species to subspecies) (cf. Splitter).

Manual.   Handbook (q.v.).

Manuscript name.   In nomenclature, an unpublished scientific name (cf. *Nomen nudum*).

Material.   In taxonomy, the sample available for taxonomic study (cf. Series, Hypodigm).

Melanism.   An unusual darkening of color owing to increased amounts of black pigment; sometimes a racial character, sometimes, as in cases of polymorphism, restricted to a certain percentage of individuals within a population (cf. Industrial melanism, Albinism).

Metatype.   A specimen compared by the author of the species with the holotype and determined by him as conspecific with it.

Metric system.   A decimal system of measures (with the meter as base) and weights (with the gram as base); the universal system for reporting measures and weights in the scientific field.

Microbiology.   The science which deals with the study of microorganisms; the biological relationship of microorganisms.

Microgeographic race.   A local race, restricted to a very small area.

Millimeter (mm.).   1/1,000 m., or 0.03937 in., approximately $\frac{1}{25}$ in. (cf. Metric system).

Mimetic polymorphism.   The occurrence within a population of several (often strikingly different) forms, each of which resembles closely a different sympatric species, in butterflies often restricted to females.

Monograph.   In taxonomy, an exhaustive treatment of a phylogenetic group in terms of all available information pertinent to taxonomic interpretation; usually involving full systematic treatment of all included taxonomic units in terms of comparative anatomy, biology, ecology, and detailed distributional analyses (cf. Revision, Synopsis).

Monophyletic. A term applied to a taxonomic category in which the contained units are all part of a single immediate line of descent (cf. Polyphyletic).

Monotypic. A category containing but one immediately subordinate zoological unit, as a genus containing but one species, or a species containing but one (the nominate or nominotypical) subspecies [for nomenclatural meaning, *see Bul. Zool. Nomencl.*, **4**:153 (1950)] (cf. Polytypic).

Multiple factors. Two or more pairs of genes with a complementary or cumulative effect (cf. Blending inheritance).

Mutation. In genetics, a discontinuous change of a genetic factor; in paleontology, a sudden change in a phyletic series of fossils.

Mythical name. A name proposed for hypothetical or mythical forms; without status in nomenclature.

Natio. Local populations within a subspecies (cf. Population, Local population, Subspecies).

Natural classification. As currently used, classification based on characters or groups of characters which indicate phylogenetic relationship (cf. Classification, Phylogeny, Artificial classification).

Natural selection. The process by which the environment eliminates the less well-adapted members of a population or causes a differential reproductive success of different genotypes; the "survival of the fittest."

Natural system. The arrangement of taxonomic categories in a hierarchy based on an evaluation of all their known characters.

Neontology. The systematics of recent organisms (cf. Paleontology).

Neoteny. Attainment of sexual maturity in an immature or larval stage.

Neotype. A specimen selected as type subsequent to the original description in cases where the primary types are definitely known to be destroyed.

Neutral term. A taxonomic term of convenience, such as form or group, which may be employed without reference to the formal taxonomic hierarchy of categories, and which has no nomenclatural significance.

New name. A new name for a preoccupied name (cf. Substitute name).

Niche (ecological). The precise constellation of environmental factors into which a species fits or which is required by a species.

Nomenclator. A book containing lists of scientific names assembled for nomenclatural, rather than taxonomic, purposes (cf. Catalogue).

Nomenclature. A system of names (cf. International Rules of Zoological Nomenclature).

Nomenclature binaire. *See* Binary nomenclature.

Nomen dubium. The name of a nominal species for which available evidence is insufficient to permit recognition of the taxonomic species to which it was applied [for nomenclatural status *see Bul. Zool. Nomencl.*, **4**:76 (1950)].

Nomen novum. New name (cf. Substitute name).

Nomen nudum. A published scientific name which does not meet the requirements for availability defined in Art. 25 of the International Rules of Zoological Nomenclature (cf. Valid name).

Nomen rejectum. Rejected name (q.v.).

Nomen specificum. Specific name (q.v.).

Nomen triviale. Trivial name (q.v.).

Nomen vanum. An indeterminate name (cf. *Nomen dubium*).

Nomina conservanda. Names whose usage has been preserved by agreement or decision in spite of actual or potential conflict with established rules of nomenclature; often applied to the Official Lists established by the International Commission on Zoological Nomenclature (cf. Official List of Generic Names in Zoology).

Nominal genus. "The concept denoted by a given generic name," as contrasted with the concept represented by a taxonomically accepted genus (International Commission).

Nominal species. "The concept denoted by a given specific name," as contrasted with the concept represented by a taxonomically accepted species (International Commission).

Nominate subspecies. Nominotypical subspecies (q.v.).

Nominotypical subgenus. That subgenus of a polytypic genus which shares with its genus the same type species and the same name [*e.g.*, *X-us* (*X-us*) *albus* in contrast to *X-us* (*Y-us*) *rufus*] (cf. Subgeneric name).

Nominotypical (or nominate) subspecies. That subspecies of a polytypic species which shares with its species the same type specimen and the same name; the subspecies of a species with the earliest valid name (*e.g.*, *X-us albus albus* in contrast to *X-us albus niger*).

Objective synonym. An absolute or nomenclatural synonym resulting from the proposal either of a replacement name for a supposedly preoccupied name or of names based on the same specimen, illustration, or taxonomic entity (cf. Synonym, Subjective synonym).

Official Index of Rejected and Invalid Generic Names in Zoology. A record of generic names suppressed by the International Commission on Zoological Nomenclature under the plenary powers or declared by the Commission to be invalid or nonexistent [*see Bul. Zool. Nomencl.*, **4**:334 (1950)].

Official Index of Rejected and Invalid Specific Trivial Names in Zoology. A record of specific trivial names suppressed by the International Commission on Zoological Nomenclature under the plenary powers or declared by the Commission to be invalid or non existent [*see Bull. Zool. Nomencl.* **4**:334 (1950)].

Official List of Generic Names in Zoology. A record of generic names (and the type species of each) which have been validated, conserved, or stabilized by the International Commission on Zoological Nomenclature through use of the plenary powers or the rendering of an Opinion [*see Bul. Zool. Nomencl.*, **4**:267–268 (1950)].

Official List of Specific Trivial Names in Zoology. A record of trivial names of species or subspecies which have been validated, conserved, or stabilized by the International Commission on Zoological Nomenclature through the use of the plenary powers or the rendering of an Opinion [*see Bul. Zool. Nomencl.*, **4**:269–271 (1950)].

Onomatophore. "Name bearer" = type (Simpson) (cf. Type).

Ontogeny. The developmental history of an individual organism from egg to adult.

Original description. The summary of characters accompanying the proposal of a name for a new taxonomic entity in conformance with Art. 25 of the International Rules of Zoological Nomenclature.

Orthogenesis. A term usually applied either to a tendency to evolve consistently in the same direction or to the concept of "predetermined" evolution toward a definite goal.

Page precedence. The principle that when two or more conflicting homonyms or synonyms are published in the same work (or portion of a work) and, as a consequence, are of the same date, the names shall have priority according to the sequence in which they first appear in the work (or portion) concerned.

Paleontology. The science that deals with the life of past geological periods (cf. Neontology).

Paratype. A specimen other than the holotype which was before the author at the time of preparation of the original description and was so designated or indicated by the original author (cf. Allotype).

Parthenogenetic. The production of offspring from unfertilized eggs.

Patronymic. In nomenclature, a dedicatory name, a name based on that of a person or persons.

Phenotype. The class in which an individual falls on the basis of visible characters, as the result of an interaction between genotype and environment (cf. Genotype).

Phyletic. Pertaining to a line of descent (cf. Phylogeny).

Phylogenetic tree. A diagrammatic presentation of assumed lines of descent, based on paleontological, morphological, or other evidence.

Phylogeny. The study of the historical development of the line or lines of evolution in a group of organisms; the origin and evolution of higher categories (cf. Classification).

Physiological race. *See* Biological race.

Physiological species. *See* Sibling species.

Plenary powers. Special powers granted by the International Congress of Zoology (Monaco, 1913; Paris, 1948) to the International Commission on Zoological Nomenclature permitting the suspension of the International Rules of Zoological Nomenclature or decisions as to how they shall apply in specific cases [*see Bul. Zool. Nomencl.*, **4**:51–56 *et seq.* (1950)].

Plesiotype. A specimen or specimens upon which subsequent descriptions or figures are based.

Polymorphism. A form of individual variability; the occurrence together in the same habitat of two or more distinct forms of a species in such proportions that the rarest of them cannot be maintained by recurrent mutation (cf. Dimorphism).

Polynomial nomenclature. A system of nomenclature consisting of a scientific designation of a species on the basis of more than three descriptive words; the antecedent of the Linnaean "binomial" system.

Polyphyletic. A term applied to a taxonomic category derived from two or more ancestral sources; not of a single immediate line of descent (cf. Monophyletic).

Polyploidy. A condition in which the nuclear complement of chromosomes is an integral multiple (greater than 2) of the haploid number.

Polytopic. Occurring in different places as, for instance, a subspecies composed of widely separated populations.

Polytypic. A category containing two or more immediately subordinate categories, as a genus with several species or a species with several subspecies (cf. Monotypic).

Population. *See* Local population.

Preadaptation. Fitness for an environment which the organism does not occupy, or an environmental relationship which it does not maintain, at the time when the adaptation appears; usually applied to a new characteristic, arising by mutation, which permits invasion of a new habitat or the development of a new environmental relationship (cf. Adaptation, Environment).

Precipitin reaction. The formation of a visible precipitate at the interface when an antigen and the corresponding antiserum are brought together (cf. Antigen, Antiserum, Antibody, Quantitative specificity).

Pre-Linnaean name. A name published prior to Jan. 1, 1758, the starting point of zoological nomenclature and the assumed date of publication for the tenth edition of Linnaeus's *Systema naturae;* such names are unavailable and may not be made available by republication in their original form after Jan. 1, 1758, nor through citation in synonymy (cf. Available name).

Primary homonym. One of two or more identical trivial names which, at the time of original publication, were proposed in combination with the same (or an identical) generic name (*e.g.*, *X-us albus* Smith, 1910, and *X-us albus* Jones, 1920); the later of such primary homonyms are to be permanently rejected; also one of two or more identical names for genera or higher categories (cf. Homonym, Secondary homonym).

Primary sexual characters. The gonads; the ovaries in females, the testes in males (cf. Accessory sex characters, Secondary sexual characters).

Protozoology. The science which deals with the study of protozoa (cf. Microbiology).

Quantitative specificity. In serology, the principle that a given kind of antibody will react more strongly, under comparable conditions, with the particular kind of antigen used in its formation than with any other substance (cf. Antibody, Antigen, Precipitin reaction).

Race. Subspecies (q.v.).

Radiation. *See* Adaptive radiation.

Rassenkreis (Rensch). A polytypic species composed of several subspecies (cf. Subspecies, Polytypic).

Recapitulation. The theory that ontogeny recapitulates phylogeny (cf. Ontogeny, Phylogeny).

Recessive. A character that is expressed in the phenotype only when the individual is homozygous for the gene producing it (cf. Dominant, Homozygous).

Règles Internationales de la Nomenclature Zoologique. The International Rules of Zoological Nomenclature adopted by the Fifth International Congress of Zoology at Berlin (1901) and subsequently amended at succeeding congresses. The French text is the official version.

Rejected name. An otherwise available name which has been permanently rejected by the International Commission on Zoological Nomenclature under the plenary powers (cf. Official Index of Rejected and Invalid Specific Trivial Names in Zoology, Official Index of Rejected and Invalid Generic Names in Zoology).

Replacement name. Substitute name (q.v.).

Reproductive isolation. A condition in which interbreeding between two or more populations is prevented by intrinsic factors (cf. Geographic isolation, Ecologic isolation, Isolating mechanism).

Reticulate evolution. Evolution "dependent on repeated intercrossing between a number of lines, and thus both convergent and divergent at once" (Huxley).

Reversion. The reappearance of an ancestral character which was not exhibited in the parental or immediately ancestral generations.

Review. Synopsis (q.v.).

Revision. In taxonomy, the presentation of new material or new interpretations integrated with previous knowledge through summary and reevaluation (cf. Synopsis, Monograph).

Saltation. Discontinuous variation produced at a single step by mutation (cf. Mutation).

Sample. That portion of a true population which is actually available to the taxonomist.

Scientific name. The binominal or trinominal designation of an animal; the formal nomenclatural designation of a taxonomic category (cf. Vernacular name).

Secondary homonym. One of two or more identical trivial names which, at the time of original publication, were proposed in combination with different generic names but which, through subsequent transference, reclassification, or combination of genera have come to bear the same (or an identical) combination of a generic and trivial name [for nomenclatural status *see Bul. Zool. Nomencl.*, **4**:97–105(1950)] (cf. Homonym, Primary homonym).

Secondary sexual characters. The characters which distinguish the two sexes of the same species but which do not function directly in reproduction (cf. Primary sexual characters, Sexually dimorphic).

Section. A neutral term usually employed with reference to a subdivision of a taxonomic unit or a series of related elements in one portion of a higher taxonomic category (cf. Higher category, Neutral term, Group).

Selection. *See* Natural selection.

Semispecies. The species of which a superspecies is composed (cf. Superspecies); semispecies are a special kind of species, not a category different from the species.

Senior homonym. The earliest published of two or more identical names for the same or different taxonomic categories (cf. Homonym, Junior homonym).

Senior synonym. The earliest published of two or more available synonyms for the same taxonomic unit (cf. Synonym, Junior synonym).

Series. In taxonomy, the sample which the collector takes in the field or the sample available for taxonomic study (cf. Material, Hypodigm); also a neutral term employed especially with reference to a sequence of taxonomic categories or forms (cf. Neutral term, Taxonomic categories, Form).

Serology. The study of the nature and interactions of antigens and antibodies (cf. Antigen, Antibody).

Serum globulin. The blood fraction in which antibodies, if present, are to be found (cf. Antibody).

Seventy-five per cent rule. The rule that population A can be considered subspecifically distinct from population B if 75 per cent of the individuals of A are different from "all" the individuals of population B (cf. Coefficient of difference).

"Sewall Wright effect." *See* Genetic drift.

Sex chromosome. A special chromosome, not occurring in identical number or structure in the two sexes and usually concerned with sex determination; the X chromosome or Y chromosome (cf. Chromosome, Autosome).

Sex-limited character. A character belonging to one sex only (cf. Secondary sexual character, Sex-linked character).

Sex-linked character. A character for which the determiner is located in the sex chromosome (cf. Sex chromosome, Sex-limited character).

Sexually dimorphic. With pronounced difference in the morphological expression (form) of the two sexes of a single species (cf. Dimorphism).

Sibling species. Pairs or groups of closely related species which are reproductively isolated but morphologically identical or nearly so (cf. Species).

Speciation. The splitting of a phyletic line; the process of the multiplication of species; the origin of discontinuities between populations due to the development of reproductive isolating mechanisms (cf. Allopatric speciation, Sympatric speciation).

Species. Groups of actually (or potentially) interbreeding natural populations which are reproductively isolated from other such groups (cf. Subspecies, Population, Reproductive isolation).

Species complex. *See* Complex.

Species group. *See* Group.

Specific name. "The binominal combination of a generic name and a specific trivial name which constitutes the scientific designation of a species" (International Commission, 1948) (cf. Species, Scientific name, Binominal nomenclature); also used by many workers and in the original Rules in place of *trivial* name.

Specific trivial name. The second term of the binominal designation of a species (cf. Species, Binominal nomenclature).

Splitter. In taxonomy, one who divides his material more finely than the average; one whose criteria for determining the level to be assigned to a given taxonomic category are such that the effect of his work is to push existing classification upward (as subfamilies to families, subspecies to species); also one who attempts to express even small differences nomenclaturally (cf. Lumper).

Standard deviation, S.D. The square root of the sum (Σ) of the squared deviations (d) from the mean, divided by N:

$$\text{S.D.} = \sqrt{\frac{\Sigma d^2}{N}}$$

Standard error (of the mean). Standard deviation divided by the square root of the sample size (N):

$$\text{S.E.}_M = \frac{\text{S.D.}}{\sqrt{N}}$$

Strickland Code. A code of nomenclature prepared by a committee of the British Association for the Advancement of Science under the secretaryship of H. E. Strickland and first published in 1842.

Subfamily. A taxonomic category intermediate between a family and a tribe (cf. Family).

Subfamily name. The scientific designation of a subfamily, recognized by the termination *inae*, which termination, by action of the International Commission on Zoological Nomenclature, may not be used for names of other categories [for minor exceptions in trivial names, *see Bul. Zool. Nomencl.*, **4**:262(1950)] (cf. Family name).

Subgeneric name. The name of an optional category between the genus and the species, enclosed in parentheses when cited in connection with a binominal or trinominal combination and therefore excluded from consideration when determining the number of words of which a specific, subspecific, or infrasubspecific name is composed [*e.g.*, *X-us* (*Y-us*) *albus rufus* is a trinominal—*see Bul. Zool. Nomencl.*, **4**:96–97(1950)] (cf. Nominotypical subgenus).

Subjective synonym. A conditional or taxonomic synonym dependent upon an author's opinion (subject to subsequent revision) that two or more available names proposed for nominally different categories actually represent a single taxonomic category (cf. Synonym, Objective synonym).

Subspecies. A geographically defined aggregate of local populations which differs taxonomically from other such subdivisions of the species (cf. Polytypic, Cline).

Subspecific name. "The trinominal combination of a generic name, a specific trivial name and a subspecific trivial name which constitutes the scientific designation of a subspecies" (International Commission) (cf. Subspecies, Nominotypical subspecies).

Subspecific trivial name. The third term of the trinominal designation of a subspecies [for nomenclatural status *see Bul. Zool. Nomencl.*, **4**:89–96(1950)] (cf. Infrasubspecific name, Subspecific name, Subspecies).

Substitute name. A name proposed to replace a preoccupied name and automatically taking the same type and type locality (cf. New name).

Superfamily. The taxonomic category immediately above the family and below the order (cf. Family).

Superspecies. A monophyletic group of entirely or largely allopatric species (cf. *Artenkreis*, Allopatric, Semispecies).

Supraspecific. A term applied to a taxonomic category or to taxonomic and evolutionary phenomena at a level higher than the species (cf. Higher category).

Sympatric. A term applied to two or more populations which occupy identical or broadly overlapping geographical areas (cf. Allopatric).

Sympatric hybridization. The occasional production of hybrid individuals between two otherwise well-defined sympatric species.

Sympatric speciation. Species formation in the absence of geographic isolation (cf. Allopatric speciation).

Synchronic species. Species which occur at the same time level (cf. Allochronic species).

Synonym. In nomenclature, one of two or more different names for the same taxonomic unit (cf. Senior synonym, Junior synonym, Objective synonym, Subjective synonym).

Synonymy. A chronological list of the scientific names which have been applied correctly or incorrectly to a given taxonomic unit, including the dates of publication and the authors applying the names; in its most abbreviated form designed for nomenclatural purposes only (cf. Full bibliographical synonymy).

Synopsis. In taxonomy, a brief summary of current knowledge of a group; the inclusion of new material or new interpretations is not necessarily implied (cf. Review, Revision, Monograph).

Syntype. "One of a number of specimens of equal nomenclatural rank which formed all or part of the material before the original author, in those cases where the author did not designate or indicate a holotype" (I.C.Z.N.) [*see Bul. Zool. Nomencl.*, **4**:186(1950)] (cf. Cotype, Lectotype).

Systematics. Taxonomy (q.v.).

Systematic serology The application of serology to taxonomic problems; comparative serology (cf. Serology).

Taxon. A taxonomic unit or category (pl., taxa).

Taxonomic category. One of a hierarchy of levels into which natural populations are classified, such as subspecies, species, genus, and family.

Taxonomic character. Any attribute of an organism or of a group of organisms by which it differs from an organism belonging to a different taxonomic category or resembles an organism belonging to the same category (cf. Biological character).

Taxonomy. The science of classification of organisms (cf. Classification, Systematics).

Teratology. The study of structural abnormalities, especially monstrosities and malformations.

Topotype. A specimen collected at the type locality.

Tribe. A taxonomic category intermediate between the genus and the subfamily.

Trinominal nomenclature. An extension of the binominal system of nomenclature to permit the designation of subspecies by a three-word name (cf. Binominal nomenclature, Subspecies, Subspecific name, Nominotypical subspecies).

Trivial name. The second or third word in a binominal or trinominal name of an animal; the specific and subspecific components in the scientific designation of an animal (cf. Specific trivial name, Subspecific trivial name, Infrasubspecific trivial name).

Type. A zoological object which serves as the base for the name of a taxonomic category (*e.g.*, a specimen which is the name bearer for a species, a species which is the name bearer for a genus, etc.)

Type designation. Determination of the type of a genus under Art. 30, Rule (*a*) of the International Rules of Zoological Nomenclature (cf. Type indication, Type selection).

Type indication. Determination of the type of a genus under Art. 30, Rules (*b*), (*c*), and (*d*) of the International Rules of Zoological Nomenclature (cf. Type designation, Type selection).

Type locality. The locality at which a holotype, lectotype, or neotype was collected (cf. Topotype).

Type method. The method of preserving the identity of a taxonomic category by fixing an included zoological object as "type."

Type selection. Determination of the type of a genus under Art. 30, Rule (*g*) of the International Rules of Zoological Nomenclature (cf. Type indication, Type designation).

Type species. The expression recommended by the International Commission on Zoological Nomenclature to refer to the concept of "a type species of a genus" [*see Bul. Zool. Nomencl.*, **4**:300(1950)] (cf. Genotype).

Typology. In taxonomy, the method of approach to classification which involves the postulate that all members of a taxonomic unit conform to a given morphological "type."

Uninominal nomenclature. The designation of a taxonomic category by a scientific name consisting of a single word; required for the categories above the species, but occasionally also advocated for the species.

Valid name. The name of a taxonomic category which is available nomenclaturally and also is recognized as valid on zoological grounds (cf. Available name).

Variance. The square of the standard deviation.

Variety. A term originally applied indiscriminately to various kinds of infraspecific forms, individuals as well as populations (*i.e.*, subspecies); in modern usage, usually limited to discontinuous variants within a single interbreeding population (cf. Subspecies, Infrasubspecific form).

Vernacular name. The colloquial designation of a taxonomic category (cf. Scientific name).

Vertical classification. Classification based upon the historical development of groups of organisms as indicated by the fossil record; classification which, according to Simpson, unites ancestral and descendent groups and separates contemporaneous groups that are diverging from a common ancestry (cf. Classification, Horizontal classification).

INDEX

317